1967

THE LIFE AND WORK OF
WILLIAM HIGGINS

Photostat of Ms. of Higgins's paper on the Human Calculus. (*Royal Society Letters and Papers*, Decade ix, No. 825. By courtesy of the Officers.) This Ms. was lost sight of for many years.

The Life and Work of
WILLIAM HIGGINS
Chemist
(1763 - 1825)

Including reprints of 'A Comparative View of the
Phlogistic and Antiphlogistic Theories' and
'Observations on the Atomic Theory and
Electrical Phenomena' by William Higgins

by

T. S. WHEELER
Dean of the Faculty of Science and Professor of Chemistry,
University College, Dublin

and

J. R. PARTINGTON
Emeritus Professor of Chemistry, University of London

PERGAMON PRESS
NEW YORK · OXFORD · LONDON · PARIS
1960

PERGAMON PRESS INC.
122 East 55th Street, New York 22, N.Y.
P.O. Box 47715, Los Angeles, California

PERGAMON PRESS LTD.
Headington Hill Hall, Oxford
4 & 5 Fitzroy Square, London W.1.

PERGAMON PRESS S.A.R.L.
24 Rue des Écoles, Paris V^e

PERGAMON PRESS G.m.b.H.
Kaiserstrasse 75, Frankfurt am Main

LIBRARY OF CONGRESS CARD NUMBER 59–12606

Printed in Great Britain by Robert Cunningham and Sons Ltd.,
Longbank Works, Alva

Contents

v

A COMPARATIVE VIEW OF THE PHLOGISTIC AND ANTI-
PHLOGISTIC THEORIES *by* WILLIAM HIGGINS

EXPERIMENTS AND OBSERVATIONS ON THE ATOMIC
THEORY AND ELECTRICAL PHENOMENA *by* WILLIAM
HIGGINS

PREFACE

AT the time when Higgins wrote the book which is the main subject of the present study, Chemistry was based on the phlogiston theory. According to this, all combustible bodies contain a principle called phlogiston which, when they burn, escapes from them in the form of fire. In 1777 Lavoisier, the French chemist, had shown on the basis of earlier experiments that whenever phlogiston was supposed to escape, oxygen is absorbed and that phlogiston has no existence. The antiphlogistic theory was still in dispute when Higgins wrote in its support. It did not begin to make general headway until after the publication of Lavoisier's *Traité Éléméntaire de Chimie* in 1789 in the same year as Higgins's volume. There was another reason why Higgins's publication showed his courage. Richard Kirwan, a prominent and highly respected Irish chemist, had written an *Essay on Phlogiston* defending the old theory, which was regarded by the French chemists as the most serious attack on their new views. Higgins's argument is largely a disproof of Kirwan and a vindication of Lavoisier, and in this he uses an ingenious and novel method, extending the idea of attraction between atoms in compounds.

This atomic theory was not especially emphasised by Higgins and (since he did not require them) he says practically nothing about atomic weights. When the antiphlogistic theory was well established, interest in its defence against the phlogiston theory receded, and Higgins's atomic theory dropped out of mind. The title, *A Comparative View of the Phlogistic and Antiphlogistic Theories*, although expressing its main object, did not suggest to later chemists that the book would contain anything of interest in their time. The theory that the atom of every chemical element has a characteristic weight belongs unquestionably to John Dalton, and it is Dalton's theory and not Higgins's which is the basis of modern atomic theory.

vii

In 1810, soon after Dalton had published his Chemical Atomic Theory, Sir Humphry Davy referred to the *Comparative View* and suggested that statements in it to some extent anticipated Dalton's theory. Many polemical discussions of the value of Higgins's ideas stem from this remark.

Higgins's is a rare book and few of those interested in the foundations of atomic theory can have an opportunity of perusing it. Further, it is difficult reading for the average chemist, for much of it is concerned with unfamiliar matter relating to the dead phlogiston theory. Not many know much of Higgins, who he was, and what he did. It seemed, therefore, appropriate to combine in one volume: an account of his life and work, a detailed discussion of his book, and an examination of the Higgins–Dalton controversy, together with a photo-reproduction of the *Comparative View*. An attempt has been made to give the reader all the facts to enable him to judge the merits of Higgins's claims.

Apart from his views on chemistry, the life of Higgins is not uninteresting. He was born in, it is thought, Collooney, County Sligo, probably in 1763. As a youth (about 1782) he was sent to work with his uncle, Dr Bryan Higgins, physician and chemist, who had a laboratory in Greek Street, Soho. William was at Oxford as lecturer-assistant from 1786-88 and then returned to London. We next hear of him as chemist at the Apothecaries' Hall, Dublin, in 1792. In 1795 he was appointed to the Royal Dublin Society's staff, first as a lecturer, later as professor. He remained with the Society until his death in 1825.

Higgins was an early type of professional chemist, going from one post to another as opportunity arose. Like many modern professors he added to his income by extra-mural work; he was from 1795-1822 part-time chemist to the Irish Linen Board.

It was while at Oxford he wrote the *Comparative View* by which he is still remembered; during the rest of his life he did little out of the ordinary, and nothing of distinction.

J. R. PARTINGTON
T. S. WHEELER

Part I

THE LIFE OF WILLIAM HIGGINS

Introduction

A GREAT DEAL has been written about William Higgins and the claims[1] he so vehemently preferred in 1814 and subsequent years to be, rather than Dalton, the originator of the atomic theory in the form current in the early nineteenth century. But in spite of much discussion little has appeared in the nature of biographical detail; what has been published is based mainly on an uncritical reliance on Sullivan's life, printed in 1849[2], of William Higgins and of William's uncle, Bryan Higgins, M.D. Sullivan's work, particularly in regard to Bryan Higgins, was based on information supplied by Captain and Mrs Nassau William Stephens[3] of Dublin. Mrs Stephens, née Blake, was a granddaughter of Bryan Higgins[4], but her memory of the past was not perfect, and Sullivan himself makes the inexplicable error of referring to her as Bryan Higgins's 'niece'[5].

It was felt, accordingly, that there was a need for an account of the life of William Higgins based as far as is possible on primary sources, and this part of the present book is an attempt to meet this need. Owing to the destruction by fire of the Irish Public Record Office in 1922, some source matter is no longer available; an effort has been made, however, to examine such relevant material as remains.

1. FAMILY AND EARLY LIFE

Dr E. MacLysaght's map of mediaeval Ireland[6] which gives the location of the principal Gaelic clans shows that the O'Higgins group lived in the south of Co. Sligo, near the Mayo border. O'Rorke[7] states that Sligo county is indebted to the O'Higgins or

Higgins family for many men of note. They possessed much land[8] before as Catholics they lost it, but they owed their celebrity to their poetic performances for which they were famous from the fourteenth century[9]. When in the seventeenth century the bardic profession decayed with the decline of Gaelic Ireland, the bardic families, with no tradition of soldiering, farming, or commerce, turned to medicine. Possibly it was in this way that a medical tradition developed in the Higgins family[10]. In addition to his uncle Bryan, William's grandfather, also a Bryan, and probably his father Thomas, were doctors.

The elder Bryan who died in 1777 was a distinguished man[11]. His grandson William was born at, it is thought, Collooney, Co. Sligo[12,13] in 1762–63[13]. We know nothing of his school-days[14]; Sullivan says merely that while still a boy William was taken to his wealthy uncle Bryan who had married an heiress and set up a laboratory in Greek Street, Soho, London[15].

2. LONDON AND OXFORD

The date of William's transfer to London is not definitely known. His uncle Bryan in a letter dated 12 January 1802[16], referring to an experiment showing the production of sound by a flame of hydrogen burning in a tube, writes that he first exhibited the experiment in 1777, and that it was afterwards shown 'by my cousin [*sic*][5], Mr Higgins, who now teaches in Dublin; who exhibited it at Sir Joseph Banks[17], and, if I am not misinformed, at Oxford, where he served the professor as operator' (lecture assistant). Bryan also states that the experiment was shown at Mr Kirwan's in 1784. Banks's house was a meeting-place for scientists from about 1777; Kirwan[18] lived in London for ten years from 1777.

Again, in the preface to his *Experiments and Observations relating to Acetous Acid, etc.*, 1786, Bryan Higgins indicates that more than one third of the book was printed in 1784, so that the experiments must have been carried out before that year. He makes no specific mention of William, but the latter[19] in a reference to this work states, 'I studied with the Doctor at this time, and assisted in making all the experiments contained in that work.' Bryan (*loc. cit.*, p. 283) writes that 'some part of every one of these experiments and mensurations was committed to the care and fidelity of my operator'. In view of the number of experiments described in the volume, which contains some 300 pages of experimental matter, and having regard to the necessity for William being trained before he could be of much use to his uncle, it is probable that he came to London some years before 1784. Apart from practice, he knew enough chemistry in that year to abandon the phlogiston theory[20].

Sullivan[2] states that after a year or two in London William went to Pembroke College, Oxford, where he graduated. This information, incorrect as regards graduation (see footnote 27, p. 34), can be amplified from Higgins's works. In his *Comparative View of the Phlogistic and Antiphlogistic Theories* (1789)[13, 21] he refers to the observations on the reduction of nitric acid he made in Dr Higgins's laboratory in the latter end of March 1785, and to a subsequent visit to Sir Joseph Banks's house[17]. He also states that he knew Dr Brocklesby[22]. In his *Essay on the Theory and Practice of Bleaching* (p. 14)[23] he mentions a mineralogical excursion he made through England in the summer and autumn of 1785, when he visited factories. In the *Comparative View* (p. 312) he indicates that the work on ammonia he was carrying out with Dr Caulet[24] was interrupted because he was obliged to set out for Oxford some time after December 1785. In the spring of 1786 he was in contact with Dr Austin[25], who was probably in Oxford at the time. We know from Foster's *Alumni Oxonienses*[13] that William matriculated at Magdalen Hall[26] on 6 February 1786. The way in which the dates fit confirms the view that the William Higgins in Foster is the one with whom we are concerned[27].

Higgins seems to have remained for about one year at Magdalen Hall, and then to have migrated to Pembroke College[28]; his name first appears on the Buttery Book of Pembroke on 16 March 1787[29]. He may have been attracted by the reputation of the Master, William Adams[30], who was said to have a deep knowledge of chemistry[31]. Well-known contemporaries of Higgins include Davies Gilbert[32], who succeeded Humphry Davy as President of the Royal Society, and James Smithson[33], who left upwards of £100,000 to found the Smithsonian Institution at Washington. In addition to Dr Austin, Higgins refers to Dr Wall[31] and particularly[34] to his learned friend, Dr Haworth[35] of St Bartholomew's Hospital, 'one of the Radcliff (*sic*) travelling fellows from Oxford, with whom I had the pleasure of being intimately acquainted at the university'. Haworth apparently shared Higgins's amusement at the failure of the reviewers of the *Comparative View* to understand the atomic theory propounded in it.

Higgins spent more than a year at Pembroke, for the College Buttery Books show that he was in residence up to the middle of 1788[36]. There are references to Oxford in his writings[37] but nowhere does he give a reason for leaving, as he did, without a degree[27]. We have seen[38] that while at the University he was an 'operator' to the professor, but it is not certain with whom he 'operated'. When Higgins matriculated in February 1786, Austin[25] was Professor of Chemistry, but resigned in August when he was appointed physician to St Bartholomew's Hospital, London, in succession to Dr J. G. Caulet, who, as indicated above, was a friend of Higgins[24]. In the *Comparative View* (p. 312) Higgins mentions that he often had the opportunity of speaking to Austin in the spring of 1786, but if he did serve Austin as operator his tenure of office must have been short.

Thomas Beddoes[39] was appointed to succeed Austin early in 1788[40], but did not occupy a chair; he is referred to as 'Reader' or 'Lecturer'; Bryan Higgins may have been writing loosely when he used the term 'professor'. As Higgins left Oxford in, probably, the following August, his period of association with Beddoes must have been brief. William refers in the *Comparative View* (p. 313), written in 1788, to a discussion with Beddoes, 'our present lecturer in chemistry at Oxford', on the reduction of nitric acid to ammonia (see p. 105 below) about July 1787. It is not clear why Beddoes was then at Oxford (cf. note 44). Meldrum[41] assumes that it was Beddoes whom Higgins served, but, as indicated above, it could have been Austin[42] or both. Higgins does not seem to have remained on cordial terms with Beddoes for in his *Experiments and Observations on the Atomic Theory* he prints (p. 7) an extract from a very formal letter from Beddoes in Oxford, dated 10 April 1789, expressing the hope that the *Comparative View* would support the phlogistonists and stating that Priestley had re-established the existence of phlogiston. The standard life of Beddoes by Stock does not mention Higgins[39].

While at Oxford, William sent to the Royal Society a paper on the analysis of the human calculus[43]. The Ms. of this paper by 'William Higgins of Pembroke College, Oxford', dated 'Oxford, 2 April 1787', is in the archives of the Royal Society[44], and there is an account of its being read to the Society on 3 April 1788[45]. The Society did not print the paper so Higgins included it as an Appendix to the *Comparative View*. It was probably at Oxford that Higgins carried out the numerous experiments on which the *Comparative View* was based[46]. He says that he discarded the phlogiston theory about 1784[20], which was before he went to Oxford. The laboratory in which he worked was in the basement of the Ashmolean Museum in Broad Street[47]. He describes the chemical 'elaboratory' some 6 ft. below ground (*Comparative View*, p. 176). A mixed crop of sodium and calcium nitrates grew on the walls every three or four months[48] and he analysed this 'nitre' mixture for his friend Dr Wall[31, 48]. Sullivan[2] says that after Higgins left Oxford he continued to work in London with his uncle Bryan for some time. Later, according to Sullivan, a coolness arose between them because of William's antiphlogistic activities; Bryan was, as William states, a 'phlogistian'[49]. Apparently Bryan cut off supplies, and William was then in what Sullivan calls 'rather adverse circumstances' for some time. On the other hand William says[50] that the *Comparative View*, which passed through two editions, in all about 1000 copies, in the course of two years, was printed and published at his own expense. As the price of the book was at least 6s.[51], Higgins for an edition of say 500 copies had presumably to find over £100 for expenses, even if the price allowed a profit. One wonders if Higgins was as 'reduced' as Sullivan suggests. The book, published in 1789 when Higgins was 26, represents his greatest achievement. On it is based his claim to be the originator of the atomic theory as applied to chemical phenomena.

We know little of what Higgins did in London until he left for Ireland in 1792. There is in the British Museum Library[52] the minutes of a meeting, held at Whitehall on 10 May 1790, of 'the Right Honorable the Lords of the Committee of Council, appointed for the Consideration of all Matters relating to Trade and Foreign Plantations'. The Committee considered 'a Memorial of Ambrose Godfrey, Chymist[53], and William Higgins of Pembroke College, Oxford[54], praying a Reward for a newly discovered method of printing Linens etc. with a printed paper therein referred to'. The memorial was sent to the Society for the Encouragement of Arts, Manufacturers etc. for an opinion on the merit and utility of the discovery. Higgins appeared before the Society on 9 November 1790, but as Ambrose Godfrey was not well enough to attend the hearing was adjourned and nothing further seems to have happened.

3. CHEMIST TO THE APOTHECARIES' HALL OF IRELAND
(1792–95)

The year of the publication of the second edition of the *Comparative View* (1791) saw developments in Dublin which were to bring William back to Ireland. On 5 May 1791 the Royal Assent was given to an Act of the Irish Parliament (31 George III, chapter 34) which came into operation on 24 June 1791, 'for the more effectually preserving the Health of His Majesty's Subjects, for erecting an Apothecary's Hall in the City of *Dublin*, and regulating the Profession of an Apothecary throughout the Kingdom of *Ireland*'[55]. The Act gave additional powers to the Corporation of Apothecaries chartered in 1745. Provision was made for a general council or court of members or subscribers who acted through a court of directors. The promoters of the Act met in February 1791, and later, as Directors, set about providing a 'Hall' which was to contain a shop for vending drugs and a laboratory for compounding chemicals. The appointment of staff then fell for consideration, and in August 1791 the Directors decided to advertise in Dublin and London papers for a chemist. In September they toyed with the idea of a combined post of chemist and apothecary, but eventually resolved 'that it must materially tend to serve this institution to have the two Offices of Chemist, and Apothecary separate'[56].

William now appears in the picture. The minutes of a general meeting of Members held on 1 November 1791 record the receipt of 'two letters from Mr Wm. Higgins in London . . . offering himself to this Corporation as Chemist on certain terms', and in December the Secretary sent a letter of appointment to Higgins. The text of the letter as entered in the Minute Book of the Hall is as follows:

No. 10 Grafton Street Dublin 26th Decr. 1791.

Sir

I am ordered by the Court of Directors of the Apothy's Hall of Dublin to inform you that they are in daily expectation of a proper Concern for an Hall. As soon as they have got such Concern, you shall have Notice thereof, and will then be engaged as Chemist at Two Hundred pounds per Ann. with apartments, Coals and Candles[57].

It is expected that you will conduct the Chemical and Galenical Preparations; and in all possible Matters, promote the Establishment and Prosperity of this Infant Undertaking. From your Character and Experience they have no Doubt but you will fulfil the expectations which they entertain of you—nor would they offer such high Emoluments to any Person, whose Knowledge and Opportunities did not entitle him to their entire Confidence.

I have, etc.

D. Moore *Secretary*.

Mr Wm. Higgins, No. 37 East Street Red Lion Square, London[58].

On 6 January 1792 Higgins replied accepting the post[59]. His letter reads as follows:

London Jany. 6, 1792, 37 East St., Red Lion Sqr.

Sir

I had the honor of receiving your letter respecting the Office which I am to hold in the new Establishment in Dublin.

You will be kind enough to transmit my best thanks to the Court of Directors for the very favourable sentiments they are pleased to entertain of me, which it will always be my particular ambition to deserve.

> I hope I shall soon have the Satisfaction of hearing that they have been fortunate in meeting with a convenient and Spacious plot of ground for the intended purpose.
>
> I have the honor, to be, Sir
>
> Yr. very Obt. Servant,
>
> Wm. Higgins.

After some preliminary difficulties owing to a defect in the title of the first site they selected, the Directors obtained a property in Mary Street, Dublin, and in March 1792 the Secretary wrote to Higgins requiring him to come over directly. On 13 April 1792 he was sworn into office and a month later (18 May 1792) the Treasurer was ordered to 'provide furniture for the small back room on the first floor for the use of our Chemist'. The scientist is ever the denizen of the small back room[60].

During 1793 and 1794 there are occasional references to Higgins in the Minutes of the Hall; he was engaged in fitting up the laboratory. As the establishment developed it became necessary to consider in detail the conditions of service of members of the Staff, and on 26 April 1794 the Directors defined their duties[61]. The officials were to have ample time to carry out their assignments, since on 29 April 1794 it was provided that 'every Officer and Servant employed in this Institution is to attend in his respective Station every Morning in Summer at Seven O'Clock and in Winter at Eight and to continue therein until at least Eight OClock in the Evening (Sundays Excepted) Note by Summer is meant from the 25th March to 25th September.' Judged by modern standards the hours of work were appalling, but they could not have been rigorously enforced since, as will be described later, Higgins found time to act in a part-time capacity for the Irish Linen Board, and to attend meetings of the Royal Irish Academy. His work in the Hall was supervised by a Committee of three directors who, for example, kept an eye on his expenditure on glass-ware ('Glass house Bills'. See Minutes of 3, 20 and 24 June 1794).

Higgins's first recorded chemical task seems to have been to analyse water from a hot spring in the Leixlip district some eight miles west of Dublin. The sample was submitted by the well-known politician the Right Honourable Thomas Conolly[62]. In view of Conolly's position the Directors fell over themselves to oblige and on 20 June 1794 Higgins was ordered to analyse the sample quickly and accurately and report to his Committee. His report was, however, not available until 8 August. The analysis was at once forwarded to Conolly together with an unaccepted fee of ten guineas he had sent[63]. On 16 September 1794, Higgins 'having complained to several Members of this Court of the great interruption in his business by the admission of every person to the Laboratory', it was resolved 'That no Person be admitted into the Laboratory after Monday the twenty-second instant unless introduced by a Subscriber'[64].

By December 1794 the premises for the Hall were ready, Higgins was given a better room, and all Members of the Company were invited to dinner at the Hall on Tuesday 23 December. But in spite of the rejoicing 1795 was not to be an easy year for Higgins. On 6 January the Directors criticised the quality of 'the red precipitate and Calcined Mercury' and the yield he had obtained of a preparation of Rochelle Salt. The Directors also referred to the number of accidental losses of material which occurred in the laboratory. Nor was that all. The Directors, who appear to have been amateurs in the matter of finance, must have seen the red light, for on 21 November 1794 they decided 'to open a set of Books and draw up the General State of the affairs of this Corporation'. The results were frightening and on 13 January 1795 it was found necessary to summon immediately a general meeting to consider the state of the funds and the expediency of application to Parliament.

The General Council held ten days later set up Committees: to approach the Lord Lieutenant[65] to ask for Government contracts; to request Henry Grattan[66] and other influential gentlemen for assistance in amending the Act so that the Hall might receive more money; to examine the possibility of obtaining £2000 as soon as possible; and to enquire into the services rendered by the officers and the cost of these officers to the Institution. The Committees were to report before the following May. On 27 May the Committee appointed to investigate the establishment reported *inter alia* that the cost of the laboratory greatly exceeded the value of the entire produce, and that the demand for chemicals did not warrant the continuation of so large an outlay. Whereupon the Governor was 'requested to inform Mr Wm. Higgins that this Corporation has no further occasion for his services'. At first Higgins seems to have taken the abrupt retrenchment of his post graciously, for on 2 June the Directors resolved: 'That the grateful and unanimous Thanks of this Court be returned to Mr William Higgins for the Masterly manner of fitting up our Laboratory—his Zeal for the good of the Institution on all occasions and for his Friendly offer of giving his advise [sic] and assistance gratuitously when called on.'

This rare feeling between employer and discharged employee did not last. The Corporation owed Higgins one year's salary due on 20 June 1795 which was not paid, so that on Tuesday 30 June we find in the Minutes: 'Mr William Higgins having importuned this Court collectively and individually for his salary due the 20th inst. and as neither the Governor or Treasurer find it convenient at present to accommodate this Company with £200 wanting for that purpose

Resolved That for the Honour of this Company Two Hundred pounds be borrowed to pay Mr Higgins. . . .'

Although Higgins can hardly be blamed for importuning the Directors for his arrears of pay, as happened all too frequently his language was such as to rankle, for on the following Friday (3 July) we find: 'Mr Higgins our late chemist having behaived [sic] to this Court in a very unbecoming manner

> Ordered
> That the Secretary write him as follows, viz.
> Mr Higgins
> The Court of Directors expect you will move your Lodgings immediately from this House in consequence of your very unhandsome Language to different Subscribers and to this Court last Tuesday.'

On 17 July the Directors adjourned consideration of a demand by Higgins for lodgings up to next quarter day, and on 1 August, his claim was further adjourned as he was out of Ireland.

Higgins does not seem to have pressed this claim further. Time heals quarrels. On 31 January 1802 Higgins was admitted an Honorary Member of the Hall in company with Cavendish, Kirwan and some others 'who had distinguished themselves in Chemistry or Natural Philosophy'.

The story of Higgins's departure from the Apothecaries' Hall, as told in the Minutes quoted, is given in detail, as some of his biographers[67] have incorrectly surmised the reasons for his transfer to the Dublin Society[68] (see p. 17) at half the salary.

4. CHEMIST TO THE IRISH LINEN BOARD
(1795–1822)

We leave Higgins in process of transfer from the Apothecaries' Hall to a post with the Dublin Society, and pause to discuss a neglected phase of his career. As had been indicated, his long hours (on paper) at the Apothecaries' Hall did not preclude his taking additional work, and early in 1795 he had been appointed 'chymist' to the Irish Linen Board at a salary of £100 per annum[69]. He says in a memorial written in 1821 (see p. 16 below) protesting at the retrenchment of this office that he did not solicit the post. From their minutes, Kirwan seems to have been highly regarded by the Board, so we can perhaps suspect his kindly influence[70]. There is no definite reference to the appointment of Higgins in the Minutes for 1795, but those of the meeting held on 1 April 1794 refer to the activities of his predecessor James Clarke, while on 28 April of the following year the Board directed that a sample of fuller's earth be sent to Mr Higgins[71].

The Linen Board which Higgins served was officially 'The Trustees of the Linen and Hempen Manufactures of Ireland' and was a typical eighteenth-century Government-nominated body, on present standards riddled by corruption. The Trustees were first appointed in 1711, mainly to control the manufacture of linen and were usually members of the legislature. They numbered seventy-two, equally divided among the provinces of Ireland. As was to be expected, the Board never functioned satisfactorily; attendance, unless a post was to be filled, was poor, particularly after the Union when the Trustees were frequently out of Ireland[72], while dishonesty was rife among the employees scattered throughout the country. In 1811 the senior Inspector General, Charles Duffin, was sentenced to three months' imprisonment and fined one mark for obtaining money from the Trustees under false pretences[73]. He was also under suspicion of conniving at frauds. The Trustees' own financial methods were frequently the subject of criticism by the Commissioners of Public Accounts[74], who had, however, a proper administrative attitude towards professional men of the chemist type, classing them with tradesmen[75]. The Board was dissolved in 1828, leaving the linen trade flourishing only in the North of Ireland, where the system of land tenure was rather more stable than in the remainder of the country[76].

With all their faults, however, the Trustees were early alive to the importance of chemistry. On 2 June 1716 the Secretary was directed by the Board to arrange for the attendance of Mr Maple, Chymist, at an 'experiment of making Pot-ashes'[77]. A return to the Government made in 1801 states that 'A Chymist was first appointed in 1782 under the appropriation to encourage the making of Potash. After his death the present gentleman was appointed'[78]. James Clarke, Higgins's predecessor, worked first on the erection of a plant for refining 'ashes' to produce pearl-ash (potassium carbonate from which carbonaceous matter had been removed by incineration at a moderate red heat). The early method of bleaching involved boiling the linen in alkaline lyes, washing it clean, and spreading it on grass for about two weeks. The whole process was repeated about six times and required perhaps six months to complete. The cloth was freed from alkali by treatment with acid[79]. Berthollet's method of bleaching[80] using 'oxygenated muriatic acid' (chlorine) was discussed by the Trustees on 23 March 1790. The minutes of the meeting in question state that Mr Kirwan attended at the request of the Board, and informed the Trustees that the chemical preparation for bleaching was composed of 'Spirit of Salt distilled on Manganese', and that Mr Barthollet [sic], an eminent chemist in Paris, seeing its effects in whitening vegetable substances, communicated his experiments to the proprietor of certain salt works there who immediately commenced its manufacture. Later, in January and February 1791, the Board arranged to offer a premium of £400 for the best formula for the new type of bleaching liquor. The entries received were carefully tested by Clarke and other officers of the Board[79].

Higgins tells us in Section IV of his *Essay on Bleaching*, published in 1799, that when he became chemist to the Linen Board he devoted a considerable portion of his time to a study of the application of chemistry to the treatment of linen. The practice of bleaching was his chief concern, possibly because of the interest taken in the subject by the Board. On 3 April 1798 the Trustees received from him a report on experiments on the application of 'oxygenated muriate of lime' (bleaching powder); the use of bleaching powder solution in place of chlorine was a considerable advance, particularly in safeguarding the health of workers. In May of the same year Higgins reported that he had, as the result of numerous experiments, shown that calcareous hepar (calcium sulphide) from quicklime and sulphur could replace the potash used in the alkali boils, with a considerable economy in the cost of materials. Further, as the new reagent was employed in the cold, there was a saving of fuel.

The essay on bleaching mentioned above was dedicated to the Linen Board. The copy in the National Library, Dublin, which was originally in the Library of the Royal Dublin Society, is inscribed 'From the Author'. The preface occupies thirty pages; the essay itself runs to seventy. In the preface Higgins explains that when he reported on 'sulphuret of lime' (calcium sulphide) to the Linen Board, the Trustees asked him to give an experimental demonstration of the process at the 'Elaboratory' of the Dublin Society. He accordingly delivered a lecture, illustrated with experiments, upon the general principles of bleaching. After the lecture John Foster, Baron Oriel (1740–1828), last Speaker of the Irish House of Commons, and Isaac Corry (1755–1813), Chancellor of the Irish Exchequer (1799–1804), suggested that it should be published. Higgins decided to deal with the whole process in detail, commencing 'with the green *flax* so as to begin at the right end of the chain . . . to take it up link after link, according to the position or arrangement which the finger of nature seemed to point out to me'.

He found it impossible, however, to keep away from controversy. Referring to his *Comparative View*[13] published nine years before, he complains that results which he published in it were later adduced as new discoveries and he points out that a 'fair author', Mrs Fulhame[81], in a book published in 1794 had put forward as her own a theory which he said he had anticipated (see p. 110).

The essay, which is written in Higgins's characteristic style, is divided into the following sections: on flax; on bleaching in the old method, with general observations on the alkalis; on bleaching with the oxygenated muriatic acid, and on the methods of preparing it; on sulphuret of lime as a substitute for potash; on bleaching with the sulphuret of lime. In the concluding portion of his essay, Higgins goes into the economics of his process, and points out that the cost of chemicals for the alkaline treatments would be halved if calcium sulphide were employed. Further as sulphur could be obtained from the Wicklow copper mines, the use of imported material would be obviated. He mentions that about 215,307 [*sic*] pounds of foreign alkalis were imported each year into Ireland for bleaching purposes. Higgins's work on the use of calcium sulphide was reprinted in *Nicholson's Journal*[82], and in the *Transactions of the Dublin Society*[83]. The Society also reprinted[84] a favourable comment on the *Essay* from the *Critical Review* for June 1801[85].

Higgins in his *Essay on Bleaching* referred to the detection of potassium sulphate, which he stated was a common adulterant of potassium carbonate. On 4 February 1801 he reported to the Trustees on a sample of potash which he had found to be adulterated adding, 'I have no doubt but this species of ingenuity is solely practised for the Irish market upon a presumption that we are not able to detect the fraud.' On 10 November 1801 he told the Trustees that oxygenated liquors are not 'calculated' for the bleaching of linens. He referred in this connection to his *Essay* (p. 50), where he had stated that oxygenated muriate of lime (bleaching powder) solutions are less liable to injure the texture of the cloth than those of oxygenated muriate of potash (potassium hypochlorite).

Higgins's work seems to have been appreciated, for on 7 June 1808 the Trustees received a Memorial from the registered

Bleachers in County Tyrone asking for the chemical establishment of the Board to be enlarged 'not only by duly appreciating and encouraging their present chemist in the exercise of his functions, but also of allowing and appointing, in co-operation therewith, some further personal aid . . . .'. The Trustees decided to make arrangements for Mr Higgins to attend two or three principal bleachers in each county to help in the new process of bleaching. In December 1810 the Trustees were specially requested to attend a meeting at which Humphry Davy was to be present to discuss the subject of bleaching. As will be clear from the attitude of the Dublin Society described later, Davy's great reputation extended to Ireland.

In May 1812 Higgins memorialised the Trustees, reminding them that in 1802 and 1803 he had stated against the opinion of expert bleachers that the use of 'detergent salt' would be injurious to linen. His predictions had turned out to be correct. In 1804 he had visited all the principal bleach greens in the north, his tour occupying two months. The Bleachers had asked for an occasional repetition of his tour. Recently he had been to Dungannon to report on the pollution of the water in the river by a distillery. Finally he pointed out that £100 when his salary was fixed was now worth £50 only, 'from the advanced price of all the necessities and comforts of life', a plea with a modern ring. The Trustees gave Higgins £100 to cover the expenses of his tours, but did not increase his salary.

One part of Higgins's duties was to examine various suggestions received by the Trustees, for example: a process for the improvement of kelp which was a source of alkaline material; a method for the determination of alkali present in potash and similar materials; regeneration of exhausted alkali by treatment with quicklime. In January 1819 Higgins reported to the Trustees the results of numerous experiments he had made on the potash content of a variety of vegetable materials. In May 1820 the Trustees were informed that sodium carbonate prepared by the Leblanc process (*Soude Factise*) had, on importation from Marseilles, attracted a duty of 50 per cent. The Board referred the matter to Mr Higgins for a chemical opinion on the properties of this new alkali before they approached the Government in regard to a remission of duty. Higgins reported that the new artificial soda was superior to the natural 'barilla' and that there should be no difference between them as regards duty. He warned the Trustees against possible adulteration of this material.

But in spite of his long service he was doomed once again to be the victim of a policy of retrenchment. In November 1821 the Trustees received from the Lord Lieutenant instructions to reduce their establishment. They appointed an Economy Committee, who recommended reductions in the salaries of most officers, and abolition of the posts of Deputy Chamberlain, Clerk of Works, Messenger, Watchman and, of course, Chymist; expert assistance is seldom regarded as essential in times of peace. The Trustees met on 19 November 1821 to implement the recommendations of the Committee. They had before them a Memorial from Higgins written the same morning saying that he was in waiting should the Trustees wish to see him. He pointed out that he had been appointed to the service of the Linen Board some twenty-seven years before, without any solicitation on his side. During that period the Board had received innumerable applications for pecuniary rewards for pretended improvements in the process of bleaching, the fraudulent nature of which he had detected. He referred to his condemnation of 'detergent salt', the use of which had ruined many bleachers, and to the advantage bleachers had received from a study of his essay on bleaching. His final paragraph is instructive: 'Men of science meet with protection in every enlightened nation; and I trust, from what I have already experienced, that it will not be withheld by your Honorable Board, particularly when I can assure them, with truth, that, upon an average of 27 years, I saved to the Board, and of consequence to the Nation, ten times my Salary.'

The argument that the application of science saves more than it costs carries little weight in times of financial stringency, and Higgins's post was abolished as from 5 January 1822, the day on which the Trustees' official year began. Thus ended his connection with the Linen Board. Actually from the financial point of view the loss of £100 per annum meant little to him; as shown later he was a wealthy man.

5. HIGGINS AND THE ROYAL DUBLIN SOCIETY
(1795–1825)

Higgins, when he left the Apothecaries' Hall, was not without alternative employment. His salary had been paid to 20 June 1795; on 18 June, the Dublin Society[68], as it then was, on the suggestion of Kirwan appointed Higgins to arrange and supervise the famous Leskean collection of minerals which it had recently purchased for some £1300[86]. The initial salary was fixed at £100 per annum. Kirwan in his recommendation referred to Higgins as skilled in mineralogy. The Society knew that Kirwan's 'needy' friend was a chemist and not a mineralogist, and decided in view of Higgins's 'extensive Skill in Chymistry' to equip a laboratory in which he could make 'Experiments on Dying [sic] Materials and other Articles, wherein Chymistry may assist the Arts'. This laboratory is believed to have been the first of its kind in Great Britain and Ireland.

The Society did not accept a recommendation of Kirwan's Committee that Higgins should also look after the Library. Sullivan[2], who states that Higgins was appointed Librarian, appears to have been misled by a certain obscurity in the minutes in regard to those recommendations of the Committee which were accepted by the Society. There is no indication that Higgins ever had charge of the Library; for example a minute dated 3 March 1796 sanctioning the tardy payment of his first half-year's salary due 18 December 1795, refers only to his service in connection with the 'Cabinet of Mineralogy'. The Library was apparently in charge of the Society's Registrar, John Brien, who disappeared in 1798—possibly he was involved in the rising.

The Irish Parliament annually granted money to the Society[87] and the 1796 Act (36 George, III chapter 16) provided £5500 *inter alia* 'towards compleating a cabinet of Irish minerals, supporting the expenses of the Leskean cabinet of minerals, and paying a salary not exceeding one hundred and fifty pounds a year, to Mr William Higgins, or such other professor of mineralogy or chymistry as they [the Society] shall from time to time appoint to the care thereof'[88]. Higgins received the £150 as from 18 June 1796. The terms of this Act as regards Higgins were repeated each year[89] until 1800, when the Irish Parliament

c

(40 George III, chapter 31) increased the grant by £10,000 and gave the two Professors of the Society a salary of £300 per annum[90]. Higgins was to attend the Laboratory and give a full course of lectures. This Act was among a large number which received the Royal Assent on 1 August 1800, immediately before the Irish Parliament ceased to exist[91].

The increase in the grant was the result of a petition made by the Society early in 1800 to the Irish House of Commons[92]. The petition pointed out the great expense the Society had incurred in purchasing and accommodating the Leskean collection of minerals and in providing and equipping a chemical 'elaboratory'. The Society had also 'established a professor of great ability to make experiments and give lectures in that science, through which manufacturers have received of late years the most decisive and rapid improvements'. The Society required extra room so that new methods in, for example, tanning and brewing, could be executed for the examination of the public. The petition also stated that just as the rules of arithmetic must be mastered before its application to book-keeping and the like, 'so, the knowledge of the general principles of *philosophic chemistry* necessarily precedes that of their application to various arts'— words as true to-day as when they were written.

To return to Higgins, in April 1796, possibly at Kirwan's behest, the Society was asked to provide apartments for William at the Laboratory because of 'his necessary Attention to Operations of great length, and the Danger he might be liable to if exposed to the Air when overheated by attending the Furnaces'. The Society was unmoved by the thought of Higgins shivering in the night air, the proposal was referred to the Committee of Agriculture, and dropped.

Higgins was not long about organising lectures. In *Saunders' News-Letter and Daily Advertiser* for 31 January 1797 there is an announcement that

'The course of Experimental Chemistry, by William Higgins, Lecturer on Chemistry and Mineralogy, will commence at the Elaboratory of the Dublin Society, in Hawkin's-street, on Monday the 6th of February next, at eight o'clock in the evening.

'For further particulars apply to Mr Higgins at the Dublin Society House, in Hawkin's-street, between the hours of twelve and four.'

Higgins's hours do not seem to have been as arduous as when he worked at the Apothecaries' Hall.

Some years later, in April 1799, the Society directed that Dr Walter Wade, their Professor of Botany, should give lectures in the chemical laboratory and instructed him to settle with Higgins convenient days and hours. Higgins seems to have reacted, for a week later it was decided that the lectures should be given in the library. In May of that year Kirwan obtained sanction for the appointment of an assistant to help Higgins in the Laboratory, at not more than half a guinea per week. Again, in March 1800 Kirwan proposed that in consideration of the great attention, trouble and fatigue shown by Higgins in the course of the last year, he should be given £150 and his salary increased to £300 per annum on condition that members of the Society should be admitted free to the chemistry lectures; lecture fees were evidently a perquisite of the professor[93]. It was decided that the proposal should lie on the table for perusal of the members. On 26 June 1800 Higgins was paid £112 10s. for the six months ending 25 June, indicating that his annual salary had been increased to £225. In a minute of 28 August his salary for the quarter ending 29 September is given as £75, and his post 'Superintendent of the Society's Cabinet of Mineralogy and Professor and Lecturer in Chemistry in their Laboratory'. As stated above, the 1800 Act had given him £300 per annum.

The minutes of the Society through the years contain many routine references to Higgins and his activities. Samples were sent to him for analysis, the price of admission to his lectures was regulated, and the expenses of running the laboratory were paid[94]. On 28 January 1802, a Committee of Chemistry and Mineralogy with fourteen members was set up to supervise the laboratory and mineral cabinet; control of expenditure over £5 was reserved to the Society. In May 1802, the Society's printers were paid £45 10s. for 650 copies of the syllabus of lectures delivered by the Professors of the Society[93].

In August 1802, the Society acceded to a request of the Irish

Commissioners of Revenue that Higgins should be permitted to proceed to London to serve on a Committee which had been set up to assist 'in ascertaining an Hydrometer which shall be hereafter made use of as the standard to judge of the strength of Spirits. . . .' In October Higgins wrote from London stating that he was afraid that he would not be able to return to Ireland for another month, being detained much longer than he had expected. He was more than optimistic. A book of Minutes which is preserved in the Government Laboratory, London, shows that the first meeting of the Committee was held on 26 January 1803; the last meeting recorded in the book took place on 22 April. Higgins was present at all thirty-eight meetings. The Committee examined the various hydrometers submitted to them with the greatest care and eventually recommended the Sikes' Hydrometer which is still used[95].

The Society appointed Mr Samuel Healy as operator to Higgins in January 1804 at £40 per annum, but in April found it necessary to compensate Healy and let him go, as Higgins could not work with him. Sanction for the appointment of a successor was at first refused; however in December 1805 the Society yielded and appointed Mr Samuel Wharmby as Assistant to Higgins; Wharmby held this post until his death in the winter of 1823–24[96].

The Society was busy in 1807 with the provision of a new laboratory and deciding that plans of laboratories should be obtained from London and the Universities. By 1810 the laboratory was completed and Humphry Davy was invited to lecture on electrochemistry in it. He also addressed the Farming Society on the application of chemistry to agriculture (see Part III, p. 131). The sale of 394 tickets yielded £672 5s. 3d. (Irish)[97] and, after paying Davy 500 guineas sterling and all expenses, the Society netted £39 7s. 9d. (Irish). It may be mentioned that Higgins himself in the next year received, in addition to his salary, 100 guineas sterling from the Society out of the profits of a lecture course. In 1813 he was granted £50.

Davy returned to Ireland in 1811, delivered a lecture course during November and December, and superintended the construction of a large voltaic battery. This time he received £750 (Irish) for 'two excellent courses' in chemistry and geological sciences. The following year the Society decided to separate the professorships of mineralogy and chemistry. A resolution was passed expressing appreciation of Higgins's work in mineralogy and stating the anxiety of the Society that Mr Higgins should devote himself to the work in which he excelled.

As always, Higgins did not have good relationships with those around him. In 1814 he was instructed not to interfere with the lectures of other Professors. In the same year the Society refused to pay £57 for printing his book on the *Atomic Theory*, but in 1815 relented and purchased 300 copies at 5s. each. Other tussles with the Society are described in the Minutes[98]. It is significant that an effort made in 1820 to have Higgins elected an Honorary Member of the Society failed, his name being withdrawn before the ballot.

In April 1817, the Napoleonic wars being over, Higgins obtained leave for six months to go to the continent for scientific business. He took advantage of his presence in London to obtain formal admission to the Royal Society on May 1; he had been elected as far back as June 1806 (see p. 25 below). In 1820 a report on the state of the Society was sent to the Government. A covering letter refers to the Professorship of Chemistry as the first instituted, and with a certain disregard of accuracy claims that Higgins had been specially brought from the University of Oxford to teach chemistry and mineralogy. The report pointed out that many excellent chemists had been formed in the school developed by Higgins and refers to his work on bleaching. In spite of the report the grant to the Society was reduced; it was the same period of retrenchment which cost Higgins his post with the Linen Board[99].

March 1823 found Higgins again out of Ireland. In the following winter Wharmby, who had served him for eighteen years, died and Higgins did not long survive him. In March 1825 he was absent through indisposition; his will is dated 28 April 1825[100], and his death was reported to the Society at the end of June. Although a Professor of Chemistry, he died a wealthy man, thanks to his family connections.

6. HIGGINS'S RESIDENCES

We know something of Higgins's residences in Dublin. When he returned from England in 1792 he had a room in the Apothecaries' Hall in Mary Street, but, as we have seen, he had to leave in 1795. The Dublin Directory for 1802 shows him among the staff of the Dublin Society and living at 6 Grafton Street, while in 1806 his address is given as College Green. A letter in the Minutes of the Linen Board indicates that in March 1808 he was living at 71 Grafton Street; he appears to have remained at this house until his death. He probably had rooms there, as the Directory gives a Richard Folds, Hosier, as occupant. The number was changed to 75 in 1809.

Although he seems to have lived in rooms in Dublin, Higgins left a considerable amount of property when he died. In 1808 he took part in the purchase of a house in Leinster Street, Dublin, for some time the home of his friend Archibald Hamilton Rowan[101]. A document in the Registry of Deeds, Dublin[102], refers to the assignment of land (over 400 acres) near Ballyhaunis, Co. Mayo, by Andrew Higgins to his cousin-german, William Higgins, Professor of Chemistry, for the sum of £2000, the assignment to take effect after Andrew's death, which occurred about 1821. In a report (1821) of a committee appointed by the Royal Dublin Society to examine the practicability of permanently reclaiming bogs and waste lands, there is a letter (p. 37) from Higgins, written from 75 Grafton Street and dated 5 April 1820, in which he refers to experiments he had in hand on the reclamation of a bog on his estate near Ballyhaunis in Co. Mayo.

Finally, in 1823 some two years before his death, Higgins purchased land in Queen's County (now Co. Leix), for £6800[103]. All his property was left to his nephew Captain Charles Higgins, and then passed to Charles's daughters, Mary Jane Josephine O'Connor, Baroness von Haeseler, and Emma Julia, Mrs Peel. The last of Higgins's property was sold by Mary and Emma in 1877[104]. (See Appendix, note 17, p. 55.)

7. PERSONAL REFERENCES TO HIGGINS IN CONTEMPORARY PUBLICATIONS

There are a few personal references to Higgins in contemporary publications. Perhaps the most striking is that of the Irish novelist, Lady Morgan. In her *Book of the Boudoir* published in 1829, she refers to a tea-party, *ca.* 1806, in Kirwan's house, at which she was present. Higgins and Archibald Hamilton Rowan were also guests. She writes (p. 75) of '. . . the good and simple Professor Higgins, with his *air de prêtre*, the very *beau-idéal* of a catholic curate from his own wild native district of Erris' [27, 105] and also (p. 76), 'As soon as Mr Kirwan had settled the constitution of acids with Professor Higgins, he turned to me, with an air of great gallantry, and said, "Let us now revert to a sweeter subject." '

Higgins's appearance seems to have belied his nature, for, as we have seen above, his hasty temper often brought him into trouble. Isaac Weld[88], giving evidence in 1836 before a Select Committee on the Royal Dublin Society, referred (Report, pp. 20, 36) to Higgins as refractory, as attempting to set the Society at defiance and as occasionally capricious and captious. Another member of the Society, Dr W. Harty[106] stated to the same Committee (Report, p. 238), which met in London, that '. . . when Mr Higgins was appointed professor of chemistry, the science was so little known in Ireland that you might as well have sought for a magician as a chemist, and Mr Higgins was considered a paragon, which he certainly then was, not only in Ireland but in this country'. Kirwan[56] refers to Higgins's ability in chemistry. Lord Tullamore, afterwards Earl of Charleville[107], in a note[108] on the analysis of turf ashes mentions a saline mass which he submitted 'to the examination of my ingenious and learned friend Mr Higgins', who 'could not detect a particle of any kind of disengaged *alkali*, though he sought it by some of the nicest tests of modern chemistry'.

Mrs Hamilton Rowan[109] writing in March 1799 to her husband in exile in America states '. . . of late I have been much taken up in attending chemical lectures, and reading sufficient to make me understand them, and from this I often find entertainment when lighter amusements have failed. Until I began I did not know how pleasant a study it was, or that it took in so much of natural philosophy.' Rowan wrote[110] on 4 June 1800 from Wilmington: 'I have put up some trifling pieces of petrification and spar, etc. for your friend Mr Higgins; I will send him a specimen of the soap-stone, which from its extreme softness when taken out of the quarry, and hardening afterwards in the air, is much used. There is a kind of beetle here, more powerful, and quicker in its operation than the Spanish flies; he shall have some of these, as also some of the locusts which have appeared this year, and are said to sink in the earth for seven or eight years, and to be as long rising. There are few persons here to assist me in the collection, and you know I am no naturalist; but trifling as these things may be, they will mark a wish to please the gentleman from whom you have received attentions which diverted your thoughts from scenes in which you have had no pleasant part to act.'

Mrs Rowan wrote[111] on 16 August 1800 with reference to Rowan's return to Europe: 'I have before said I am promised letters of recommendation, as soon as it is known where we mean to live; in what style they will be I cannot say, but I think the Chancellor will do the best he can for us; and from men of science here I shall have letters to men of the same sort in Germany. Ten thousand thanks for your thinking of my good friend Higgins.'

Thomas Egan, M.D., M.R.I.A., in a paper on the 'Nature of Gravelly and Calculus Concretions in the Human Subject' writes of 'our own learned and ingenious professor, Mr William Higgins', and again (p. 274) of 'My ingenious friend, and master in chemistry, Mr Wm. Higgins'[112].

Finally, we may recall that Sullivan[2], writing a little over twenty years after Higgins's death, stated, 'William Higgins appears to have been a man of peculiar habits, possessing very great abilities, and singularly comprehensive views upon science, but totally deficient in energy, and in the ambition of working out to the end any happy ideas in science which might strike him, and in the peculiar tact of putting his opinions forward in such a manner as to call immediate attention to them, without which the most important discoveries may remain for years neglected and barren. He was incapable of making his age comprehend him. His style of lecturing was very quaint, and a number of laughable anecdotes are still remembered of circumstances the result of this quaintness, but which our space, and our respect for his memory, forbid us dwelling on.'

8. HIGGINS AND THE ROYAL IRISH ACADEMY

Higgins became a Member of the Royal Irish Academy on 22 March 1794. He was elected to the Council and the Committee of Science in 1796–98, 1800, 1802, 1804, 1806, 1809, 1814 and 1820–22[113]. His attendances at the meetings of the Council and of the Committee of Science were irregular, averaging about 30 per cent. In these years the Academy went through a difficult period particularly after the Union, when many of its Members were frequently out of the country. The Committee of Science ceased to function in 1810 and was not revived until 1838. Higgins was not prominent at any of the meetings, at least his name seldom appears in the minutes. In 1800 he reported unfavourably on a project which involved the use of common heath plants in tanning. In 1801 he presented a copy of his course in chemistry for the year 1802[93], and in 1814 a copy of his book on the *Atomic Theory*[13].

He was an original member of the Royal Irish Academy Dinner Club which was founded in 1816, and in the period covered by the extant minute book, 1816–21, attended some 70 per cent of the dinners, five of which were held annually. He was also, from its inception, a member of the Kirwanian Society, founded in Dublin in 1812[114], as a tribute to Kirwan, for the cultivation of chemistry, mineralogy and other branches of natural history. The Hon. George Knox[115] was president of the Society and one of the vice-presidents was Dr Robert Blake, who was married to Anne, elder daughter of Bryan Higgins[116]. Bryan himself was an honorary member of the Society which is not listed in the Dublin Directory after 1819.

9. HIGGINS AND THE ROYAL SOCIETY

Higgins was elected a Fellow of the Royal Society on 12 June 1806. In his certificate of election which is preserved in the archives of the Society, he is described as 'Professor of Chemistry

to the Dublin Society. A gentleman distinguished for his knowledge in chemistry and other branches of natural philosophy
and author of a work on the new system of chemistry and of a
treatise on bleaching'[79].

His proposers were Charles Hatchett[117], the Hon. George
Knox[115], Richard Lovell Edgeworth[39], Humphry Davy[118], and
A. G. Eckhardt[119]. Hitherto it has been thought that Higgins
never signed the obligation in the Charter Book of the Society;
actually he did so and, as stated (see p. 21), obtained admittance
on 1 May 1817. The reading of his paper on the analysis of the
human calculus to the Society on 3 April 1788 has been mentioned (p. 5). This paper was communicated by Dr David
Pitcairn, F.R.S.[120].

10. PAPERS PUBLISHED BY HIGGINS

Higgins published only eight papers in the years in which he
practised chemistry. Five[121] like his *Atomic Theory*[13] were
polemical, dealing with his claims to have propounded a chemical
atomic theory in his *Comparative View*[13]; one was an extract
from his essay on bleaching[82]. Of his two experimental papers the
first[122], published in 1811, gave an analysis of a meteor which
fell in Co. Tipperary in August 1810. In 1818 he wrote the
second[123] which dealt with a shower of meteors which fell in Co.
Limerick in September 1813. He attempted to explain the
heating of meteors in falling, by assuming accumulation of
electricity collected in moving through the atmosphere[93, 124].
Reference may again be made to the account of his work on the
analysis of the human calculus which he read to the Royal
Society and printed as an Appendix to the *Comparative View*[43-45].

11. CONCLUSION

Such then was the career of William Higgins. His name is
current in chemical circles, yet in Ireland his memory has died.
His grave is unknown. Circulars to all of the name of Higgins
listed in Irish Directories and letters to newspapers published
in the Republic brought no information to supplement that
from available documents. There is no explanation of why,
having published when he was 26 a book containing ideas in

advance of his time, he wrote nothing further on the subject for twenty years and did little out of the ordinary in chemistry. He then attempted in five papers[121] and his *Atomic Theory*[13] to sustain his claim to have anticipated Dalton who applied the atomic theory to chemistry in the early years of the nineteenth century. His attempt was unsuccessful and he died a disappointed man.

In recent years there has been a growing appreciation among chemists of the value of Higgins's contribution to chemistry. It is difficult, however, to assess his status in relation to the useful application of the atomic theory to chemical phenomena. Since 1814 many people, fifty at least[125], have written to dispute the subject, yet the controversy between 'Daltonians' and 'Higginsians' flares up at intervals and dies down still unextinguished. The remainder of this book is devoted to an examination of Higgins's contribution to chemistry.

Notes to Part I

1. The claims have more recently been discussed by Partington, *Annals of Science*, 1939, *4*, 245; *Nature*, 1955, *176*, 8; and Wheeler, *Endeavour*, 1952, *11*, 47; the matter is more fully examined in Part III of the present book. The particulars of Higgins's life given in Part I are largely taken from articles by Wheeler in *Studies*, Dublin, 1954, *54*, 78–91, 207–215, 327–331 (which have been reproduced by permission of the Rev. R. Burke-Savage, S.J., editor of that journal).

2. W. K. Sullivan, *Dublin Quart. J. Medical Science*, 1849, *8*, 465–495. An account of this Irish chemist (1823?–90) is given in *Studies*, 1945, *34*, 21, 36. Sullivan was about 26 when he wrote on Bryan (see Appendix) and William Higgins; too young, perhaps, to verify all his references.

3. See Appendix, particularly note 14 (p. 55).

4. This is clear from the wills of: (i) Bryan Higgins (in Somerset House, London); (ii) his daughters, Mrs Anne Blake and Mrs Charlotte Golding (abstracts in Public Record Office (P.R.O.), Dublin); (iii) Mrs Anne Blake's daughter, Elinor Stephens, née Blake, whose will is one of those of which a complete copy is available in the P.R.O., Dublin. Most of the records were destroyed by fire in 1922.

5. Sullivan states that Bryan Higgins died in 1820, but his will was proved in January 1819. There is a discrepancy between the year of Bryan's birth indicated by Sullivan (1736–37) and that listed in the record of students at Leyden University (*ca.* 1741). This record is said to be unreliable in regard to the age of students. (R. W. Innes Smith, *English-speaking Students of Medicine at the University of Leyden*, 1932.) The entry reads 'Higgins (Higgius) Bryan, Hibernus, Oct. 5, 1765, *aet.* 24, Med.' Again the property in London owned by Bryan Higgins was in Lincoln's Inn (his will) and not in King's Inns (Sullivan). There is a King's Inns in Dublin, but not in London. William nowhere says that Bryan was his uncle and Bryan (*Nicholson's Journal*, 1802, *1*, 130) refers to William as his cousin. Davy (*Discourse to the Royal Society*, November 1826; *Award of a Royal Medal to John Dalton, F.R.S.*; *Works*, 1840, 7, 95–96), uses the word 'relation'. Sullivan, however, is probably correct about the uncle–nephew relationship. The Oxford Dictionary states that 'cousin' was formerly often applied to nephew or niece.

6. In the National Library, Dublin.

7. Archdeacon T. O'Rorke, *History of Sligo*, 1890, *2*, 505.

8. There are references to the possessions of the O'Higgin or O'Huiginn family in the records (in the P.R.O., Dublin) of *Exchequer Inquisitions* (*post mortem* and on attainder) for the county of Sligo (Elizabeth–Charles I). O'Higgin also figures in the genealogies in the Mss. *Linea Antiqua* by Roger O'Ferral in the National Library, Dublin. It has not, however, been found possible to link any of these references with direct ancestors of

28

William's grandfather, Bryan (see Appendix). Owing to the land sequestration and the Penal Laws this hiatus is common in Irish genealogy.

9. See (Miss) Eleanor Knott, *The Bardic Poems of Tadgh Dall O'Huiginn* (1550–91). *Irish Texts Society*, 1922, *22*; 1926, *23*. This work contains details of Exchequer Inquisitions relating to O'Huiginn property and also a genealogy to 1650. Miss Knott believes that the name Higgins is from the Norse for a 'viking'.

10. The authors are indebted to Dr Eileen MacCarvill of University College, Dublin, for this suggestion. It is of interest to note that Dr John Higgins (*ca.* 1678–1729), the son of Dr Patrick Higgins, whose family came originally from Connaught, rose to be Chief Physician to the King of Spain. (Marquis Patrick MacSwiney, *Studies*, 1939, *28*, 63–84.)

11. See Appendix, note 2, p. 50.

12. Bryan the elder resided in Collooney, about six miles south of Sligo. Sullivan (footnote 2), says William was born in Co. Sligo. (See Appendix, note 4, p. 50) Lady Morgan (p. 23) refers to the Erris district of Co. Mayo as William's native place.

13. William's statement in his *Experiments and Observations on the Atomic Theory* (1814, p. 7), that he was a very young man in 1788 when he started work on his first book (*A Comparative View of the Phlogistic and Antiphlogistic Theories*, 1789), led previous biographers to assume that he was born about 1766. To William writing when he was over 50, 25 must have seemed young to be engaged in polemics with the great. However, thirty years ago, R. T. Gunther (*Notes and Queries*, 1929, *157*, 421; 14 December 1929), drew attention to an entry in Joseph Foster's *Alumni Oxonienses* (1715–1886) (1888, *2*, 657), which reads: 'Higgins, William, s. Thomas, of Mayo, Ireland, gent. Magdalen Hall, matric 6 Feb., 1786, aged 23', and which shows that William was born in 1762–63. (see note 27 below). It was in the *Comparative View* that Higgins put forward his new ideas on the atomic theory.

   The thanks of the authors are due to Mr Edward Keane of the P.R.O., Dublin, and to Mr Lionel E. Salt, formerly Bursar of Pembroke College, Oxford, who independently informed them of the entry in Foster, and to Mr J. C. T. MacDonagh who directed their attention to the entry in *Notes and Queries*.

14. Since the Higgins family was Catholic, it would have been difficult for him to be educated at other than ephemeral 'hedge-schools'. On the chance that he might have gone to a school under the protection of the State, enquiries have been made about the archives of some of the eighteenth-century schools in the Sligo district. Records for the Higgins period have not, however, been found. The authors' thanks are due to Mr T. H. Blackburn, Headmaster, Sligo Grammar and High School, and Mr W. T. Ardill, who have kindly assisted in these enquiries.

15. In the *Comparative View* (p. xii), William states: 'I am indebted to Dr Higgins for my first instructions in chemistry who is a phlogistian.' (Some account of the life of Bryan Higgins is given in the Appendix and in Part III, p. 124.) There is a description and plan of Bryan Higgins's laboratory in *The Operative Chemists* by Samuel Frederick Gray (London, 1828). The authors are grateful to Mr E. C. Cripps who drew their attention to this reference; see also J. C. Hanbury, *Chemistry and Industry*, 1952. 300.

In those days it was necessary for Irish Catholic students to go abroad for professional education. Of thirty-six medical graduates of the University of Edinburgh between the years 1784–90, four were Scottish, six English, one Dutch, one American, and the residual twenty-four, Irish. Kendall, *Proc. Roy. Soc., Edinburgh*, 1952, *63*, 348, 392.

16. *Nicholson's Journal*, 1802, *1*, 130. William himself in the *Comparative View*, p. 164, states that he could not follow up an investigation because he was 'busy in assisting at a public course of chemistry, at Oxford' (see Part II, section on 'The Presence of Bile in Blood', p. 108).

17. Sir Joseph Banks (1743–1820), was President of the Royal Society from 1778 until his death. His house in Soho Square, London, purchased in 1777, became a meeting place of scientists (*Dict. of Nat. Biog.*; *Journal of Sir Joseph Banks*, London, 1896). Higgins (*Comparative View*, 309–310) mentions a visit to Banks's house about April 1785, to show his method of reduction of nitric acid to ammonia by means of tin (see Part II, p. 105). William Austin, who was a friend of Higgins (see note 25), mentions (*Phil. Trans.*, 1788, *78*, 379–388) the exhibition of this experiment at Sir Joseph Banks's house, some years before (see Sir Henry Lyons, *The Royal Society (1660–1940)*, Cambridge, 1944).

18. Richard Kirwan (1733–1812), the famous Irish chemist, was, as will be seen from the text (pp. 11, 17, 18, 23, 33, 37), William Higgins's patron and friend. He lived in Newman Street, London, from 1777 to 1787, when he returned to Dublin. His London house, like that of Sir Joseph Banks, was a rendezvous for famous scientists of the day. Higgins (*Phil. Mag.*, 1818, *51*, 172), refers to his 'illustrious friend Kirwan'.

A letter written by John Lloyd, F.R.S. to Banks on 13 August 1783 states that Kirwan, whom Lloyd had earlier visited in Dublin, seemed. quite lost and discontented in Ireland and would, if his daughters were settled, probably return to England. When Kirwan first went to Ireland Banks gave him a letter to Thomas Percy, Bishop of Dromore, requesting him to introduce Kirwan to the literati of Ireland. (Information supplied by Mr Warren R. Dawson.)

Kirwan bequeathed his books to the Royal Irish Academy in which they now are. This was his second library, however, for by an odd chance his first library is in the 'Salem Athenaeum' in Salem, near Boston, Massachusetts. In 1780 he had his books sent in the British ship *Mars* from Galway to London where he was residing. The ship was captured off the English coast by an American privateer. The privateer's captain took his prize into Beverly near Salem on 9 February 1781.

The following advertisement appeared in the Salem *Gazette and General Advertiser* of 3 April 1781:

AT BEVERLY

That Copper Bottom fast sailing frigate built ship MARS, burthen 450 tons, more or less, is pierced for and did mount 24 carriage Guns,
captured by the Ship Pilgrim, Joseph Robinson, Commander, Will be sold,
On Wednesday, 11 Instant at X o'clock. For the inventory of Tackle, Apparel, and Furniture, apply to J. Hiller or J. Grafton.

The books were bought on 12 April 1781 by an association of local gentlemen. The record written by the Rev. Joseph Willard, afterwards President of Harvard University, states that 'all 116 volumes were sold for the sum of eight hundred and fifty eight pounds, ten shillings in paper money; the exchange at that time between the paper Currency and Gold or Silver being at the Rate of seventy five pounds in Paper for one in Silver, equal to $38. 16.

'The Cheapness of this purchase arose from the disposition of the Gentlemen who owned the Ship to favor the Purchasers all in their power.'

The list of books is given below; included are 'a few additions by gift of members' which are not distinguished. It is recorded that the *Transactions of the Philosophical Society in London* and of the *French Academy of Arts and Sciences*, which were among the volumes in Kirwan's library, were at first purchased locally to be used for wrapping paper, but were later added to the new library. There are many more than 116 volumes (see above) in the list—some are obviously later than 1780. The catalogue is given with misspellings as printed.

Folios

R. Boyle's Works, 5 vols.   Harris's Lexicon Technicum, 2 vols.

Quartos

Philosophical Transactions, a-bridged, 10 vols.

Philosophical Transactions, at large, from Vol. 47 (1753) to vol. 98 (1808).

Memoires de l'Academie Royale des Sciences, Depuis 1666 jusqu'à 1699, 11 vols.

Histoire de l'Academie Royale des Sciences from 1699 to 1790.

Miscellaneous Berelinensia, 7 vols.

Ames's Art of Printing.

Buffon Histoire Naturelle, 15 vols.

Johannis Bernoulli Opera, 4 vols.

Jacobi Bernoulli Opera, 2 vols.

C. Wolfii Elementa Mathesees, 5 vols.

I. Newtoni Principia, 4 vols.

Traitè des Sections Coniques.

Maclaurin's Fluxions, 2 vols.

Smith's Optics.

Priestley's Optics.

Franklin on Electricity.

Knight on Attraction and Repulsion, Mercator's Sailing, and Bird's Method of Dividing Instruments, Mr. Winthrop's Lecture on Earthquakes. Bound together.

Arbuthnott's Tables of Ancient Measures, etc.

Memoirs of ye American Academy.

Transactions of ye American Philosophical Society, 6 vols.

Index to the Philosophical Transactions.

Mahon's Principles of Electricity.

Sprat's History of the Royal Society.

Encyclopedia Britanica, 18 vols, with Appendix, 3 vols.

Costard's History of Astronomy.

Transactions of the Royal Society, Edinburgh, 5 vols.

Fabricii Bibliotheca Graeca, 14 vols.

Pennant's Artic Zoology, 3 vols.

Taylor's Proclus, 2 vols.

Octavos

Leadbetter's Astronomy, 2 vols.

Newton's Arithmetic.

Keil's Introduction to Philosophy.

Keil's Astronomical Lectures.

Stewart's Tracts.

Rehault's Physics.

Maupertuis' Figure of ye Earth.

Goldsmith's Philosophy, 2 vols.

Priestley on Electricity, 2 vols.

Priestley's Philosophical Experiments, 2 vols.

Stewart on ye Distance of ye Sun from ye Earth, Winthrop's 2 lectures on Comets, Winthrop's Lectures on ye use of ye Transit of Venus, Oliver's Essay on Comets. Bound together.

Spallanzini Dissertations, 2 vols.

Sir John Pringle Discourse to the Royal Society.

Jefferson's Notes on Virginia.

Ingenhouz Experiments on Vegetables.

Darwin's Botanic Garden, 2 vols.

Repertory of Arts and Manufactures, Series 1, 16 vols; Series II, 13 vol.

Pennant's British Zoology, 4 vols.

Spallanzani's Tracts.

Newton's Optics.

Kirwan on Climates.

Tilloch's Philosophical Magazine, 32 vols.

The captured books became the nucleus of the Salem 'Philosophical Library'. An offer of remuneration was afterwards made to Kirwan who generously declined it, expressing his satisfaction that his erstwhile library had found so useful a destination. (See Essex Institute, Salem, *Historical Collections*, vol. 9, pt. 2, pp. 17, 18.)

In 1810 the Philosophical Library was united with the Social Library (founded in 1760) to form the Salem Athenaeum. Nathaniel Hawthorne was connected with this latter institution.

Donovan in the *Proc. Roy. Irish Acad.* (see below) says that the books were despatched from Galway on 5 September 1780 in a vessel belonging to that port and were captured a few days later by an American privateer. He says that the captain of the privateer was Thomas Kirwan who was descended from the Irish Kirwans. He also states that the privateer seized the library only and allowed the vessel to proceed. To balance those errors, the Salem records say that the captured ship was taking the library to a literary institution in Quebec.

The authors' thanks are due to the staffs of the Irish Consulate at Boston and of the Essex Institute, Salem, for helpful information. They are indebted to Mrs George F. Brown, Librarian of the Salem Athenaeum, who in March 1957 gave one of us (T.S.W.) many details. It was interesting to see at Salem, Kirwan's characteristic signature which appears so often in his library in the Royal Irish Academy. Unfortunately the books were not set apart as the 'Kirwan Library' but were placed with others of their class, with no direct way of identifying them as part of that library. There are three or four having the characteristic Kirwan signature and one having the engraved book-plate of Richard Kirwan, *The History of the Royal Society*, London, 1734.

A Calendar of the correspondence of Sir Joseph Banks by Mr Warren R. Dawson, published in 1958, contains seven letters from Kirwan all written from Dublin between 1788 and 1802. He mentions in a letter dated April 1797, that about 1400 copies of Volume 2 of his Mineralogy printed in Dublin were captured the previous September by a French privateer and taken to Morlaix in Finisterre. He had, accordingly, sent a copy to London for reprinting. Kirwan also remarks: 'Experimental Philosophy has as yet made no progress here. Higgins gives good chymical lectures, but is attended but by professional men or Mechanics, yet in time I hope they may kindle a spark of curiosity in some breasts; to all appearances that time is as yet distant.'

The authors are grateful to Mr Warren R. Dawson for supplying a proof of his abstracts of the Kirwan letters and to the authorities of the British Museum for photostats of the originals.

For an authoritative life of Kirwan see (V. Rev.) P. J. McLaughlin, *Studies*, 1939, *28*, 461, 593; 1940, *29*, 71, 281. Other material of biographical interest is contained in: Lady Morgan, (see p. 23 and note 105, p. 45) *The Book of the Boudoir*, 1829, 54–89; John O'Reardon, *National Magazine*, Dublin, 1830, *1*, 330, 469; Pickells, *British Association*, Cork, 1843 *Transactions*, 39; *Proc. Roy. Irish Acad.*, 1850, *4*, 481; M. Donovan, *Proc. Roy. Irish Acad.*, 1850, *4*, Appendix No. viii, p. lxxxi; J. O'Neill Mackle, *Reminiscences of Dr Richard Kirwan*, 1862 (in National Library, Dublin); J. Reilly and N. O'Flynn, *Isis*, 1930, *13*, 298–319.

19. *Phil. Mag.*, 1816, *48*, 410; see also *Comparative View*, p. 249.
20. *Comparative View*, p. xi.
21. pp. 309–313.
22. Dr Richard Brocklesby (1722–97) (see *Dict. Nat. Biog.*), was born in Somerset, and educated in Ireland with Edmund Burke. He studied medicine at Edinburgh, graduated M.D. at Leyden and practised in London. See *Comparative View*, p. 310. He was a friend of Johnson, being mentioned by Boswell, and was a subscriber to Bryan Higgins's *Society for Philosophical Experiments and Conversations* (see note 53), which met in 1794. His famous nephew, Thomas Young (1773–1829), physician, physicist and Egyptologist, was also a member (see Arago, *Records of General Science*, 1836, *3*, 245. Arago confuses Bryan and William Higgins and in an editorial note states, wrongly, that William was Bryan's son.)

Higgins (*Comparative View*, p. 91) refers to a visit to the Royal Society with Dr Brocklesby to see Cavendish's experiment on sparking nitrogen and oxygen. He mentions an accident to the apparatus that had occurred the day before the visit. In the published account of the work (*Phil. Trans.*, 1788, *78*, 261) the date of the accident is given as 23 January 1788. The authors' thanks are due to Dr D. C. Martin, Assistant Secretary of the Royal Society, for help with this reference. (See Part II, p. 66.)

23. Published in 1799. The work is discussed in Section 4, p. 13.
24. Dr John Gideon Caulet, M.D. (1750–86), who was educated at Cambridge, was one of the physicians at St Bartholomew's Hospital. Higgins (*C.V.*, 310–312), refers to his chemical work, and incidentally calls him 'Caulett'. (See W. Munk, *Roll of the Royal College of Physicians of London*, 1878, *2*, 338.)
25. Dr William Austin (1754–93), a friend of Higgins (see for example *Comparative View*, 62, 71–80, 312–313; note 17, above), was a physician with a knowledge of chemistry. He obtained the degree of M.D. at Oxford in 1783, and practised in Oxford, being physician to the Radcliffe Infirmary. In 1785 he was appointed University professor of chemistry,

D

but resigned when on 10 August 1786 he became physician to St Bartholomew's Hospital, London, in succession to Dr J. G. Caulet. He did much to improve the teaching of chemistry in the hospital. There is a passing reference to Higgins in a treatise on the stone (p. 100) by Austin (London, 1791). (Information kindly supplied by Dr Gweneth Whitteridge, Archivist to St Bartholomew's Hospital; see also *Dict. Nat. Biog.*)

26. Magdalen Hall became independent of Magdalen College in 1602, and was converted into Hertford College, Oxford, in 1874. The Principal of Hertford College writes that the records of the old Magdalen Hall have been destroyed by fire. Mr Colin A. Cooke, Bursar of Magdalen College, Oxford, kindly assisted in the enquiries. R. T. Gunther (*Early Science at Oxford*, 1937, *11*, 254; see also *Notes and Queries*, 1929, *157*, 421; 14 December 1929), says of Magdalen Hall: 'Although small in size, the Hall was great in attainment, at least as far as its scientific members were concerned.'

27. Mr Lionel E. Salt, Fellow and formerly Bursar of Pembroke College, Oxford, considers that the entry in Foster (note 13 above), refers to the William Higgins of this article, since it would have been most unusual for a student not to have matriculated and to have escaped inclusion in Foster. *The Dictionary of National Biography* which states that Higgins did not matriculate is probably in error. Although the Foster entry assigns William's father, Thomas, to Co. Mayo, and not to the neighbouring Co. Sligo, Irish gentry of the time moved about leasing estates for short periods. Again, Foster often gives the son's birthplace as the father's residence. (See Appendix, note 4.) While William Higgins matriculated, he did not graduate, though Sullivan states the contrary (see p. 3).

28. Mr Salt (see note 27) states that migration from one College to another was then common.

29. It may here be mentioned that A. N. Meldrum (*New Ireland Review*, 1909–10, *32*, 350), mentions that he was not able to obtain the slightest information about William Higgins from the then authorities of Pembroke College. Not only did Mr Salt search his Buttery Books, but he very kindly sent a photostat of a page of a Buttery Book containing Higgins's name and assisted frequently with advice. The authors wish to express their deep appreciation of Mr Salt's assistance.

Since these notes were first compiled one of us (T.S.W.) has had, through the courtesy of the Bursar, Mr G. R. F. Bredin, C.B.E., an opportunity of inspecting the Buttery Books of Pembroke College, Oxford. These show that though William Higgins ceased to reside in the College in August 1788, his name remained on the books and he visited the College at intervals. He stayed there for a few days in March, June, and September and, for the last time, in December 1790. His name then disappears from the books.

30. William Adams (1706–89), divine, Master of Pembroke College (1775–89), was a friend of Johnson who visited him at Oxford in 1784. Gilbert[32], Smithson[33], and Beddoes[39] were at Pembroke under Adams. (See Douglas Macleane, *History of Pembroke College, Oxford*, 1897; *Pembroke College (Oxford College Histories)*, 1900; R. T. Gunther, *Early Science at Oxford*, 1923, *1*, 60–64; 1937, *11*, 277; *Notes and Queries*, 1929, *157*, 421; 14 December 1929; *Dict. Nat. Biog.*)

31. Dr Martin Wall, F.R.S. (1747–1824), reader in chemistry at Oxford

(1781–85), stated that Adams was 'considerably deep in chemistry'. (R. T. Gunther, *Early Science at Oxford*, 1923, *1*, 64; D. Macleane, *History of Pembroke College, Oxford*, 1897, 393.) An interesting account of Wall's lectures in chemistry based on the letters of a student, John James (1760–86; *Dict. Nat. Biog.*), is given by Gunther (*op. cit.*, *1*, p. 61). In 1785 Wall was elected Lichfield professor of clinical medicine at Oxford. He is mentioned by Higgins on p. 177 of the *Comparative View*. Further details of Wall's life are given by W. Munk (*Roll of the Royal College of Physicians of London*, 1878, *2*, 372; see also *Dict. Nat. Biog.*).

32. Dr Davies Gilbert (1767–1839), president of the Royal Society (1827–30), matriculated at Pembroke College on 12 April 1785, and obtained the degree of M.A. in 1789. He brought Davy to the notice of Beddoes (note 39 below). R. T. Gunther (*Early Science in Oxford*, 1937, *11*, 279; *Notes and Queries*, 1929, *157*, 421) refers to Davies Gilbert as Gilbert Davies.

33. James Smithson, F.R.S. (1765–1829), founder of the Smithsonian Institute at Washington, matriculated at Pembroke College, Oxford, in 1782, and was soon distinguished as a student of mineralogy and chemistry. *Dict. Nat. Biog.*

34. *Phil. Mag.*, 1819, *53*, 405.

35. Dr James Haworth (*ca.* 1762–1823), matriculated 7 December 1782, at Brasenose College, Oxford. He was awarded a Radcliffe travelling fellowship in 1791, and was the first of the travelling fellows to visit the New World. He was appointed a physician to St Bartholemew's Hospital in 1802. (W. Munk, *Roll of the Royal College of Physicians*, London, 1878, *3*, 11; see also *A Picture of the Present State of the Royal College of Physicians of London*, 1817, 81.)

36. Information supplied by Mr L. E. Salt, See note 29.

37. E.g., *C.V.*, 164, 176, 300, 312–313.

38. See note 16 and corresponding text (p. 2).

39. Thomas Beddoes (1760–1808), chemist and physician, matriculated at St Johns' College, Oxford, in 1775, but in 1776 migrated to Pembroke. Later he studied medicine in London and Edinburgh and obtained the degree of M.D. (Oxford) in 1786. He was appointed public reader in chemistry in 1788, and attracted the largest class that had been assembled in chemistry in Oxford since the thirteenth century. (See Robinson, *Annals of Science*, 1955, *11*, 137.) He resigned his readership in 1792, and in 1798 he established a 'Pneumatic Institution' at Clifton for the treatment of disease by inhalation and, there engaged Humphry Davy as its superintendent. He married in 1794, Anna, sister of Maria Edgeworth (1767–1849), the Irish novelist and daughter of Richard Lovell Edgeworth (1744–1817), writer and educationalist (*Dict. Nat. Biog.*; J. E. Stock, *Memoirs of the Life of Thomas Beddoes, M.D.*, London, 1811). Davy described Beddoes, perhaps unfairly: 'As little fitted for a Mentor as a weather-cock for a compass.' He contributed several papers to the Royal Society and one to the Chemical Society of the University of Edinburgh in 1785–86, and in 1789 informed Black as he informed Higgins (see p. 5) that Priestley had overthrown Lavoisier's theory. (Kendall, *J. Roy. Soc. Edinburgh*, 1952, *63*, 350, 392.) Beddoes had at first adopted the theory (see Crell's *Annalen*, 1789, I, 32, 45 (why he abandoned it)). He translated Scheele's *Chemical Essays* (1786), added notes to E. Cullen's translation of Bergman's *Essays* (1784–88), and

published *Chemical Experiments and Opinions, Extracted from a Work published in the last century*, Oxford, 1790, in which he drew attention to Mayow's *Tractabus Quinque*, Oxford, 1674, and gave extracts from it. See Partington, *Isis*, 1956, *47*, 217.

40. Implied by Stock (note 39), p. 18.

41. *New Ireland Review*, 1909–10, *32*, p. 351.

42. Mr L. E. Salt (notes 27–29 above) states that appointments earlier than the nineteenth century were made as funds permitted; the level of the appointment was similarly determined. Thus Austin, resigning as professor in 1786, was not succeeded by Beddoes as reader until 1788.

43. *Comparative View*, pp. xiii, 283.

44. *Letters and Papers*, Decade ix, No. 82. Higgins seems to have had an interest in medical chemistry. In the paper (see p. 304 of the *Comparative View*), Higgins refers to a discussion with Beddoes, who did not become reader until 1788. As the paper was finished before April 1787, the discussion may have taken place when Beddoes was in Oxford to receive the M.D. in December 1786 (see p. 66 below).

45. *Journal Book of the Royal Society*, p. 169. The authors thank the Officers and Librarian of the Royal Society for this information.

46. Higgins states (*Phil. Mag.*, 1816, *48*, 364; 1819, *53*, 405; *Atomic Theory*, p. 7), that he wrote the *Comparative View* in 1788 and published it in March 1789. A second edition was published in 1791 (see note 13).

47. Information kindly supplied by the late Dr. F. Sherwood Taylor, Director of the Science Museum, London. The building now houses the Museum of the History of Science of which Dr Taylor was formerly Curator. The Ashmolean Museum was founded by the English antiquarian, Elias Ashmole (1617–92). Dr Taylor stated that nitre still grows on the walls of the room in which Higgins worked. A bottle containing nitre and labelled 'Nitre from the walls of the Museum' was recently found by the present Curator, Dr C. H. Josten. (See Part II, p. 67.)

48. *Comparative View*, p. 177. John James (note 31) refers to Wall's interest in nitre. (Gunther, *Early Science in Oxford*, 1923, *1*, 63; *Dict. Nat. Biog.*)

49. See note 15. A later work of Bryan [*Minutes of the Society for Philosophical Experiments and Conversations*, 1795 (see note 53)], shows that he afterwards adopted Lavoisier's views.

50. *Atomic Theory* (see note 13), p. 10.

51. The *Monthly Review*, 1789, *81*, 197, gives the price as 7s. The *Analytical Review*, 1789, *4*, 177, the *English Review*, 1790, *15*, 188, and the *Critical Review*, 1790, *70*, 545, state 6s. Messrs John Murray, London, who published the *Comparative View*, have kindly made a search of their records, but have been unable to find any reference to their transactions with William Higgins.

52. British Museum Mss., No. 38392/f/104. See also Board of Trade, Minutes (B.T. 5), Volume 6, p. 204, Public Record Office, London; Roy Soc. Arts, London, Minute Book, 19 May 1790, and Minutes of the Committee of Manufactures, 9 November 1790; Madison, note 53 below.

53. The Ambrose Godfrey mentioned was probably a grandson (*d*. 1797), of Ambrose Godfrey Hanckwitz (1660–1741), Boyle's assistant, two of whose sons, Ambrose and John, carried on their father's business as a manufacturing chemist in Southampton Street (see note 58) on the south side of Covent Garden where it was continued until 1916–17 as a

purely pharmaceutical concern under the name of Godfrey and Cooke. The third son, Boyle, settled in Dublin, and his son Ambrose succeeded to his uncle's business. Ambrose Godfrey and Charles Gomond Cook [sic] both of Southampton Street, were subscribers to Bryan Higgins's 'Society for Philosophical Experiments and Conversations' which was established on 25 January 1794 with a subscription of five guineas. The first Chairman was Field-Marshal Conway, friend of Horace Walpole, and it met for a period of six months at Higgins's house in Greek Street, Soho. See note 22 and Appendix note 5, also pp. 115, 124. The list of subscribers is given in the *Minutes* published in 1795. Cooke is mentioned in Ambrose Godfrey's will (Somerset House, London; Probate Book (Exeter), folio 239). (See R. B. Pilcher, *Royal Institute of Chemistry Lectures*: 'Alchemists in Art and Literature', 1933, 45; 'A Century of Chemistry: From Boyle to Priestley', 1940, 8, 22; *Ambix*, 1938, 2, 17; see also *Dict. Nat. Biog.*; M. E. Weeks, 'Discovery of the Elements', Easton, Pa., 1959; Madison, *Notes and Records of the Royal Society of London*, 1955, *11*, 159; *Annals of Science*, 1955, *11*, 64.)

54. On the title page of the *Comparative View*, Higgins also describes himself as of Pembroke College, Oxford; see also p. 5 above.

55. See the *Acts of the Irish Parliament* and the *Journal of the Irish House of Commons*. The Hall is now called the 'Apothecaries' Hall'. The account of Higgins's connection with the Hall is based on the actual Minute Book. Capitals, spelling and punctuation in extracts from the minutes are as in the somewhat capricious original. We are greatly indebted to a previous Registrar, the late Dr J. T. Daniel, and to his successor, Miss Mary J. Barnett, now Mrs Carroll, who made the Minute Book freely available. Sullivan was forced to depend on a few abstracts made by a medical friend, Dr Charles H. Leet, and these have had to serve other biographers.

56. The Directors were ahead of most moderns in their appreciation of the difference between a chemist and apothecary. It is of interest to note that Dr John Berkenhout in the preface to his *First Lines of Theory and Practice of Philosophical Chemistry* (London, 1788), writes, 'Persons, who know nothing more of Chemistry than the name, naturally suppose it to be a trade exercised by the shopkeepers, called *Druggists and Chemists*, who are thought to be chiefly employed in preparing medicines for the use of apothecaries. . . .' There are several references to Bryan Higgins in Berkenhout's book.

In a paper (*Trans. Roy. Irish Acad.*, 1794, *5*, 244) on 'Experiments on a New Earth found near Stronthian [sic] in Scotland', Kirwan states that he was assisted in his experiments 'by Mr Higgins, superintendent of our Apothecaries Hall, whose chemical abilities are well known, and likely to be eminently useful to this country'. Higgins was chemist not superintendent; the latter term never occurs in the Minute Book. Kirwan has misled a number of Higgins's biographers.

57. Higgins's salary with no income-tax would together with his lodging and perquisites (10 tons of coal and 50 lbs. of candles per annum) amount to about £1000 per annum at present values. (Information supplied by Senator Professor George O'Brien, Litt.D.) He was under 30, so that his salary compares well with that of a modern chemist of the same

age. Higgins was the best paid of the Hall's officials, the Apothecary (the next in rank) received £80 per annum (Meeting of 8 April 1794). The salary first fixed for the chemist was £150 per annum.

58. The rate-books (in Holborn Town Hall) for the Red Lion Square area give the name of the householder in 1791 as Eleanor Newton with the name Mary Scott in pencil above it. For 1792–93 the name is Henry Scott. It would seem, therefore, that Higgins lived in lodgings. (Information supplied by Mr Edmund Nicholls.) No. 37 Dombey Street, formerly East Street, in Holborn, near Southampton Row, was destroyed in an air raid in the last war. Higgins's residence was near Godfrey and Cooke's business (see note 53 above). Another son of Oxford, one greater than Higgins, was later associated with East Street; Cardinal Newman's parents lived at No. 13 in 1822. (O'Faolain: *Newman's Way*, London, Longmans Green, 1952.)

59. In connection with the laboratory of the Apothecaries' Hall, see *History of the City of Dublin*, by J. Warburton, J. Whitelaw and R. Walsh, 1818, *2*, 747.

60. Higgins's appointment dated from 20 March 1792; he was not appointed in 1791 as previous biographers have stated. Every officer upon appointment had to give security for the faithful discharge of his duty. (Minute, dated 14 September 1791.)

61. Higgins's duties were listed as follows: 'to receive Such Simples from the Committee of Directors (as may be necessary) To Prepare the Chymicals or Galenicals Ordered by the Court or Committee of Directors and to give a Receipt or Receipts for the Same to prepare all Such Chemicals and Galenicals as may be ordered by the Committee of Directors and none other in the Best Possible Manner to endeavour to turn all caput Mortuums and Residuums to advantage and to have a general attention to Oeconomy to lay before the Court of Directors or any Committee appointed by it for the purpose of attending to his Department an Account of all preparations made by him and their respective Products and at least once in every Week lay before the Court of Directors an Account of all Utensils Received, Impaired, or Broken, and lay before the Same Court or Committee all Chymicals and Galenicals when finished for their Imputition. To lay before the Court of Directors or its Committee any alteration or Amendment that he may deem proper to Make in the Laboratory or its Vaults.'

62. Thomas Conolly (1738–1803) was member for Londonderry in the Irish Parliament (1761–1800), while in the British Parliament he was member for Malmesbury (1759–68), and for Chichester (1768–84). He held various offices in Ireland and was one of those who advocated the Union of the two Parliaments. The *Dictionary of National Biography* quotes that 'bad as a statesman, worse as an orator, he was as a sportsman, preeminent'.

63. It may be of interest to give the results of an analysis of a water as carried out in 1794; the extract is from the Minute Book of the Hall.

A Wine Gallon of the new Spa, such as sent to me and said to be lately discovered near Leixlip on the Estate of the Rt. Honble. Mr Connolly [*sic*] contains of Muriated Mineral Alkali dried in the Temperature of 200 Fraenheits

[*sic*] Thermom.	30.37
Muriated Vegetable Alkali	2.07
Vitriolated Vegetable Alkali	.7
Muriated Lime	8.73
Vitriolated Lime	1.0
Aerated Lime	13.44
Muriated Magnesia	.97
Argil or Clay	.50
Silex or Earth of Flints	.25
Bituminous matter	.14

Found to yield in the temperature 212

Barometer 29.35 Thermometer 70	Cubic Inches
of Fixable Air	1.50
Atmospheric Air	2.15

This is a very detailed analysis for the time.

64. This is perhaps an indication of Higgins's tendency to be difficult. At the same meeting the Directors sanctioned the appointment of an assistant to Higgins at £50 per annum.

65. William Wentworth, Earl of Fitzwilliam (1748–1833), was appointed Lord Lieutenant of Ireland in December 1794, but was recalled within three months on account of his desire for Catholic Emancipation. He was succeeded by the Earl of Camden (1759–1840), who had some responsibility for a policy which led to the rising of 1798.

66. Henry Grattan (1746–1820) played a prominent part in obtaining legislative independence for Ireland in 1782. He strongly opposed the union of the British and Irish Parliaments. He was one of the greatest of Irish statesmen and orators. (See *Dict. Nat. Biog.*)

67. Sullivan (see note 2 above) wrote: 'Whether the Company thought the salary so very high, that they did not think any amount of work on the part of their chemist sufficient, or for some other reasons, Higgins did not remain with them more than two or three years.' Actually he was there from 20 March 1792 to 20 June 1795.

Meldrum (*New Ireland Review*, 1909–10, *32*, 352) wrote, 'He [Higgins] gave up a post at the Apothecaries' Hall worth more than £200 a year for one at £100, and no reason has ever been offered for this. I suggest that with his uncle's (Bryan Higgins) example before him he had felt the impulse to give lectures and take pupils in chemistry, that he was not at liberty to do so at the Apothecaries' Hall, and that he went to the Dublin Society in the expectations that there he might teach if he would.'

McLaughlin (*Three Centuries of Irish Chemists*; edited by D. Ò. Raghallaigh, Cork University Press, 1941, 3) states that the Dublin Society 'stole' Higgins from the Apothecaries' Hall.

68. In 1820 the title 'Dublin Society' was changed to 'Royal Dublin Society', when George IV, as a mark of appreciation of the loyal address presented by the Society on his accession, was pleased to become its Patron.

69. The account of Higgins's work with the Irish Linen Board is based on the Proceedings (Minutes) of the Board Meetings. There appears to be no complete set of these Minutes in Dublin since the destruction of the Public Record Office in 1922. However, the broken sets in the National

Library, the Library of the Royal Irish Academy and in University College Library, provide for the period of Higgins's connection with the Board a set from which the only volumes missing are those for 1800 and 1802–1804. An account of the early work of the Board is given in *Precedents and Abstracts from the Journal of the Trustees of the Linen and Hempen Manufactures of Ireland to the twenty-fifth of March, 1737* (published 1784). These were compiled by James Corry who was in the service of the Board from 1790 until the Board was dissolved in 1828. Corry succeeded his father as Secretary in 1795; father–son succession was an eighteenth-century method of superannuation. He found later that his father had died owing the Board over £13,000. The defalcation was discovered by the Commissioners of Public Accounts in 1805 (Minutes of 15 October 1805); Corry then stated that he had always intended to repay this money when certain sums legally due to him became available. The Trustees accepted his promise to repay, which finally he did in 1812. The story of repayment as told in the minutes is epic, recalling Sir Walter Scott's struggles to discharge his liabilities. Corry was in fact an unusually good type of public servant, honest, diligent and able. The Commissioners of Public Accounts who, like their modern counterparts, did not lightly praise, frequently bore testimony to Corry's merits (see, for example, *Proceedings of the Board for 1810*; first half-year, Appendix XIX; *Proceedings*, 1821; Appendix, p. 53). The Trustees (Minutes of meeting of 1 December 1812; see also Minutes of meeting of 3 March 1812), referred to Corry as 'a fair and honorable man, a faithful, zealous, and disinterested public Officer'. They frequently complimented Corry on his work. (See, for example, Minutes of Meeting of 4 September 1810.)

70. A paper by Kirwan, in the *Trans. Roy. Irish Acad.* (1790, *3*, 3), on the *Alkaline substances used in Bleaching and on the Colouring Matter of Linen-yarn*, contains references to Clarke who was Higgins's predecessor.

71. A return from the Board to the Government dated 6 October 1801, which lists their staff, states that he was appointed in 1795.

72. '. . . that the Body is too numerous, that the attendance of the Members is too fluctuating, and on many occasions, any attendance whatever is difficult to be obtained.' (*Report of the Commissioners of Public Accounts for 1819*; Appendix to Proceedings of the Board for 1821, p. 54.) The average attendance of Trustees for the latter half of 1810 was six; at nine out of twenty-one meetings less than four were present. In 1814 the average attendance was four. (See *Report of the Commissioners of Public Accounts for 1814*; Appendix to *Proceedings of the Board for 1816*, p. 8; also *Journal of the Irish House of Commons*, 1782, *20*, 453.)

73. Appendix to the *Proceedings of the Board* for 1810 (first and second half-years), and *Proceedings* for 1811, pp. 14, 15, 40, 74; also *Freeman's Journal* (Dublin), 2 March 1811. The following unfilial gem from a Memorial by Charles Duffin, Jnr., who, following the custom of the time, held the post jointly with his father with reversion on his father's death, is worth quoting: 'The formal communication of those circumstances', i.e. the behaviour of father, 'must lead, I fear, to the discontinuance in office of your senior Inspector General; in contemplating which event, filial affection might be, perhaps, permitted to indulge its sorrows; but other duties tear me from them, and claim their feelings too; for that event will call me from

the place of *son*, in the numerous family that surrounds me, to undertake the premature anxieties of a *father*.' (*Proceedings of the Board for 1810*, second half-year, Appendix IV.) However, though the son had taken time by the forelock by seeking his father's post before the holder had been dismissed, the Trustees abolished the Inspector Generalship.

74. 'We disallowed, in former Accounts, additional Salaries, granted contrary to Law, by the Trustees of the Linen Board, to several of their Officers. In the present Account, the Trustees seem to have paid these illegal Salaries under the name of *Gratuities*. Considering the change of name to be an evasion of the Law . . . we have disallowed them all.' (*Report of the Commissioners of Public Accounts for 1815*; *Proceedings of the Board for 1817*; Appendix, p. 1.)

75. 'We are, perhaps, censurable in allowing one hundred Pounds to a Chymist and one hundred pounds to an Architect, for their annual Services, as being unauthorized Salaries; but considering these Persons as professional Men or Tradesmen . . . we conceived we were warranted in allowing the Sums paid. . . .' (*Report of the Commissioners of Public Accounts for 1817*; *Proceedings of the Board for 1819*; Appendix p. 9.)

76. There appears to be no detailed history of the activities of the Board, but some account is given in *The Rise of the Irish Linen Industry* (C. Gill; Oxford, 1925), and in *The Linen Trade of Europe* (J. Horner; Belfast, 1920).

77. *Precedents and Abstracts from the Journals of the Trustees to 25 March, 1737*, p. 16; see note 69.

William Maple, a friend of Dean Swift, was one of the founders of the Royal Dublin Society in 1731. He was 'operator' in chemistry to Trinity College, Dublin, and also keeper of the Irish Parliament House. It was through his influence that the newly formed Society was enabled to meet in one of the committee rooms until suitable premises were found. In 1727 the Irish Parliament presented Maple with £200 for discovering a method of tanning leather by the root of *Tormentilla erecta* and in 1729 he published a pamphlet entitled *A Method of Tanning without Bark*. Maple acted as a curator and registrar to the Dublin Society from 1731 until his death which took place on 18 January 1762 at, some say 91, others 101; he was also honorary secretary from 1755 to 1762. There is a bust of Maple by Cunningham at the headquarters of the Royal Dublin Society at Ballsbridge, Dublin. (See Berry, *History of the Royal Dublin Society*, Macmillan, London, *passim*.)

The Minute Book of the Governors of Steevens Hospital Dublin, states that about 1732, before the hospital was opened, 'The Governors voted a sum of £40 to be paid to Mr William Maple towards fitting up the Apothecary's Shop and providing medicines' (Information kindly supplied by Dr F. S. Bourke).

78. See notes 70 and 71.

79. Methods of bleaching were discussed by Higgins in his *Essay on the Theory and Practice of Bleaching, wherein the Sulphuret of Lime is recommended as a Substitute for Pot-Ash. Dublin, 1799*. (See p. 14 above.) At that time potassium carbonate was 'mild pot-ash or alkali' and potassium hydroxide 'caustic pot-ash or alkali'. Higgins recommended the latter to bleachers for the alkali treatment. He obtained the idea of using calcium sulphide from Kirwan's work (note 70). There is a report on

the manufacture of 'ash' in Ireland in the *Journal of the Irish House of Commons* (1788, 25, CCCCXIII).

The *Essay on Bleaching* was published in both London and Dublin. The London edition has the following on the title-page:

> An Essay on the Theory and Practice of Bleaching, wherein the Sulphuret of Lime is recommended as a Substitute for Pot-Ash. By William Higgins, M.R.I.A. Professor of Chemistry and Mineralogy at the Repository of the Dublin Society. London: printed for the Author; and sold by Vernor & Hood, No. 31, Poultry, 1799. Price Two Shillings. Pp. xxxii +71.

The title-page of the Dublin edition reads as follows:

> An Essay on the Theory and Practice of Bleaching, wherein the Sulphuret of Lime is recommended as a Substitute for Pot-Ash. By William Higgins, M.R.I.A. Professor of Chymistry and Mineralogy at the Repository of the Dublin Society. Dublin: Printed by B. and J. Williamson, Grafton-street, Printers and Stationers to the Right Hon. and Hon. the Trustees of the Linen-Board, 1799. No price. Pp. xxx +71.

Higgins also published *Essay on the Sulphuret of Lime, as a Substitute for Pot-Ash; or a new method of Bleaching* in *Trans. Dublin Soc.* for 1799, Dublin, 1800, 1. (See note 83.)

80. *Mémoire sur l'acide marin déphlogistiqué*, *Journal de Physique*, 1785, 26, 321. An interesting account of the development of this process is given by Samuel Parkes in his *Chemical Essays* (London, 3rd ed., 1830, 387). *Essai sur le Blanchiment*, by R. O'Reilly (Paris, 1801), contains information on the bleaching practice of the time and refers to Higgins's work (pp. 122–131). Berthollet (1748–1822) was the first of the French chemists to adopt (1785) Lavoisier's theory.

81. See p. 110.

82. *Nicholson's Journal*, 1800, 3 (1st series), 253. There is also a reference to Higgins's use of calcium sulphide in a *Dictionary of Chemistry*, by A. and C. R. Aikin (1807, 1, 146).

83. *Trans. Dublin Soc. for 1799*, 1800, 1, Pt. 1. In this paper Higgins includes from the *Essay* (p. 15), a method for showing the presence of potassium sulphate in potassium carbonate based on the lesser solubility of the sulphate which was a common adulterant of the carbonate.

84. *Trans. Dublin Soc. for 1800*, 1801, 2, Pt. 1, 482. There is a reference on p. 488 to O'Reilly's *Essai sur le Blanchiment* (note 80 above), which mentions Higgins's work on bleaching.

85. *Critical Review*, 1801, 32, 222–224. The relevant page of the copy of the Journal in the National Library, Dublin, is marked, possibly by Higgins, for extraction. Much of the library of the Royal Dublin Society was transferred to the National Library about 1880.

86. The Leskean collection was one of the best of its time; it consisted of 7331 specimens. It had originally been assembled by Nathaniel Gottfried Leske, Professor of Natural History at Marburg. In the Preface to this *Elements of Mineralogy*, 2nd edition, 1794, Kirwan stated that the collection was 'the most perfect monument of mineralogical ability now extant'. (See also H. F. Berry, *History of the Royal Dublin Society*, 1915, 156.) The collection, which was transferred to the National Museum,

Dublin, has unfortunately been broken up and distributed and many
specimens are no longer available.

87. Acts of the Irish Parliament from 1761 to 1800 sanctioned regular
grants to the Dublin Society. Sums of between £5000 and £15,500 were
involved. (H. F. Berry, *History of the Royal Dublin Society*, 1915, 209,
and *passim*; *Journal of the Irish House of Commons*; *Statutes of the Irish
Parliament*.) The Act of 1795 was not passed by the Irish House of Lords,
because their Lordships objected to a provision enabling the Society
more effectively to recover money due to it.

88. Higgins (*Phil. Mag.*, 1819, *53*, 405) refers to his appointment as Professor
of Chemistry to the *honourable* the Dublin Society by the act of parliament
which established the professorship. Isaac Weld (1774–1856; there is a
memoir of Weld in the *Journal of the Royal Dublin Society*, 1858, *1*,
151–179), who was honorary secretary of the Society from 1828 to 1849
and vice-president from 1849 to 1856, said in evidence before a Select
Committee on the Royal Dublin Society, 22 April 1836 (p. 20), that
Higgins believing he held office by virtue of an Act of Parliament
attempted at times to defy the Society, 'but, however, they brought him
a little to his senses, by showing that they could leave him out at the
annual general election for professors and officers'. Weld studied under
Higgins from about 1799 to 1801 (*Memoir*, p. 162; *Select Committee*, p.
35.) He did not regard Higgins as a good teacher (*Select Committee*, p. 36;
see also text, p. 23.

89. The sum of £5500 was granted in 1797–99 (1797, 37 George III, c. 41;
1798, 38 George III, c. 43; 1799, 39 George III, c. 45).

90. In addition to Higgins there was Walter Wade, M.D., Professor of Botany
and Superintendent of the Botanic Gardens whose chair was established
by the 1797 Act.

91. It was suggested by Isaac Weld (see note 88 above) in *Observations on the
Royal Dublin Society* (1831, p. 2), and by some biographers of Higgins,
that the Irish parliament had a special concern for the Society, because
the 1800 Act granting money to the Society received the Royal Assent on
1 August 1800, the day before the Act of Union came into force. Actually
eighty-four Acts received the Royal Assent on that day, and there
appears to be no special significance attaching to the date of assent.

92. See *Trans. Dublin Soc. for 1799*, 1800, *1*, Part 1; *Journal of the Irish House
of Commons*, 1800, *19*, 35.

93. *A Syllabus of a Course of Chemistry for the year 1802*, published in 1801,
runs to eighty-eight pages and contains material covering forty-one
lectures. In the 'Advertisement' Higgins stated that he had annually
delivered the course since his appointment as Professor of Chemistry and
Mineralogy by act of parliament in 1796. He also writes that 'A work
formed upon the arrangement which I have adopted, and which I have
found by experience to be free from some inconveniences, attendant
upon those of other professors, is already in forwardness and will, ere
long, be submitted to the public judgement.' The promised textbook,
though again mentioned in Higgins's *Atomic Theory* (p. 18), never
appeared. The lectures cover a wide field; a first introductory lecture
refers to 'the happy effects of chemical philosophy on the human mind'.
The following lectures deal with attraction, the atmosphere, caloric,
gases, meteorology, water, vegetation, brewing, fermentation, distillation,

alkalis, acids, earths, metals. There is no definite reference to the
atomic theory though later he claimed (*Phil. Mag.*, 1819, *53*, 405) that
it always formed part of his annual course of lectures. There are, however, entries such as 'On the combustion of sulphur, or its union to oxygen—experiments and theory'. There are similar references to 'theory'
in regard to the oxides of nitrogen and the action of sulphuric acid on
iron. The topics which carry this reference are those discussed by Higgins
in the *Comparative View* in relation to his atomic theory. There is also in
the library of the Royal Dublin Society a syllabus of Higgins's course of
twenty-four lectures, delivered on Mondays, Wednesdays and Fridays
between October 1821 and January 1822. The lectures have advanced
with the times, for there are references to the atomic theory and to
metals such as sodium and rhodium discovered since the syllabus
described above was published. Higgins also refers to his theory of electrical phenomenon which he published in 1814 in his *Atomic Theory*. (See
Phil. Mag., 1818, *51*, 81, and p. 26 above).

The distinguished Irish chemist, Sir Robert Kane (1809–90; see 'The
Natural Resources of Ireland', Royal Dublin Society, 1944, and *Studies*,
1944, *33*, 158, 316), stated in 1868 before a Commission on the Science
and Art Department in Ireland that as a schoolboy he attended lectures
in chemistry in the Royal Dublin Society. If this was before 1825, he
heard Higgins lecture. He nowhere mentions Higgins in his writings.
The minutes of the Dublin Society for 17 March 1796 record the grant
of permission to Doctor James McNevin [*sic*] to study mineralogy in the
Society's cabinet under the direction of Mr William Higgins. This may
have been Dr William James MacNeven, (or MacNevin) (1763–1841;
for details of his life see McLaughlin, *Studies*, 1940, *29*, 73 and *Dict.
Nat. Biog.*), who was removed from his office of Physician to the House
of Industry, Dublin, for his part in the patriot activities which culminated
in the rising of 1798 (see *Minutes of the Meeting of the Acting Governors of
the House of Industry, Dublin*, 15 November 1798). He was banished by
the Government and, after travel on the continent, went to the United
States where he became Professor of Chemistry in the College of
Physicians and Surgeons of the University of the State of New York
(1811–26). He is best known for his early recognition of the atomic theory.
In his 'Exposition of the Atomic Theory' (*Annals of Philosophy*, 1820, *16*,
195–214; 289–293; 338–350; reprinted in the *Journal de Physique*, 1821,
92, 274–288; 376–401; 444–458) he criticises Higgins's lack of industry
in not persevering with the development of his early ideas on the atomic
theory and adds that 'celebrity without labour is neither legitimate nor
attainable in the walks of science'. It is noteworthy that both MacNeven
and Sullivan (note 2), were critical of their fellow-countryman. As pointed
out above MacNeven may have had personal contact with Higgins. (See
p. 136.)

94. The total annual expenses of the Department of Mineralogy and Chemistry (one Professor) in 1803 was £643 14s. 6d. In 1819 when there
were Professors of Chemistry, Mineralogy and Mining the annual cost
was about £1500.

95. Further details of the work of the Committee are given by F. G. H. Tate
in *Alcoholometry* (London, 1930; p. 5). The famous chemist, W. H.
Wollaston (1766–1828; see *Dict. Nat. Biog.*), was a member. Our thanks

are due to the late Dr G. M. Bennett, F.R.S., Government Chemist, London, who kindly made available the original minutes of the Committee, and also provided photographs of a typical entry.

96. Dr J. O'Reardon in his life of Kirwan (*National Magazine*, 1830, *1*, 333) says that Samuel Wharmby, a native of London, was for forty years Kirwan's assistant in his numerous experiments. He died a few months after Kirwan. The Samuel Wharmby who was Higgins's assistant was possibly a relative. (See also M. Donovan's *Life of Kirwan*; *Proc. Roy. Irish Academy*, 1847–50, *4*, Appendix 8, p. cxiv.)

97. The currencies were amalgamated in 1821; 21/- sterling equalled 22/9 Irish currency.

98. See, for example, *Minutes of the Committee of Chemistry*, 2 February 1818.

99. See *Proc. Roy. Dublin Soc.*, Vol. 66 (4 November 1819–21, August 1820), pp. 101, 148 and Appendix.

100. See Deed No. 1854/20/203, dated 10 August 1854, in Registry of Deeds, Dublin. Higgins was succeeded by Edmund Davy (1785–1857) a cousin of Sir Humphry's (see *J. Chem. Educ.*, 1953, *30*, 302). His chair eventually became the Chair of Chemistry in the Royal College of Science for Ireland which was merged with the Chair of Chemistry in University College, Dublin, in 1926, (Cocker and Wheeler, *Nature*, 1952, *169*, 575; Wheeler, *J. Roy. Inst. Chem.*, 1953, 77, 113).

101. Deed No. 636/45/435,583 in the Registry of Deeds, Dublin: see also Deed No. 1853/22/21 for the sale of the house by Baroness von Haeseler and Emma Julia Higgins (see appendix). Archibald Hamilton Rowan (1751–1834) was a distinguished Irish patriot who, as a United Irishman, was exiled from Ireland from 1794 to 1806. (For an account of his life see Harold Nicholson, *The Desire to Please*, London, 1945; see also p. 23 above).

102. No. 733/506/500,241, dated 22 October 1818.

103. Deed No. 787/343/532,478, dated 30 October 1823, in the Registry of Deeds, Dublin.

104. Information obtained in the Office of the Land Commission, Dublin (Anthony Blake Estate, 1895; Rec. No. 1685; Box No. 243). The assistance of Messrs Charles J. Reddy and Son, Solicitors, Dublin, is gratefully acknowledged.

105. Sydney, Lady Morgan, née Owenson (1783?–1851) was, in her day, a well-known novelist. She is best remembered for *The Wild Irish Girl*, 1806. The tea-party to which she refers took place soon after Hamilton Rowan's return from exile. (See note 101 above.) Erris is a district in County Mayo.

106. Dr William Harty (1781–1854) was physician to the Dublin prisons. (*Dict. Nat. Biog.*)

107. Charles William Bury (1764–1835) F.R.S., became Baron Tullamore in 1797, Viscount Charleville in 1800 and Earl of Charleville in 1806. He served as President of the Royal Irish Academy (1812–22), and as Vice-President of the Royal Dublin Society from 1803 to 1822.

108. *Trans. Roy. Irish Acad.*, 1799, 8, 137.

109. *Autobiography of Archibald Hamilton Rowan* (Dublin, 1840), pp. 337–338.

110. *Autobiography*, pp. 348–349.

111. *Autobiography*, pp. 339–340.

112. *Trans. Roy. Irish Acad.*, 1805, *10*, 235.

113. By an error his name is given in the minutes as Robert Higgins, but his signature is opposite the corresponding member number in the Academy Roll. The Council of the Royal Irish Academy is divided into a Committee of Science and a Committee of Polite Literature. A number of authors following Meldrum (*New Ireland Review*, 1919–10, *32*, 352) have stated, incorrectly, that Higgins was on the Council of the Royal Irish Academy from 1796 to his death.

114. The Dublin Directory for 1814 says that the Kirwanian Society was founded in February 1812 (Kirwan died in June) for the cultivation of chemistry, mineralogy and other branches of natural history. It met once or twice monthly from November to May. Volume 2 of the minutes preserved in the library of the Royal Irish Academy, covers the period from 8 March 1815 to 11 February 1818. The Society had some fifty members and papers were read at the meetings. The pages of the Minute Book not used by the Society are filled with details of experiments on illumination written in the 1830's by Michael Donovan (1791–1876), Secretary and Treasurer of the Kirwanian Society. He was a doctor and a chemist, published many papers in chemistry and physics, and *A Treatise on Chemistry*, London, 1832. He taught chemistry at the Apothecaries' Hall, and was its Governor in 1829. For a full account of the Kirwanian Society see McLaughlin, *Studies*, 1954, *43*, 441.

115. The Hon. George Knox (1765–1827), F.R.S. (for scientific papers see Royal Society list), was member for Dublin University in the Irish and Imperial parliaments, and was Vice-President of the Royal Dublin Society from 1820 to 1827. (Information kindly supplied by Professor Dudley Edwards and Mr Thomas P. O'Neill.) His sons, George James Knox and Thomas Knox, suffered damage to health attempting to isolate fluorine. (See for example, *Phil. Mag.*, 1836, *9*, 107; *Proc. Roy. Irish Acad.*, 1838, *18*, 127; *Compt. rend. Acad. Sci.*, Paris, 1846, *23*, 960; 1847, *24*, 434; M. E. Weeks, *Discovery of the Elements*, Easton, Pa., 1959.)

116. See Appendix, note 11.

117. Charles Hatchett (1765–1847), F.R.S., was a distinguished chemist of the time. He discovered the element niobium. (*Dict. Nat. Biog.*, M. E. Weeks, *Discovery of the Elements*, Easton, Pa., 1945.)

118. Davy, who, as mentioned above (see p. 20), had lectured to the Dublin Society in 1810 and 1811, was the first (*Phil. Trans. Roy. Soc.*, 1811, Pt. 1, 15), to draw attention to Higgins's claim to be the originator of the 'chemical' atomic theory (see p. 131).

119. Anthony George Eckhardt's (of The Hague in Holland) certificate of election to the Royal Society dated 2 June 1774, states he had 'distinguished himself by some Ingenious Inventions of great publick Utility'. He took out a patent for printing designs on textiles and paper shortly before he became a member of the Royal Society. He and his brother, Francis Frederick, carried on, reputedly, the best wall-paper manufacturing business in London from about 1786–96. They went bankrupt owing to the high labour costs of producing an artistic product. Information kindly supplied by Mrs Ada Leask.

120. Dr David Pitcairn (1749–1809), became physician to St Bartholomew's Hospital in 1780. He was a subscriber to Bryan Higgins's *Society for Philosophical Experiments and Conversations* which met in 1794 (see note 53 above). William Higgins seems to have known, in addition to Pitcairn,

the following physicians attached to this hospital: Dr J. G. Caulet (note 24 above); Dr W. Austin (note 25 above); Dr James Haworth (note 35 above). Dr Gweneth Whitteridge, Archivist to St Bartholomew's Hospital, has kindly searched the records of the hospital but has found no reference to either Bryan or William Higgins. Dr D. C. Martin, Assistant-Secretary of the Royal Society, has kindly had examined the Indexes of the letters and papers of the Society for the period 1790–1825. No reference to correspondence with William Higgins has been found.

121. *Phil. Mag.*, 1816, *48*, 363–371 and 408–417; 1817, *49*, 241–250; 1818, *51*, 81–91; 161–172; 1819, *53*, 401–410.

122. *Phil. Mag.*, 1811, *38*, 263–268; *Dublin Society's Minutes*, 1811–12, passim.

123. *Phil. Mag.*, 1818, *51*, 355–358. See H. J. Seymour, *Proc. Roy. Dublin Soc.*, 1947, *24*, 157–164.

124. *Atomic Theory*, 1814, p. 33; *Phil. Mag.*, 1818, *51*, 357.

125. The following references to the work of William Higgins have been traced and examined: *Monthly Review*, 1789, *81*, 197; *Analytical Review*, 1789, *4*, 177; *Critical Review*, 1790, *70*, 545; *English Review*, 1790, *15*, 188; *Monthly Review*, 1800, *31*, 442; *Critical Review*, 1801, *32*, 222; William Henry, *Epitome of Chemistry*, 2nd ed., 1801, 65; 3rd ed., 1805, 163; 4th ed., 1806, 156; the *Epitome* then became the *Elements of Experimental Chemistry*: references to Higgins occur in, e.g., 6th ed., 1810, *1*, 422; 9th ed., 1823, *1*, 403; 10th ed., 1826, *1*, 413; 11th (last) ed., 1829, *1*, 44, 432; Humphry Davy, *Phil. Trans. Roy. Soc.*, 1811, Pt 1, 15; *Elements of Chemical Philosophy*, 1812, *1*, Pt. 1, 107; Thomas Thomson, *Annals of Philosophy*, 1813, *2*, 32; Jacob J. Berzelius, *Annals of Philosophy*, 1813, *2*, 445; T. Thomson, *Annals of Philosophy*, 1813, *2*, 445; John Nash, *Phil. Mag.*, 1814, *43*, 54; T. Thomson, *Annals of Philosophy*, 1814, *3*, 329; W. H. Wollaston, *Phil. Trans. Roy. Soc.*, 1814, 5; *Ann. Chim.*, 1814, *90*, 138; William Crane, *Phil. Mag.*, 1814, *43*, 113; T. Thomson, *Annals of Philosophy*, 1814, *4*, 52; H. G. de Claubry, *Journal de Physique*, 1817, *84*, 392; *Phil. Mag.*, 1817, *50*, 406; James Watt, *Annals of Philosophy*, 1817, *9*, 407; *Monthly Review*, 1817, *82*, 379 (the copy in the National Library of Ireland is annotated by Higgins); John Murray, *Elements of Chemical Science*, 1818, 28; *Weekly Freeman* (Dublin), 16 January 1819; *Freeman's Journal* (Dublin), 22 January 1819; *Dublin Magazine*, 1819, *1*, 191; 1820, *2*, 110; M. H. Klaproth and F. Wolff, *Supplemente zu dem chemischen Wörterbuch*, Berlin, 1819, *4*, 134; J. L. G. Meinecke, *Journal für Chemie und Physik*, 1819, *26*, 296 (he thought the *Comparative View* was published in 1799); John Murray, *System of Chemistry*, 4th ed., 1819, *1*, 127; Abraham Rees, *The New Cyclopaedia*, 1819, *28*, article on 'Proportions, Definite, in Chemistry'; *34*, article on 'Theory, Atomic, in Chemistry'; William J. MacNeven (see note 93), *Annals of Philosophy*, 1820, *16*, 195, 289, 338; *J. de Physique*, 1821, *92* 274, 376, 444; Samuel Parkes, *The Chemical Catechism*, 10th ed., 1822, 232; *A Catechism of Chemistry* (revised by William Barker), 1837, 65; *The Chemist*, 1825, *2*, 55; Humphry Davy, *Discourses to the Royal Society* on 30 November 1825 and 1826; Edward Turner, *Elements of Chemistry*, 1st ed., 1827, 132; 3rd ed., 1831, 179; Thomas J. Graham, *Chemical Catechism*, 1829, 35; Charles G. Daubeny, *Introduction to the Atomic Theory*, 1st ed., 1831, 33; 2nd ed., 1850, 23; Anon., *Brit. Quarterly*

Review, 1845, *1*, 157; H. Kopp, *Geschichte der Chemie*, 1843–47, *passim*; William K. Sullivan, *Dublin Quart. J. Medicine*, 1849, 8, 465; William C. Henry, *Memoirs of the Life and Scientific Researches of John Dalton*, London, The Cavendish Society, 1854, 75, 78–79, 217; W. Barker, *Journal of the Royal Dublin Society*, 1856–57, *1*, 421; Robert A. Smith, *Memoirs of the Literary and Philosophical Society of Manchester*, 1856, *13*, 1; George Wilson, *Religio Chemici*, 1862, 318, 346; Sir John F. W. Herschel, *Familiar Lectures on Scientific Subjects*, 1866, 453; A. Wurtz, *Dictionnaire de Chimie*, Paris, 1869, *1*, 75 (article by P. Schützenberger); H. Kopp, *Die Entwickelung der Chemie in der neureren Zeit*, 1873, *passim*; M. M. P. Muir, *A Treatise on the Principles of Chemistry*, 1884, 8; R. Jagnaux, *Histoire de la Chimie*, 1891, *1*, 317; E. von Meyer, *History of Chemistry*, 1891, 184; T. E. Thorpe, *Humphry Davy, Poet and Philosopher*, 1896, 146; J. W. Mellor and E. J. Russell, *J. Chem. Soc.*, 1902, *81*, 1273; A. N. Meldrum, *Brit. Assoc. Report*, 1908, 78, 668; *Mem. Lit. Phil. Soc., Manchester*, 1908, *52*, No. 10, 9; 1910, 11, *55*, No. 4, 8, 14; *New Ireland Review*, 1909–10, *32*, 275, 350; H. E. Roscoe and C. Schorlemmer, *Treatise on Chemistry*, 1920, *1*, 35; E. F. Smith, *Old Chemistries*, New York, 1927; J. H. White, *Science Progress*, 1929, *24*, 300; T. R. Gunther, *Notes and Queries*, 1929, *157*, 421; J. Reilly and D. T. MacSweeney, *Sci. Proc. Roy. Dublin Soc.*, 1929, *19*, 139; J. E. Marsh, *The Origins of Growth and Chemical Science*, 1929, 77; A. Wolf, *Outline of Modern Knowledge*, 1931, 40; R. T. Gunther, *Early Science at Oxford*, 1937, *11*, 254; J. R. Partington, *A Short History of Chemistry*, 1937, 166, 178; *Annals of Science*, 1939, *4*, 269; Thomas Dillon, *Studies*, 1939, *28*, 51; Edward R. Atkinson, *J. Chem. Educ.*, 1940, *17*, 3; D. O'Raghallaigh, *Three Centuries of Irish Chemists*, Cork, 1941, 6; J. R. Partington, *Phil. Mag. Comm. Number*, 1948, 63; R. Hooykaas, *Chemisch Weekblad*, 1948, *44*, 407; J. R. Partington, *Annals of Science*, 1949, *6*, 126; Frederick Soddy, *The Story of Atomic Energy*, London, 1949, *passim*; Leonard K. Nash, *The Atomic Molecular Theory*, Harvard, 1950, 14; T. S. Wheeler, *Studies*, 1950, *39*, 6; J. R. Partington, *Nature*, 1951, *167*, 120, 735; F. Soddy, *Nature*, 1951, 167, 734; T. S. Wheeler, *Endeavour*, 1952, 11, 47; see Ref. 1. The *Dict. Nat. Biog.* has articles on Dalton and Higgins.

A number of these references are discussed in Part III.

Appendix

THE HIGGINS FAMILY[1]

BRYAN HIGGINS, M.D., of Collooney, Co. Sligo; *d.* 1777[2]

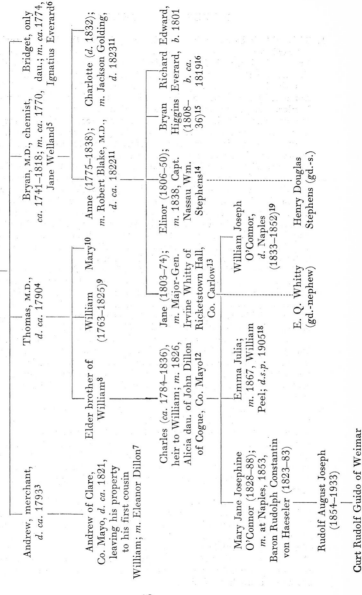

NOTES TO APPENDIX

1. This table is based on information supplied by the Irish genealogists Mr Edward Keane, Mr J. C. T. MacDonagh a descendant of the elder Bryan Higgins, and Dr R. C. Simington, and on material obtained from the Irish Public Record Office and the Registry of Deeds. Information has also been supplied by the Public Record Office and the War Office, London, by Mr Edmund Nicholls, London, and by H.M. Consul-General, Naples. Many, too numerous to mention, including various solicitors in Dublin, have also helped. Herr Curt von Haeseler of Weimar, who was traced by a letter to the *Stadtverwaltungsdirektor* of Weimar, has been most courteous in answering queries. Legal documents in Dublin had shown that Mary Jane Higgins had become Baroness von Haeseler of Weimar. The authors' best thanks are due to all those mentioned.

2. The name of Bryan Higgins disappeared in 1777 from the rent-roll (Mss. No. 2175 and 3050–3053, Nat. Library, Dublin) of the Cooper family, the landlords of Collooney, and was replaced by the 'Widow Higgins'. Andrew Higgins is shown as tenant from March 1789; in 1793 the property is described as 'formerly Andrew Higgins' and the phrase 'late Higgins' persists for the plot or garden involved up to 1813. Mr James Higgins of Dublin, who comes from Collooney, states that a plot in Collooney is still called 'Higgins's Gardens'.

   Faulkner's Dublin Journal for 7–10 March 1778 refers to the death of Bryan Higgins, M.D., of Collooney, Co. Sligo, at an advanced age. There is another reference to Bryan Higgins in Deed No. 399/56/262,861, of 24 January 1774 (Registry of Deeds, Dublin), a deed of intermarriage between Bridget, only daughter of Bryan Higgins of Collooney, 'doctor of physik', and Ignatius Everard of Neenanagh, Co. Mayo.

   O'Rorke (*History of the Parishes of Ballysodare and Kilvarnet, Co. Sligo*, 1878), refers (p. 51) to the opinion of the celebrated Dr Higgins of the last century on the salubrity of the Collooney climate; later (p. 79) he states that 'In the house now occupied by Dominick Brenan, resided, a century ago, Dr Higgins, the most distinguished physician of Connaught, or perhaps, of Ireland, in his day.'

3. Andrew Higgins signed the Catholic Qualification Rolls at Collooney in 1778. These Rolls, set up in 1774, contained the names of Catholics who swore loyalty to the Crown, and were then relieved of some of the restrictions imposed by the penal laws, for example, they obtained rights in regard to the enjoyment and disposition of land. Lists of those who signed the Rolls are preserved in the Public Record Office, Dublin. Andrew had, probably, to sign on receipt of property on his father's death.

4. Thomas Higgins, M.D., signed the Catholic Qualification Rolls at Collooney in 1782. His name appears on the Intestacy Index for 1790, in the Public Record Office, Dublin. (See note 10, below). Foster's *Alumni Oxonienses* (see note 13, p. 29), gives Thomas Higgins as 'gent' of Co. Mayo. Sadleir in the preface to Burtchaell and Sadleir's *Alumni Dublinenses* says that Foster always describes the father of each student as residing at what was merely the son's birthplace and that this practice has caused much confusion.

50

It has not been found possible to discover where Bryan the elder qualified in medicine. He is not on the graduate rolls of Cambridge, Dublin, Edinburgh, or Oxford, nor on W. Munk's *Roll of the Royal College of Physicians, London*; these records are, however, incomplete in some instances. (See note 5 below relative to Bryan the younger.)

As regards Thomas Higgins, Miss Jean M. Simpson, Reference Assistant in the Library of the University of Edinburgh, to whom our thanks are due, writes (25 October 1955):

'A Thomas Higgins is on our register as having matriculated at Edinburgh in Arts subjects under Adam Ferguson, professor of Philosophy in 1762, and in medicine, 1762–3, 1764–5, and 1764–5, but did not apparently graduate here.'

No reference to a Thomas Higgins has been found in Munk or on the Graduate rolls of Cambridge, Dublin, or Oxford.

The Edinburgh dates are a little unexpected if Thomas was married in 1759. (See conjectural genealogical table p. 58.)

5. For accounts of the life of the younger Bryan Higgins see references in notes 1, 2, 4, 5, 14, 53 above, Meldrum (*New Ireland Review*, 1909–10, *32*, 275), and the *Dictionary of National Biography*. Further details are given below and in Part III, p. 124. In addition to the material given in these references, the following information obtained from the University of Leyden with the help of Drs G. van der Lee and W. P. Jorissen, and of the Secretary to the Curators of the University, may be of interest (see also note 5 to Part I of the main text). Bryan Higgins, 'Hibernus', enrolled at the University of Leyden on 5 October 1765, at the age of 24. He passed the medical examination on 2 November of the same year and ten days later he defended the following seven theses to qualify for the degree of M.D.: (1) venesection is seldom suitable for the treatment of fever in large cities; (2) putrefaction involves a loss of fixed air; restoration of the air removes it; (3) venereal disease can be cured without salivation; (4) there are as yet no remedies to break up stone in the bladder; (5) the juice of millipedes has no definite healing properties, apart from the effects which the mind can cause, when it is moved by something revolting, disgusting, and horrible; (6) alkaline salts are septic inside, but antiseptic outside the human body; (7) in practice simple remedies are preferrable to complex. (We are indebted to Professor J. J. O'Meara for the translation of this and other material from the Latin.)

It will be noted that, as Meldrum (*loc. cit.*) points out, Bryan Higgins did not study medicine at Leyden; he came there merely to obtain a degree. It is not known where he received his medical training. Priestley (*Philosophical Empiricism*, 1775, p. 43; this volume is polemical, attacking Bryan Higgins; see p. 52 below) states that Higgins's mistaken view that fixed air consists of common air and phlogiston was obtained from Dr Cullen. (See Part III, p. 124.) This might suggest that Bryan Higgins received his medical education in Edinburgh, where William Cullen (1710–90), was appointed joint professor of chemistry in 1756. However Priestley is very unreliable.

An interesting reference to Bryan Higgins's lectures occurs in a letter dated 1 November 1791, from Robert Howard to his son Luke Howard (1772–1864; *Dict. Nat. Biog.*); our thanks are due to Mr G. E. Howard of 'Howards of Ilford', for information in regard to this letter.

There is in the library of the British Museum (Add. Mss. No. 38221/ f/236) a letter dated 25 February 1787 from Bryan Higgins of Greek Street, Soho, to Lord Hawkesbury saying that he had 'something of moment to communicate to his lordship, relative to the Treaty with France', and asking for an interview. He mentions the Earl of Stanhope as supporting this application. Charles Jenkinson, Earl of Liverpool and Baron Hawkesbury (1727–1808), held a number of ministerial offices, among them the presidency of the Board of Trade (1786). Charles Stanhope, third Earl of Stanhope (1753–1816), politician and man of science (F.R.S., 1772), constructed two calculating machines and invented a printing press and the lens which bears his name. He was a member of Bryan Higgins's *Society for Philosophical Experiments and Conversations* (see pp. 37, 124) which met in 1794. Lady Hester Stanhope was his daughter.

Sullivan (note 2, p. 28) says Bryan was in Russia in the service of the Empress Catherine the Great between 1780 and 1790. There is no reference in the *Proceedings of the St Petersburg Science Academy* for 1780–90 to Bryan being present at any of the meetings. Mr John Jordan who has made a special study of Irishmen who served in Scandinavian countries has kindly had a search made in the State Library at Helsingfors which has much Russian material, without result. Dr A. V. Topchiev, Chief Secretary of the Academy of Sciences of the U.S.S.R., has informed us in answer to an enquiry that a search of both State and Academy archives yielded no information in regard to a sojourn of Bryan Higgins in Russia between 1780 and 1790.

Bryan Higgins was a friend of Boswell and of Johnson (see note 22, p. 33). There are, for example, references in Boswell (Life and Diary) to visits by Higgins, Boswell, Johnson, and others to 'Mr Beauclerk's' on 16 May 1778 and 24 April 1779.

Professor René Fric of the University of Clermont has kindly drawn our attention to two letters received by Lavoisier from de Magalhaens, written in 1775 (see *Oeuvres de Lavoisier, Correspondance*, ed. by R. Fric, Paris, 1957, Fasc. II, pp. 504–8, with a summary of B. Higgins's *Syllabus*). The first letter accompanied a copy of Higgins's *A Syllabus of the Discourses and Experiments, With which the Meetings of the Subscribers are to be opened, after the Course of Chemistry is concluded* (76 pp.; another publication, *Syllabus of Doctor Higgins's Course of Philosophical, Pharmaceutical, and Technical Chemistry*, n.d. (1778?), 112 pp., is quite different and is of a practical character). The second letter accompanied a copy of Priestley's *Philosophical Empiricism* (86 pp., with a list of Priestley's books at the end), which consists almost entirely of an unpleasant personal attack on Higgins, in reply to a chance remark of the latter: 'conceits of acid air, vitriolic air, acetous air, nitrous air, &c. corrected', made in his *Syllabus* (p. 27).

Priestley had attended Higgins's course and was 'favoured' with the use of chemicals (see Priestley, *Experiments and Observations on Air*, 1775, 2, pp. 23, 70, 80, 82, 86, 114), but probably not gratuitously as Meldrum (*New Ireland Review*, 1909–10, *32*, pp. 275, 350) suggested, since Priestley announced in his *Philosophical Empiricism* that he was able to buy red precipitate from Cadet in Paris more cheaply than from Higgins.

Bryan Higgins also published *A Philosophical Essay concerning Light*

(1776, containing a slightly modified reprint of the *Syllabus* of 1775. A copy of a separate reprint of the 1775 Syllabus (London, J. Robson and Co. and B. Law, 1776) is in the Library of University College, London); *Experiments and Observations made With the View of Improving the Art of Composing and Applying Calcereous Cements* . . . , 1780; *Experiments and Observations relating to Acetous Acid* . . . , 1786; *Minutes of the Society for Philosophical Experiments and Conversations*, 1795 (German translation, 1803); *Observations and Advice for the Improvement of the Manufacture of Muscovado Sugar and Rum*, in several parts, 1797–1803 (see Higgins, *Phil. Mag.*, 1806, *24*, 308); and papers in the *Philosophical Transactions* and *Nicholson's Journal*. He discovered acetone, independently observed the absorption of gases on charcoal, invented the 'chemical harmonica' (a jet of hydrogen burning in a glass tube; see p. 2) and found that sparks are emitted when copper nitrate crystals are wrapped in tinfoil. In 1781 he was granted a patent for making caustic soda from common salt by converting this into sodium sulphate, reducing this to sulphide by heating with coal, and fusing the sulphide with lead, when caustic soda floated to the surface; he thus partly anticipated the Leblanc process. Bryan Higgins's remarks (1775–76) on 'saturation' and his speculations on the combination of atoms, which he assumed had 'polarity' or were endowed with attractive forces acting in definite directions which in gases cause them to approach in a certain order, were undoubtedly the source of William Higgins's interest in the subject (see Meldrum, *loc. cit.*; Partington, *Annals of Science*, 1939, *4*, 245).

J. H. de Magalhaens or Magellan (1722(3)–90) of the family of the celebrated navigator lived in London for many years. He had a wide range of interest in science. He was elected to the Royal Society in 1774 and was a correspondent of the Paris, Madrid, and St Petersburgh Academies.

6. A study of the *Alumni Dublinenses* shows that Ignatius Everard, merchant, of Co. Sligo, had at least three sons, Patrick (*b.* 1775), Bryan Higgins, gentleman farmer, and Richard, a barrister (*b.* 1781). Bryan Higgins Everard had two sons who went to Trinity College, Dublin; Ignatius Houston (*b. ca.* 1809), and Richard Houston (*b. ca.* 1811). Support is lent to the relationships shown in the table by that fact that one of Anne Blake's (née Higgins) sons had Everard as a Christian name. We know that Anne was a daughter of the younger Bryan (note 11 below).

7. See p. 22. The Cooper papers in the National Library, Dublin, contain a list of freeholders dated 1796 (Mss. 3136). This list includes the name of Andrew Higgins of Brooklawn, Co. Mayo. He is also referred to in Deeds Nos. 561/306/377, 334, 12 July 1804, and 576/422/392,842, 16 January 1806. Andrew, then of Clare, Co. Mayo, died about 1821 (list of Wills and Intestacies, Public Record office, Dublin, 1821). The names of Ignatius and Bryan Everard (see preceding note) occur in the deeds in conjunction with that of Andrew. Apart from the land he inherited from Andrew, William, in 1823, bought land to the value of £6800 in Queen's County (now Co. Leix). See p. 22.

8. The existence of this elder brother is postulated because Charles, William Higgins's nephew (see note 12 below), who was born about 1784, would seem to have been too old to be the son of a brother younger than William.

9. The date of William's birth is fixed as 1762–63 by the entry in Foster's *Alumni Oxonienses* (see note 13, p. 29). He was 23 when he matriculated on 6 February 1786.

10. Betham in his abstracts of Administrations (in the Public Record Office, Dublin) gives Robert Harmon, the husband of Mary, daughter of Thomas Higgins, M.D., as Administrator of the estate of Thomas Higgins. The date of the grant is 30 November 1790.

11. Bryan Higgins's will (Somerset House, London), besides indicating the date of his marriage, shows Anne Blake and Charlotte Golding, to be his daughters. There are abstracts of their wills in the Public Record Office, Dublin. Anne is buried in the Blake family grave in Mount Jerome Cemetery, Dublin. William left £100 each to Anne and Charlotte (Deeds Nos. 816/303/549,838 and 819/40/551,375, 20 July 1826, Registry of Deeds, Dublin).

    Robert Blake, Anne's husband, was a distinguished Dublin dentist who in 1821 became State Dentist. He was Vice-President of the Kirwanian Society (see note 114, p. 46). His thesis for the degree of M.D. (Edinburgh, 1798), on the structure and formation of the teeth, was published in an enlarged form in Dublin in 1801, and was regarded as the best work on the subject, of the period in which it was written. It is dedicated to Bryan Higgins. In the preface Blake states that the anatomical preparations were made in Dublin in 1795. (See *History of the Royal College of Surgeons in Ireland* by Cameron, 1886; pp. 49. 106.)

12. Charles Higgins's relationship to William is shown by a Minute of the Council of the Royal Dublin Society, dated 9 May 1822, thanking Captain Higgins, nephew of Professor Higgins, for the gift of a packet of rare foreign seeds. Charles was 19 when he was commissioned in the York Rangers in July 1803. When the regiment was disbanded, he was posted in 1805 to the Royal Africa Corps as lieutenant. However, he wisely transferred to the 46th Foot (South Devonshire Regiment), otherwise he would have had to go to West Africa, in those days almost certain death. During Charles's period of service, the 46th were in the West Indies (1809–10), New South Wales and Tasmania (1813–17), and in India (1817–23). (This information was supplied by the War Office and the Public Record Office, London; see also J. J. Crook's *Historical Records of the Royal Africa Corps*, 1925.) Charles was married on 10 May 1826 (*Freeman's Journal* (Dublin), 11 May 1826), by Dr Daniel Murray, Archbishop of Dublin; he died in Dublin on 8 May 1836 (*Freeman's Journal*, 14 May 1836). An abstract of his will, which was dated 28 April 1836, is in the Public Record Office, Dublin. The Honourable George Knox (see note 115, p. 46), was a trustee of Charles's marriage settlement (Deed No. 813/479/548,215, 9 May 1826; Registry of Deeds, Dublin).

13. The records available show that Robert and Anne Blake had five daughters and at least two sons. Jane Whitty (née Blake) is buried with her husband in the Blake family grave in Mount Jerome, Dublin. Major-General Whitty (1788–1855) fought as a captain at Waterloo and was later Governor of Malta. Mr E. Q. Whitty of Bedford, grand-nephew of the Major-General, who was traced through legal records in Dublin, has kindly supplied information about this branch of the family. There remains no tradition of the Higgins connection.

14. Bryan Higgins's granddaughter, Elinor Stephens, née Blake, was the source of much of Sullivan's information (note 2, p. 28) about the Higgins family. Her will, which is available in the Public Record Office, Dublin (Reference P.C. 492; 1A/24/21), is, as she left numerous legacies, a guide to her relations. Her husband, Captain Nassau William Stephens, was born at Stockton-on-Tees on 3 January 1807. He served in the 94th Regiment from 8 November 1827, until he sold out on 7 June 1838, shortly before his marriage to Elinor. They lived at 12 Holles Street, Dublin, until her death in 1850. He then returned to England, and was appointed captain in the 2nd Cheshire Militia on 30 December 1854. He resigned on 30 January 1861, and became Adjutant of H.M. Lancashire Rifle Volunteers. He died in Preston on 9 July 1868. There is an abstract of his will in the Public Record Office, Dublin. (Information supplied by the War Office and the Public Record Office, London, by Messrs H. T. Dix and Sons, Solicitors, Dublin, and by Mr H. D. Stephens, grandson of Captain Stephens.)

15. There is a reference to the will of Bryan Higgins Blake in the Public Record Office, Dublin. His approximate date of birth is given by his age of entry to Trinity College, Dublin (*Alumni Dublinenses*).

16. Richard Everard Blake matriculated at Trinity College, Dublin, in 1837, at the age of 18 (*Alumni Dublinenses*). His sister Elinor Stephens (note 14 above), left him a miniature of her grandfather, Bryan Higgins, possibly one to which reference was made by Sullivan (note 2, p. 28). Foster's *Alumni Oxonienses* gives Richard Everard Blake, third son of Richard Everard Blake of Llanl-yan, Carmarthen, as matriculating at Magdalen Hall on 13 April 1872, at the age of 21. No will of Richard Everard Blake has been traced in the Irish, English or Welsh probate records, and the whereabouts of the miniature remains unknown. Sullivan states that it was painted by the Irish miniature painter John Comerford (*ca.* 1762–1832), but it is not included in the list of known works of this artist.

17. The genealogy of the von Haeseler family is given in the German publication *Brief Adel.* Our thanks are due to Mr G. J. Bernfeld who consulted the publication in the Vienna State Library. Mary Jane's date of birth is given in her marriage certificate as 14 October 1831, but as she was baptised in St Andrew's Church, Dublin, on 25 September 1828, she seems to have subtracted a few years from her age. Herr Curt von Haeseler of Weimar, grandson of Mary Jane Higgins, kindly loaned family photographs, some of which were taken in Dublin. He also supplied information in regard to his grandmother and her sister Emma Julia Peel. It should be mentioned that the Baroness von Haeseler visited Ireland about 1853, and in 1876–77 to dispose of the Higgins land in Co. Mayo and Queen's County (Co. Leix). Information was supplied by Messrs C. J. Reddy and Sons, Solicitors, Dublin, and by the Land Commission, Dublin. Deeds No. 1854/20/202, 9 July 1853, and 1854/20/203, 10 August 1854, in the Registry of Deeds, Dublin, relate to these lands. The latter document gives the date of William Higgins's will as 28 April 1825. See notes 100 and 104, p. 45.

18. See *Burke's Landed Gentry*, 1939, p. 1780. Messrs Maxwell, Weldon and Co., Solicitors, Dublin, have a copy of the marriage settlement of

William Peel and Emma Julia Higgins. Her will was traced in Somerset House, London by Mr Edward Nicholls.

19. William Joseph O'Connor Higgins died in Naples in December 1852 at the age of 19. (Information supplied by the British Consul-General, Naples.) His sister, Mary Jane Josephine O'Connor Higgins, registered the death in the Consulate. She was married in April 1853 in the Consulate at Naples to Baron Rudolph von Haeseler. A search of the Naples newspapers for 1852–53 by Miss Laura Motzo (arranged by the Department of External Affairs, Dublin), yielded no additional information.

ADDITION TO APPENDIX

SINCE this Appendix was prepared, the first portion (1763–71) of an Index (1763–1922) to a Dublin newspaper, the *Freeman's Journal*, now in course of preparation in the National Library, Dublin has become available.

The following marriage reference has been found:

Freeman's Journal (Dublin), 19–22 October 1765.

'At Killuny, in the County of Sligo, Mr James Tiernan, of Bride-street, Merchant, to Miss Higgins, Daughter of Thomas Higgins, Esq.; an eminent Physician.'

Genealogical problems are encountered if Thomas Higgins had a daughter who was married in 1765 (? *b.* 1747), a son, William, born in 1763, and a sister Bridget (*m. ca.* 1774; see p. 51). A further search uncovered an additional reference in:

Sleator's Public Gazetteer (Dublin), 19–22 October 1765.

'Mr James Tiernan of Bridge-street [*sic*] married to Miss Higgins of Killoony in the co. of Sligo.'

Finally in *Faulkner's Dublin Journal*, 19–22 October 1765, there is the entry:

'At Killuny in the County of Sligo, Mr James Ternan [*sic*] of Bride-street, Merchant, to Miss Higgins, Daughter of Bryan Higgins, Esq.; an eminent Physician.'

It fits better with the other genealogical data if Mrs Tiernan (Ternan) was the elder Bryan's and not Thomas's daughter, though Bridget Higgins who married Richard Everard about 1774 is given as the *only* daughter of Bryan Higgins (see notes 2 and 6 to Appendix). The inaccuracies of eighteenth-century journalism are exemplified in these extracts. There is, it may be mentioned, a Bridge Street in Collooney. (Information kindly supplied by Mr L. P. MacEachmharceagh.)

If Mrs Tiernan was Bryan's daughter the following conjectural table emerges:

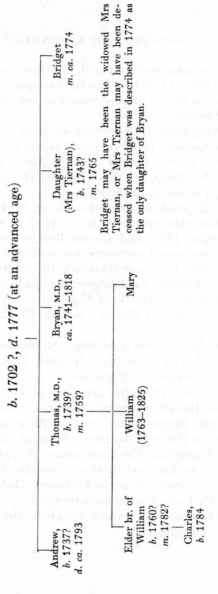

BRYAN HIGGINS, M.D.,

b. 1702 ?, *d.* 1777 (at an advanced age)

Andrew,
b. 1737?
d. ca. 1793

Thomas, M.D.,
b. 1739?
m. 1759?

Bryan, M.D.,
ca. 1741–1818

Daughter
(Mrs Tiernan),
b. 1743?
m. 1765

Bridget may have been the widowed Mrs
Tiernan, or Mrs Tiernan may have been de-
ceased when Bridget was described in 1774 as
the only daughter of Bryan.

Bridget
m. ca. 1774

William
(1763–1825)

Mary

Elder br. of
William
b. 1760?
m. 1782?

Charles,
b. 1784

58

Acknowledgments

THE AUTHORS are indebted to many correspondents who have helped in compiling material for this biography. They have indicated in the notes some of those who assisted but it would be impossible to name all. They wish, however, specially to mention His Grace, the Archbishop of Tuam, who had enquiries made in his archdiocese in an attempt to trace the grave of William Higgins. The Right Rev. Monsignor R. J. Glennon, Chancellor of the Archdiocese of Dublin kindly searched for particulars of the marriage of Captain Charles Higgins. The Irish Genealogists, Mr Edward Keane, Mr J. C. T. MacDonagh, Dr E. A. MacLysaght, and Dr R. C. Simington, the British Genealogist, Mr Edmond Nicholls, and Herr Curt von Haeseler of Weimar provided much biographical material. The authors' thanks are also due to the Librarian of the National Library, Dublin, Dr R. J. Hayes, and his Staff (particularly Mr P. Henchy), the Registrar (Dr H. H. Poole) and the Librarian (Mr D. J. Clarke) of the Royal Dublin Society, and the Secretary (Dr A. Farrington), and the Library Staff of the Royal Irish Academy. Professor John Read, F.R.S., provided references. Dr Michael Tierney, President of University College, Dublin, very kindly made available facilities for the work. Finally the authors wish to express their gratitude to Mrs J. F. Conan for her interest and her help in the collection and the preparation of the material for this biography. In addition to innumerable letters written in quest of information, she typed many drafts of the Mss.

Part II

HIGGINS AND THE ATOMIC THEORY

Introduction

IN MARCH 1789 Higgins, then aged 26, published in London *A Comparative View of the Phlogistic and Anti-phlogistic Theories*, which he had written the year before; it had also been printed in 1788[1]. The book which contained many experimental results was a detailed refutation of Kirwan's *Essay on Phlogiston* (London, 1787), and the great work of Higgins's life. He states in the Preface (p. xi) that he adopted Lavoisier's views about 1784. Lavoisier's *Traité* was not published until 1789 and the new theory was not well known before this, so that Higgins was an early convert. On the ideas outlined in the *Comparative View* rests Higgins's claim (discussed in Part III) to have anticipated Dalton as the originator of the atomic theory in its nineteenth-century form. As Thomson[2] said, the work did not attract attention when it was published. Four contemporary reviews have been traced[3], and none gives any indication that the book was regarded as more than an excellent exposition of the case against the phlogiston theory. Indeed, a notice of Higgins's *Essay on Bleaching* which appeared in the *Monthly Review* for 1800[4] cited the review of the *Comparative View* published in that journal in 1789[3], and stated that the earlier book made only a slight impression on the public.

An unsigned review of Higgins's *Atomic Theory* published in 1817[5] also refers to the poor reception of the *Comparative View*. Higgins of course thought otherwise. He claimed[6] that 'My atomic theory of chemistry is so mathematically correct, that all visionary hypotheses fell prostrate before it, and it was from it *alone* that the phlogistic doctrine received its fatal blow.' He

61

stated that he was the first in Great Britain to adopt the anti-phlogistic doctrine, thus extending a claim he made in 1799[7]. This earlier restricted claim that he was the first in England to adhere to Lavoisier, and to write in support of him in the English language was, literally, correct[8], since Black[6,9], who had accepted Lavoisier's theory before 1784, lived in Scotland and did not publish his conversion, and a spirited defence of the antiphlogistic theory written in 1784 by Richard Lubbock[10] was in Latin[11]. As the first English work to support Lavoisier the *Comparative View* is of great historical interest[12].

Higgins also stated[6] that when the *Comparative View* was published, the scientific world was so anxiously engaged in the phlogiston controversy that his novel mode of investigation (the atomic theory) was overlooked; he added, '. . . and indeed I was not much surprised at it, for the science was not at that time sufficiently ripe for so unusual a style of reasoning.' Bryan Higgins, however, had used it before him[13]. Higgins further claimed that some twelve months after his book appeared, Priestley was the only 'phlogistian' in England, and that Kirwan himself, the formidable champion of the phlogiston theory, recanted as soon as he read the book, 'and declared in the presence of many philosophical gentlemen now living in Dublin, that it was that work alone induced him to change his opinion, and that nothing the French philosophers brought forward had any influence on him; this appears from his notes in answer to the French at the end of the English translation'.

Higgins here refers to the fact that Kirwan's *Essay on Phlogiston* which has been mentioned above had been translated into French by Madame Lavoisier and published (1788) with refutations of the various sections by Lavoisier (Introduction; sections, 1, 2, 3, 11), Berthollet (4, 5, 6), de Fourcroy (8, 9, 10), de Morveau (7, conclusion), and Monge (12)[14]. Kirwan replied in 1789 in a second English edition of the *Essay*, containing a translation of the French notes (in which he says nothing of Higgins), but on 26 January 1791 he wrote to Berthollet thus[15]: 'Enfin je mets bas les armes, et j'abandonne le phlogistique. Je vois clairement qu'il n'y a aucune experience avérée qui atteste la production de l'air fixe par l'air inflammable pur; & cela étant, il est impossible de soutênir le systême du phlogistique dans les métaux, le soufre, &c. Sans des expériences décisives nous ne pouvons soutenir un systême contre des faits avérés. . . . Je donnerair moi-même une réfutation de mon Essai sur le phlogistique.' In a letter to Crell published in May 1791[16], Kirwan declared that he had abandoned the phlogistic system because he knew of no single, clear, decisive experiment by which one could establish that fixed air is composed of oxygen and phlogiston, and without this proof it seemed to him impossible to prove the existence of phlogiston in metals, sulphur, or nitrogen.

It will be seen that Higgins's claim to have converted Kirwan receives no confirmation from Kirwan's statements. Higgins possibly thought that, as Kirwan was unconverted in 1789 when he published the translation of the French chemists' notes, it must have been the *Comparative View* which came later that turned him early in 1791. Higgins also asserted[17] that his book altered the views of Bryan Higgins, Black, and Cavendish, but again published confirmatory evidence is lacking. Indeed, Cavendish never announced that he gave up the phlogiston theory[18]. We know[6, 9, 11] that Higgins was wrong in claiming to have influenced Black. Thomson thought[19] that it was the answer of the French chemists to Kirwan that was really responsible for the prevalence of the 'Lavoisierian theory' in Britain.

Summary of the Comparative View

The book extends to 316 pages of which pp. 283 to the end relate to analytical work on the 'human calculus' (see 'Topical Allusions' below). The divisions of the main work are into an introduction; of the composition and decomposition of water; of the composition of acids; of the vitriolic acid; of the nitrous acid; of the marine acid; of the calcination of metals *via sicca*; of the calcination of metals by steam, and the decomposition of water; of the reduction of metallic calces by charcoal, and the formation of fixed air; of the solubility of metals; of the precipitation of metals by each other. Since the book was written to combat Kirwan's *Essay on Phlogiston* (1787), there is some correspondence in the chapter headings in both books.

Higgins's refutation of Kirwan is about twice the length of that of the French chemists. He states in the *Comparative View* (p. 281) that about two-thirds of his book had been printed before he saw the French version of the *Essay on Phlogiston*. The date of publication of the French translation of Kirwan (1788) supports this statement. A comparison of Higgins's and the French chemists' remarks suggests that the *Comparative View* was written without reference to the French work. The large number of original experiments described by Higgins are in accord with this view.

The Introduction to the *Comparative View* refers to the rapid advance in chemistry in the preceding twelve years (say 1776–88). Recent chemical discoveries apparently of small value might prove to be of utility, for example, the discovery of phosphoric acid in bones may be of importance in medicine. The utility of many facts may depend on the discovery of one. To derive value from facts it is necessary to have a sound theory such as Lavoisier's antiphlogistic doctrine. Higgins says that he was obliged to have recourse to a mode of reasoning rather novel in chemistry. He had considered phlogiston as a substance chemically united to bodies in a solid state, and then enquired into the nature of such compounds, and whether the different phenomena in chemistry were consistently explicable on such principles. He had also endeavoured to determine whether the same phenomena were as explicable by supposing that the different bodies which unite to oxygen attract it, independent of a common principle or phlogiston.

Higgins says that he had frequently repeated most of the numerous experiments he quotes. He had been obliged to introduce several diagrams to explain his meaning. He had adopted the antiphlogistic theory four years before (*ca.* 1784), but so many able philosophers (Cavendish, Priestley, Kirwan, Black, Bryan Higgins) persisted in the old doctrine that he found it difficult to summon resolution enough to begin his book. He had written with conviction, otherwise he would have joined his countrymen in defence of the doctrine in which he had received his early instruction in chemistry from Dr Higgins, a phlogistian. He apologises for his lack of experience in proof reading.

In giving a summary of the points made by Higgins in the *Comparative View*, it would seem best to deal with: (1) his *obiter dicta*, (2) his topical allusions, (3) his arguments against the phlogistonists, (4) his atomic theory, and (5) his other claims to novelty.

1. OBITER DICTA

Higgins had a tendency to moralise as shown by the following examples: (i) 'Speculative reasoning must ever fall to the ground when put to the test of experiment' (Introduction, p. iv); (ii) 'Notions early imbibed will not be readily exchanged for new ones; the slow but sure hand of time alone can dispel those clouds which never fail to eclipse truth at her early appearance' (Introduction, p. v); (iii) 'Although I do not think sulphur contains phlogiston, or the solid matter of light inflammable air, I by no means suppose it to be a simple body, but to be, relatively to our knowledge of chemistry, as simple as the earths, or the two fixed alkalies; all of which I make no doubt will be analysed at some future period[20], when the science of chemistry will be more cultivated than at present, by men of genius, fortune, and leisure' (p. 120); (iv) 'A concatenation of facts, which regularly correspond with each other, will always bring truth to light; although a number of facts ever so well understood or arranged, are seldom without a few, which may separately admit of a quibble. . . . But happily for mankind, the most ingenious projects, which the most fertile imagination can produce to suppress truth, generally appear, sooner or later, as so many evidences in her favour' (p. 131); (v) 'I think a series of experiments made on this subject (action of nitric acid on blood) (see p. 108 below), could not fail of being productive of some benefit to mankind. For how can chemistry be better applied than in those investigations, which may tend to throw light on the different disorders incident to man?' (p. 164); (vi) 'As these facts cannot be satisfactorily accounted for, I think it better to suspend my opinion, than to attempt plausible explanations, which are generally more productive of evil than good, and only serve as so many allurements to decoy us out of the right path' (p. 173); (vii) 'Thus we find that chemistry is still in its infancy, and that

F

there is a good deal to be done in order to bring it to perfection'
(p. 178).

2. TOPICAL ALLUSIONS

(i) 'I have annexed an Analysis of the Human Calculus, which
I hope will be acceptable as well to my medical as chemical
readers. I was the more induced to publish it, as being delivered
in to the Royal Society in the year 1787, and read at one of their
spring meetings in the year 1788' (Introduction, p. xiii). The
paper was read at the meeting of 3 April 1788. It was this
reference which led to the discovery of the complete Ms. of the
paper in the archives of the Society (*Letters and Papers*, Decade
ix, 82; p. 5, above).

(ii) 'Mr Cavendish repeated his process for making nitrous
(nitric) acid (passing an electric spark through nitrogen and
oxygen) on a tolerable large scale last spring (footnote: Anno
1788). Dr B——y[21], another gentleman, and myself, have had
the pleasure of seeing it. The tube which confined the airs and
soap-lees was accidentally raised out of the mercury the day
before, which gave me an opportunity not only of seeing but of
tasting the nitre' (p. 91). The *Journal Book of the Royal Society*
(Meeting of 17 April 1788) records that Cavendish repeated his
experiment on the sparking of a mixture of nitrogen and oxygen
confined over mercury with soap-lees floating on the metal in the
apartments of the Royal Society in presence of the President and
some Members. This was because several able experimenters
such as Lavoisier had been unable to repeat the experiment
which Cavendish had first described some three years before. In
the published account of the work[21] it is mentioned that on 23
January 1788, the bent tube in which the gases were contained
was by accident raised out of the confining mercury. We know,
therefore, that Higgins did visit the Royal Society on 24 January
1788 (see p. 33 above). It will be remembered that he read his
paper there on 3 April of that year[22].

(iii) Higgins's description (p. 176) of the laboratory at Oxford
in which he worked reads: 'The chemical elaboratory at Oxford
is near six feet lower than the surface of the earth. The walls
are constructed with common lime stone, and arched over with

the same; the floor is also paved with stone. . . . There is an area adjoining it on a level with the floor, which, though not very large, is sufficient to admit a free circulation of air. The ashes and sweepings of the elaboratory are deposited in it. There is a good sink in the centre of this area, so that no stagnated water can lodge there. The p——y which is seldom frequented, is over ground, and unconnected with the elaboratory. Notwithstanding all this, the walls of the room afford fresh crops of nitre every three or four months.'

Higgins goes on to say how he analysed these crops which still grow on the walls of this room. A bottle labelled 'Nitre from the walls of the Museum' and containing nitre was recently found by the Curator of the Museum of the History of Science (Dr C. H. Josten). This is the building in Broad Street which housed the chemical laboratory, and is better known as 'The Old Ashmolean'.

Since Dr John Kidd, Professor of chemistry at Oxford, published an account of the efflorescence in 1814[23], it is possible that the specimen was collected by him. (See Part I, note 47, p. 36.) Analysis of a sample of the nitre kindly supplied by Dr Josten yielded the following figures; those found by Higgins are also given.

	Now found	Higgins
Per cent soluble nitre	28.5	28.1
K as KNO_3	20.2	18.8
$Ca(NO_3)_2$	None	9.3
	$CaCO_3$ also present	

3. ARGUMENTS AGAINST THE PHLOGISTONISTS

(i) Section I of the *Comparative View* states (p. 2) that the determination of the composition of water by Lavoisier and Cavendish was 'one of the most interesting discoveries that ever was made in Chemistry'. It threw light, for example, on the different stages of fermentation. Higgins thought that water contains by weight six of oxygen to one of hydrogen, and by volume exactly two to one. He refers to Priestley's belief that the water produced in the Cavendish experiment is originally present in the hydrogen and oxygen, and that 'nitrous acid' is

formed by the union of their ultimate particles. Higgins rejects
this view, because he had found[24], with excess of hydrogen and
with pure gases, that no acid was obtained on inflammation;
with excess of oxygen, acid was formed, particularly if nitrogen
was present (see also *Comparative View*, 92 ff). He also points
out that the acid is not found in the slow combustion of hydrogen
in oxygen. He had condensed up to half a gallon of oxygen in
this way but could not detect even a trace of acid. He draws the
correct conclusion that any acid formed on sparking is due to the
presence of adventitious nitrogen. He affirms his belief that
water is composed of hydrogen and oxygen. Because gases hold
water in 'solution', it is not to be inferred that water is a necessary ingredient in them, 'chemically united to the real gravitating matter of the different airs' (p. 6). If oxygen is mainly
water why is not hydrogen produced when iron is calcined in
oxygen as it is when iron is calcined in steam? (p. 7).

(ii) In Section III (p. 18) Higgins deals with sulphuric acid
and opposes Kirwan's view that 'sulphur consists of a basis, or a
radical principle, which, when saturated with phlogiston, constitutes sulphur, but with fixed air (carbon dioxide) vitriolic acid
(sulphuric acid); and when combined partly with one and partly
with the other, volatile sulphureous acid (sulphurous acid or
sulphur dioxide)[25]. Higgins points out that Kirwan's view requires that the combustion of sulphur in oxygen involves the
union of oxygen to the phlogiston of the sulphur. This union
should according to Kirwan give water[26]; 'therefore it appears
to me, that his doctrine is a little contradicted in this process'.
Kirwan thought that hydrogen was pure phlogiston combined
with fire (see note 29, p. 115 below).

Higgins also states that he had condensed some 100 cubic
inches of oxygen by the combustion of hydrogen in a jar inverted over lime-water. The hydrogen was produced from iron
free from rust, and sulphuric acid diluted with three volumes
of water, and was washed with soap-lees to retain adventitious
carbon dioxide and traces of sulphuric acid. He could detect no
carbon dioxide in the water produced. Further, he considers it
unlikely that substances so different in properties as carbon
dioxide and water could be the same compound in different

modifications as Kirwan thought, and feels that Kirwan cannot continue to maintain that sulphuric acid contains carbon dioxide. He gives at length reasons against Kirwan's views on sulphur, and the compounds which it forms with oxygen. Later (p. 32; see also p. 120—quoted above on p. 65) he points out that although lime and similar earths had not been decomposed yet they are probably compounds. However, until resolved, they must be regarded as simple substances and for this reason sulphur, phosphorus, nitrogen, and the metals should be regarded as simple bodies. Again, hydrogen is formed when steam is passed over pure sulphur. If sulphur is a compound of a certain basis and phlogiston, and water is composed of oxygen and phlogiston 'would (p. 33) the dephlogisticated air (oxygen) of the water quit its own phlogiston, to unite to the phlogiston of the sulphur?' Finally (p. 35) '. . . all the phenomena above recited are only explicable by leaving out phlogiston, and supposing sulphur to be a simple substance, whose ultimate particles attract dephlogisticated air with forces inherent in themselves, independent of phlogiston or concrete inflammable air, as an alkali does an acid. . . .'

(iii) In Section VI of the *Comparative View* (p. 219), Higgins discusses the calcination of metals in the dry way. He says that 'The antiphlogistians suppose that metals are simple bodies, which unite to dephlogisticated air, and form calces. . . . The phlogistians, on the contrary, are of opinion, that metals are composed of two principles, viz. metallic bases, and phlogiston (or light inflammable air), in a solid state.' He shows real chemical insight when he remarks (p. 225), 'Indeed, there are some circumstances in which bodies will decompose others of superior attraction, when exposed to heat; as, for instance, phosphoric acid will decompose vitriolated tartar (potassium sulphate); but this proceeds from the extreme fixity of the alkali and phosphoric acid, and the volatility of vitriolic acid'[27]. He also states (p. 225) that '. . . we could account for the calcination of mercury, and the decomposition of the calx again when exposed to a stronger heat, on the same principle that copper and zinc, or gold and mercury, or tin and mercury, unite in a low heat, and separate again in a higher degree'.

Higgins points out (p. 227) that if metals are composed of fixed bases and so volatile a substance as hydrogen, it is strange that they cannot be separated even at high temperatures. 'Surely all the metallic bases are not the same. Therefore we should suppose that there might be one or more amongst them all, that would be so little tenacious of their phlogiston as to yield, if not the whole, a portion of it when urged with a fierce heat.' He heated iron filings in a small glass retort to a temperature sufficient to melt the glass, but obtained only a trace of hydrogen. He also (p. 228) heated lead, tin, and other metals to the melting-point of cast iron in a well-closed, deep crucible, but obtained no change in their constitution. He thinks (p. 231) that any carbon dioxide 'obtained as well during the calcination of metals, as afterwards from their calces, depends upon some impregnation in the materials, and does not in the least tend to prove the existence of phlogiston in metals. Iron quickly calcined by fire, or in the nitrous (nitric) acid, will not yield a particle of fixable air (carbon dioxide), though rust of iron will afford it in abundance.' Higgins concludes (p. 237) that in experiments of this kind 'the fixable air proceeds partly from some impurities in the material, but chiefly from the absorption of fixable air from the atmosphere'.

4. ATOMIC THEORY

Higgins made no effort to present his atomic theory systematically. He used it solely to assist him in his discussion of the case against phlogiston. He put forward new ideas vaguely and without emphasis on their novelty as if they were generally current at the time he wrote. It is necessary, therefore, to systematise the presentation of his views, and for this purpose they are discussed below under the following heads: (i) Composition of molecules; (ii) Law of gaseous volumes; (iii) Law of multiple proportions; (iv) Use of symbols. Interatomic bonds and forces; (v) Reaction mechanisms.

Composition of Molecules

Nitric oxide—In Section II (p. 8) Higgins discusses Kirwan's criticisms of 'Mr Lavoisier's Table of affinities of the Oxygenous

Principle'[28]. He (p. 13) cites various chemical reactions to show the anomalies which occur when one seeks to determine affinity; for example, iron will not rust in dry air, but will do so in the presence of water. This result indicates that iron decomposes water and that the hydrogen so liberated re-combines with the oxygen of the air (see p. 110 below). He finds it difficult to account for this. He goes on (p. 14): 'It is true, all this may be justly attributed to fire[29] which from its attraction to bodies, counteracts their chemical union to one another: but, from the following considerations, I think some other power must interfere[30]. It is generally allowed, and justly, that nitrous air (nitric oxide) consists of dephlogisticated air (oxygen) and phlogistic (nitrogen) in the proportion of two of the former to one of the latter.' Hence he concludes 'every ultimate particle of phlogisticated air must be united to two of dephlogisticated air; and these molicules [*sic*][31] combined with fire constitutes nitrous air'. He repeats this statement (p. 132) writing: 'Nitrous air, according to Kirwan (see p. 78 below), contains 2 of dephlogisticated to 1 of phlogisticated air. According to Lavoisier, 100 gr. of nitrous air contain 32 gr. of phlogisticated air, and 68 of dephlogisticated air. I am myself of the former philosopher's opinion: I likewise am of opinion, that every primary particle of phlogisticated air is united to two of dephlogisticated air, and that these molecules are surrounded with one common atmosphere of fire.' (See p. 81 below.)

Higgins does not make it clear whether his two to one refers to composition by volume or by weight (see pp. 77, 78, 86, 87 below), although his quotation of Lavoisier's result seems to suggest that Higgins here was thinking of proportions by *weight*. In his *Atomic Theory* (p. 119) he says that he referred to the ratio by volume[32]. Actually, with the crude measurements of the time, volume and weight ratios would not differ greatly for nitrogen and oxygen. (See p. 72 below.) Further, the figures Higgins gives are inaccurate; nitrogen and oxygen combine to form nitric oxide in equal proportions by volume, and as 28 is to 32 by weight.

He expands his ideas in regard to nitric oxide in a manner characteristic of his method of thought. He states (p. 14) that if the volume associated with a particle of that gas is equal to that associated with a particle of oxygen, then 100 cubic inches of nitric oxide should under standard conditions weight about 98 grains $(2 \times 34 + 30)$, since 100 cubic inches of oxygen and of nitrogen weight 34 and 30 grains, respectively. But the weight is only 37 grains. 'Hence (p. 15), we may justly conclude, that the gravitating particles of nitrous air are thrice the distance from each other that the ultimate particles of dephlogisticated air are in the same temperature, and of course their atmosphere of fire must be in size proportionable.'

Higgins is wrong in his calculations; the distance factor should be $\sqrt[3]{3}$ approximately[33]. He remarks that, having regard to the large repelling atmospheres of nitric oxide, it is surprising how readily this gas as compared with nitrogen unites with oxygen. For this and other reasons he concludes (p. 16) that 'the attractive forces of bodies are not to be estimated by the facility of compounding, but rather by the difficulty of decompounding these again'. He did not, accordingly, accept Kirwan's criticisms of Lavoisier's 'Table of Affinities'[28]. It should be stressed that Higgins was then unaware of the importance of his atomic ideas, and was solely concerned with attempts to refute Kirwan.

Sulphur dioxide—On p. 36 of the *Comparative View* Higgins plunges into his atomic theory. He says that 100 grains of sulphur require about 100 of 'the real gravitating matter' of oxygen to form sulphur dioxide. He goes on: '. . . and as volatile vitriolic acid (sulphur dioxide) is very little short of double the specific gravity of dephlogisticated air (oxygen), we may conclude, that the ultimate particles of sulphur and dephlogisticated air, contain equal quantities of solid matter; for dephlogisticated air suffers no considerable contraction by uniting to sulphur in the proportion merely necessary for the formation of volatile vitriolic acid. Hence we may conclude, that, in volatile vitriolic acid, a single ultimate particle of sulphur is intimately united, only to a single particle of dephlogisticated air, and that, in perfect vitriolic acid, every single particle of sulphur is united to 2 of dephlogisticated air, being the quantity necessary to saturation.'

Higgins's views are here obscure. A possible reading lies in the fact that he had a vague idea that equal volumes of gases under the same external conditions contain in some instances the same number of particles (see 'Law of Gaseous Volumes' below). Hence as oxygen combines with an equal weight of sulphur to give its own volume of sulphur dioxide (with consequently twice the specific gravity of oxygen), each atom of oxygen forms one molecule of sulphur dioxide which for simplicity he wrote SO rather than $S_n O$. This formula involves the assumption that the atoms of sulphur and oxygen are equal in weight (see also $C.V.$, p. 81). And as Higgins thought that sulphuric acid (p. 36) 'contains 2 parts of dephlogisticated air, and 1 of sulphur, exclusive of water', he wrote sulphuric acid, SO_2[34]. His assignment of this formula is in line with his approach to the formulae of the oxides of nitrogen (see 'Law of Multiple Proportions', below). At that time it was not realised that acids contained hydrogen, and the distinction between an acid and its anhydride was not understood.

Water—We come now (p. 37) to one of the most quoted statements in the book. Higgins writes: 'As 2 cubic inches of light inflammable air require but 1 of dephlogisticated air to condense them, we must suppose that they contain equal numbers of divisions (ultimate particles), and that the difference of their specific gravity depends chiefly on the size of their ultimate particles; or we must suppose that the ultimate particles of light inflammable air (hydrogen) require 2 or 3, or more, of dephlogisticated air to saturate them. If this latter were the case, we might produce water in an intermediate state, as well as the vitriolic (sulphuric) or the nitrous (nitric) acid, which appears to be impossible; for in whatever proportion we mix our airs, or under whatsoever circumstance we combine them, the result is invariably the same. This likewise may be observed with respect to the decomposition of water. Hence we may justly conclude, that water is composed of molicules[31] formed by the union of a single particle of dephlogisticated air to an ultimate particle of light inflammable air, and that they are incapable of uniting to a third particle of either of their constituent principles.'

Hydrogen sulphide—Higgins believed that the available evidence indicated that hydrogen sulphide consisted of a suspension or solution of sulphur particles in hydrogen (pp. 13, 72, 73, 77,

80). He sparked hydrogen sulphide with an equal volume of oxygen (p. 78) and he found that when allowance had been made for impurities present in the gases, about half a volume of sulphur dioxide remained. He knew that hydrogen sulphide contained its own volume of hydrogen which would remove half a volume of oxygen as water; the residual half volume of oxygen, therefore, gave its own volume of sulphur dioxide. The specific gravity of the latter gas is approximately twice that of oxygen, and of hydrogen sulphide when a deduction is made for the hydrogen present. Hence, per unit volume, the number of particles in sulphur dioxide is equal to the number of particles in oxygen, and to the number of sulphur particles in hydrogen sulphide. But Higgins thought (see p. 73 above) that the particle number of hydrogen per unit volume is half that of oxygen, so that the number of ultimate particles of sulphur in hydrogen sulphide is twice the number of those of hydrogen; hence hydrogen sulphide is HS_2. Higgins deduced nine to five in error in the *Comparative View* (p. 81) but changed the figure to 18 to 9 in his *Atomic Theory* (p. 84).

Higgins used figures for gaseous specific gravities in grains per 1000 cubic inches, taken from Kirwan's *Essay on Phlogiston*, and these he prints in the Introduction. As stated above he thought that hydrogen sulphide contained gaseous sulphur and its own volume of hydrogen, so that the specific gravity of the sulphur gas present was given by deducting the specific gravity of hydrogen (2·613) from that of hydrogen sulphide (34·286). The resulting figure (31·673) was approximately equal to the specific gravity of oxygen (34), and half that of sulphur dioxide (70·215).

Higgins's arguments about hydrogen sulphide, both in the *Comparative View* and in an amended version in the *Atomic Theory*, are unclear, and the outline given above is a paraphrase. He had already (see under 'Sulphur Dioxide', p. 72 above) deduced the composition of sulphur dioxide and the equality in weight of the sulphur and oxygen particles. The explosion experiment confirmed these results.

These extracts illustrate the manner in which Higgins applied the atomic theory to chemistry. His combination of the results of chemical experiments with figures for specific gravity show real chemical insight. His claim to have anticipated Dalton will be discussed later (Part III).

Law of Gaseous Volumes

It will be clear from what has been written under 'Composition of Molecules' that Higgins foreshadowed the Law of Gaseous Volumes announced by Gay-Lussac in 1808. This law states that 'When gases take part in chemical change, the volumes of the reacting gases and those of the products, if gaseous, are in the ratio of small whole numbers.' Higgins claimed priority in regard to this law when he pointed out[35] that Thomas Thomson in an article on the 'Atomic Theory' which appeared in the *Encyclopaedia Britannica*[36] in 1815 failed to notice any of Higgins's contributions to the subject. Thomson himself[37] and Wollaston[38] had previously conceded Higgins's claim in this field. The importance which Higgins attached to it is shown by the footnote which appears in an attack on Dalton's views on the composition of the nitrogen oxides[39]. This footnote is worth quoting: 'My *Comparative View* was published twenty years before Mr Dalton's *New System of Philosophy* appeared, and Gay Lussac had written some time after him[40]. It will be found by any person who will take the pains of carefully perusing my work, that I was perfectly acquainted with the proportions in which gases combine in volumes; it was the groundwork, together with their specific gravities, on which my entire system rested: and without this knowledge no human being could attempt to estimate the different proportions in which they unite particle to particle; and much less the relative size, and of course the relative weight, of those particles; for the specific weight of the ultimate divisions of all kinds of ponderable matter is the same—their size or diameter only constitutes the difference.' It may be noted that Higgins takes it as obvious that the density of the matter constituting atoms was the same for all atoms. This had been assumed by Demokritos and the early Greek atomists. He goes on:

'Without a previous knowledge of the foregoing principles, we might as well attempt to ascertain the weight of the most distant fixed stars, as those of particles, atoms, or molecules of matter . . .'.

This footnote amplifies Higgins's prior statement[41]: 'Now the doctrine of the proportions in which particles unite to particles, or atoms to atoms, could only be deduced from a previous knowledge of the specific gravity of simple gases and of their components in the gaseous state, and of the proportions in which they unite volume to volume. The whole of my Atomic System was founded on those principles, and without this preliminary knowledge I could not advance a single step.'

Apparently Higgins thought that gases have 'particle numbers' which are equal or in a simple ratio; that is to say that equal volumes of gases under the same conditions of temperature and pressure contain numbers of particles which are equal or in a simple ratio. Avogadro[42] began his discussion of Gay-Lussac's law of volumes by saying that it suggests that 'very simple relations also exist between the volumes of gaseous substances and the numbers of simple or compound molecules which form them'.

Higgins's views (see above under 'Composition of Molecules') in relation to some of the gases with which he dealt may be summarised as follows (references are to *Comparative View*):

Nitric oxide
(pp. 14, 132)

Two volumes of oxygen and one of nitrogen give three volumes of nitric oxide. (He does not use the word 'volume' here but the context on p. 14 implies it.) Nitric oxide is NO_2. The particle numbers of nitrogen and oxygen are equal. The particle number of nitric oxide is one third that of oxygen.

Sulphur dioxide
(pp. 36, 80)

One volume of oxygen gives one volume of sulphur dioxide. Sulphur dioxide is SO. The particle numbers of sulphur dioxide and of oxygen are equal.

Water
(p. 37)

Two volumes of hydrogen combine with one of oxygen. Water is HO. The particle number of oxygen is twice that of hydrogen.

Hydrogen sulphide   Hydrogen sulphide contains its own volume
  (p. 78)   of hydrogen and the sulphur dispersed in it
                     has the same particle number as oxygen.
                     Hydrogen sulphide is, therefore, HS_2. Hig-
                     gins (p. 81) wrote H_5S_9 in error.

Law of Multiple Proportions

Higgins's statements on the constitution of oxygen compounds of nitrogen ($C.V.$, pp. 132, 164, 171)[43] foreshadow the law of multiple proportions[44]. Higgins writes obscurely and his arguments on the composition of the oxides of nitrogen are difficult to follow, particularly as he does not clearly differentiate between proportions by weight and by volume (see p. 71 above). Although he nowhere explicitly states the law of multiple proportions, his words and diagrams leave no doubt that he believed that if two elements, such as oxygen and nitrogen, or oxygen and sulphur, form more than one compound, and if A and B represent the particles of the elements, then (i) one compound is AB, as Bryan Higgins had assumed and Dalton was later to assume, and (ii) the other compounds contain two, three, etc., B particles united to one A particle, and can be formulated as AB_2, AB_3, etc. Dalton also assumed this, but (on the basis of experimental results) he also assumed that such compounds as A_2B_3 are possible. The law of multiple proportions is thus implicitly contained in Higgins's scheme.

Scheele[45] knew that nitric oxide, nitrous acid, nitrogen dioxide, and nitric acid stood in that order. He also knew that ammonia was converted into an inert gas by oxidising agents. Higgins may not have known of Scheele's views, though he twice refers to the 'celebrated Scheel' in the Section on 'the Marine Acid' ($C.V.$, pp. 179, 197). He sets out his own ideas on the oxygen compounds of nitrogen as follows ($C.V.$, pp. 133, 171):

Compound	Higgins's formulation using modern symbols
1. 'Dephlogisticated nitrous air' (Nitrous oxide, N_2O)	NO
2. 'Nitrous air' (Nitric oxide, NO)	NO_2

Compound	Higgins's formulation using modern symbols
3. 'Red nitrous vapour, or the red nitrous acid' (Possibly a mixture of nitric oxide and nitrogen dioxide which would dissolve in water to form nitrous acid)	NO_3
4. 'Pale or straw-coloured nitrous acid' (Possibly nitrogen dioxide dissolved in nitric acid)	NO_4
5. 'Colourless nitrous acid' (Nitric acid)	NO_5

On p. 164 of the *Comparative View* Higgins discussed Priestley's discovery of nitrous oxide and refers to the gas as 'the last stage of nitrous acid'. He himself had found that when nitric oxide was kept over water and iron it formed first nitrous oxide and then nitrogen and ammonia. From his experiments he concluded (p. 165): 'that which is called dephlogisticated nitrous air (nitrous oxide), is common nitrous air (nitric oxide), deprived only of a portion of its dephlogisticated air (oxygen).' Again he writes (p. 166): 'These facts leave no room for doubt, but that dephlogisticated nitrous air contains less dephlogisticated air than common nitrous air.' Higgins, following Kirwan, thought (*C.V.*, pp. 14, 132; see p. 71 above) that nitric oxide was formed from one volume of nitrogen and two of oxygen: he wrote it NO_2 and consequently he assumed that nitrous oxide is NO. Kirwan's statements refer to the weight ratio but his densities (*C.V.*, p. xiv) give much the same volume ratio.

Nitrous and nitric oxides were established as definite compounds when Higgins wrote. His next two compounds are less well defined. He believed (*C.V.*, p. 84) that three volumes of nitric oxide united with one of oxygen to give 'red nitrous vapour'. As he thought (*C.V.*, p. 14) that one volume of nitrogen and two volumes of oxygen give three volumes of nitric oxide, it follows that 'red nitrous vapour' contained one volume of nitrogen and three of oxygen and was, therefore, NO_3[46]. Similarly (p. 84) the 'straw-coloured nitrous acid' appeared to contain one volume of nitrogen and four of oxygen, and was, therefore, NO_4.

The red nitrous vapour was probably a mixture of nitric oxide and nitrogen dioxide which would dissolve in water to form mainly nitrous acid; the pale product may have been nitrogen dioxide dissolved in nitric acid. The quantity of nitrogen dioxide dissolved was less than in the red fuming acid as now used. It is difficult to obtain accurate results from experiments on mixing nitric oxide with air or oxygen over water[47].

In 1817 Higgins discussed Dalton's views on the volume composition of the oxides of nitrogen. He states that by 'red nitrous vapour' he, in 1789, meant subnitrous acid, that is the solution in water of the oxide containing one volume of nitrogen and one and a half of oxygen[48]. By 'pale nitrous acid' Higgins claims that he had referred to 'nitrous acid gas', the product of mixing two volumes of nitric oxide with one of oxygen, that is nitrogen dioxide, or rather its solution in water. He remarks (see preceding paragraph) on the difficulty of obtaining consistent results in experiments of this kind; 'variations depend upon the manner in which the gases are mixed, and the surface which they present to water'. Dalton observed this before[47, 49].

N_2O_3 *and* NO_2—We may here indicate briefly how the confusion existing in Higgins's day about N_2O_3 and NO_2 was eventually removed. Higgins wrote all oxides with 'N' where N_2 is correct. Dalton (see above) in spite of his neglect of Gay-Lussac's law of volumes, had in 1803 assumed the correct formulae: N_2O, NO, N_2O_3[50]. Higgins also had NO_2 for nitrogen dioxide, but Dalton thought that NO_2 was nitric acid[51, 52].

The ambiguities were not cleared up until 1816. Gay-Lussac[53] distinguished experimentally between N_2O_3 and NO_2, and Dulong[54] showed that the product obtained by heating lead nitrate is NO_2 and not N_2O_3 and water as Gay-Lussac thought. The clarification of the position in regard to nitrogen pentoxide and nitric acid is given below.

Nitric acid—The development of knowledge on the composition of nitric acid merits special consideration. It was in Section IV (p. 82) of the *Comparative View* that Higgins discussed this acid. He was concerned with proving that Kirwan was wrong in holding that nitric acid contained hydrogen and carbon dioxide in addition to nitrogen and oxygen. Higgins in 1814[55] stated that he found (*C.V.*, p. 83) that nitric acid contained one part of nitrogen to five of oxygen, while Lavoisier had observed one of nitrogen to four of oxygen. What he actually said in the *Comparative View* is shown by five excerpts which, at the cost of some repetition, are given below.

On p. 83, Higgins wrote (excerpt 1): 'I mixed the different products of (the decomposition of) a quantity of pure nitre, and found by exposure to liver of sulphur that one-sixth was left unabsorbed. This was the utmost degree of purity in which I obtained dephlogisticated air from nitre.

'According to Mr Lavoisier, 100 grains of nitrous (nitric) acid contain $79\frac{1}{2}$ of dephlogisticated air, and $20\frac{1}{2}$ of phlogisticated air, which is not quite four to one. But his experiments contradict this; for whatever mode he adopted to decompose nitrous acid, it appeared that the proportion of dephlogisticated air was nearly as five, to one of phlogisticated air[56].

'Mr Cavendish[57] has proved, that nitrous acid may be formed by taking the electric spark in a mixture of three parts phlogisticated air, and seven of dephlogisticated air, which is but $\frac{1}{7}$ more of dephlogisticated air than nitrous air contains. This may apparently contradict Mr Lavoisier's as well as my own estimation of the proportion of the constituent principles of nitrous acid when in its perfect state.'

Again (excerpt 2; pp. 105–106), Higgins describes a quantitative experiment by Lavoisier on the action of charcoal on potassium nitrate[58]. Using the figures recalculated to British weights and measures by Kirwan[59] he writes (p. 106): 'Mr Lavoisier was justly led to conclude from this experiment, that nitrous acid was composed of dephlogisticated and phlogisticated air, and that the latter was in the proportion of $\frac{1}{5}$ of the whole of the acid; and likewise, that fixable air was composed of the matter of charcoal and dephlogisticated air.' And (p. 107): 'In my opinion, 100 gr. of pure nitre contain, of

		Correct
Caustic alkali	57 grains	46.6 as K_2O
Dephlogisticated air	27	39.5
Phlogisticated air	6	13.9
Water	10	?
Total	100	100

Lavoisier gives[60] for potassium nitrate:

Caustic alkali	57.5
Oxygen	33.8
Nitrogen	8.7
	100.0

Kirwan[61] gives:

Caustic alkali	53.5
Acid	34
Water	12.5

On p. 132 we have (excerpt 3): 'In my opinion, the purest nitrous acid contains 5 of dephlogisticated to 1 of phlogisticated air. Nitrous air, according to Kirwan, contains 2 of dephlogisticated air to 1 of phlogisticated air (see below). According to Lavoisier, 100 gr. of nitrous air contain 32 gr. of phlogisticated air, and 68 of dephlogisticated air (see below under discussion of excerpts). I am myself of the former philosopher's opinion: I likewise am of the opinion, that every primary particle of phlogisticated air is united to two of dephlogisticated air, and that these molecules are surrounded with one common atmosphere of fire.' (See p. 71 above.)

On p. 143 (excerpt 4; the figures are Kirwan's recalculations[62], which are slightly in error), Higgins states: 'Mr Lavoisier, to whom we are chiefly indebted for reducing this useful science into a rational system, and expelling that gloom which had overwhelmed it for all ages past, took 945 gr. of nitrous acid, whose specific gravity was 1.316, and to this he added 1104 gr.[63] of mercury (Footnote—*Mem. Par.*, 1776, p. 670)[64]. The whole of the mercury was dissolved, and he obtained 273,234 cubic inches of nitrous air. He afterwards exposed the mercurial salt to a red heat, and obtained from it 287,742 cubic inches of dephlogisticated air, at the same time that the mercury was revived.' And then, after much discussion, on p. 155 (excerpt 5): 'The quantity of nitrous air obtained was 273,234 cubic inches, or 101,09 gr. and the dephlogisticated air amounted to 287,743. (This is an error for Kirwan gives, as Higgins does above, 287,742 cubic inches, or 97.83 gr.) The above quantity of pure nitrous air contains 91.78 (? 91.078; see below) cubic

G

inches of phlogisticated air, and 182,156 cubic inches of dephlogisticated air which, in addition to the quantity expelled
from the calx, make 469,898 cubic inches of dephlogisticated air;
which, subtracting 14,512 cubic inches (? 287.742 – 273.234
= 14.508) from them, make five of dephlogisticated air to one
of phlogisticated air, being the exact proportion of perfect
nitrous acid.' (See p. 86 below.)

Note on Lavoisier's work on nitric acid—A brief statement of
Lavoisier's experiments used by Higgins may be interpolated
here. The weights and measures are those used in Lavoisier's
publications. The experiment with mercury and nitric acid was
published in two forms, in 1776 and 1779[64]. Lavoisier dissolved
2 oz. 1 gros of mercury in 2 oz. of nitric acid of sp. gr. 1·31607
(about 50 p.c.) and collected the nitrous air (NO) over water. He
evaporated the solution to dryness and a white salt (mercuric
nitrate) remained. He obtained 'soixante-douze' (1776) or (1779)
190 cu. in. of nitrous air. On heating the salt he collected 10 to
12 cu. in. of gas which he thought was common air [he must
have lost a little NO_2 in the water] and obtained a residue of red
precipitate (HgO), on heating which he collected 234 (1776) or
224 (1779) cu. in. of 'plus air que l'air common' (i.e. O_2) and
recovered the 2 oz. 1 gros of mercury. Thus he obtained 190
cu. in. of nitrous air, 12 cu. in. of common air, and 224 cu. in.
of air better than common air (1779). The 12 cu. in. of common
air he supposed resulted from the mixture of 24 (1776) or 36
(1779) cu. in. of nitrous air and 24 (1776) or 14 (1779) cu. in.
of air better than common air (oxygen), 'd'après les expériences
de M. Pristley [*sic*]'. Thus for 2 oz. of nitric acid or calculated for
1 lb. by multiplying by 8:

	1776		1779	
	2 oz.	1 lb.	2 oz.	1 lb.
Nitrous air	196	1568	226	1808
Purest air	246	1968	238	1904
	442	3536	464	3712

all in cu. in. Priestley's experiments seem to be those (*Experiments and Observations on Air*, 1775, vol. 2, pp. 45–49) in which

he says he mixed equal volumes of nitrous air and dephlogisticated air (O_2) over water and the dephlogisticated air was
'diminished to almost one-half of its original quantity'. This
gives the 24 vols. and 24 vols. of Lavoisier's 1776 figures, leaving
12 vols. (Priestley does not say the residue is common air.)

In its formation the 12 cu. in. of common air used up 24 cu. in.
nitrous air and 24 cu. in. oxygen, and we should have expected
Lavoisier to have added these to the volumes, giving $190 + 24$
$= 214$ of nitrous air and $234 + 24 = 258$ oxygen. Instead he
added 6 of nitrous air, giving $190 + 6 = 196$, and 12 of oxygen,
giving $234 + 12 = 246$.

The 1779 corrections seem to be based on Priestley's alternative result when he says that 5 half-volumes ($5 \times 7 = 35$) of
nitrous air could be added without appreciably diminishing the
original volume (14) of pure air. Then the residue would have
been 14, not 12 as Lavoisier found. He may have increased 35
to 36 because Priestley says the air (oxygen) from red lead
took 6 half-volumes instead of 5 (which is wrong if air contains
$\frac{1}{5}$ of oxygen), and Lavoisier may have taken 12 instead of 14
because Priestley says 'appreciably'. For the densities of the
gases Lavoisier took 1 cu. in. $NO = 0.4$ grains and 1 cu. in.
$O_2 = 0.55$ grains, and hence 1 lb. of nitric acid contains:

	1776			1779		
Nitrous air	1 oz.	—	$51\frac{1}{2}$ gr.	1 oz.	2 gros	$3\frac{1}{5}$ gr.
Purest air	1 oz.	7 gros	$2\frac{1}{2}$ gr.	1 oz.	6 gros	$32\frac{1}{5}$ gr.
Water	13 oz.	—	18 gr.	13 oz.	7 gros	$36\frac{3}{5}$ gr.

(The last figure should be 12 oz. instead of 13 oz.)

Although he obtained nearly equal volumes of nitric oxide
and oxygen by decomposing nitric acid, Lavoisier found that
on mixing $7\frac{1}{3}$ vols. NO and 4 vols. O_2 over water the $11\frac{1}{3}$ vols.
were reduced to $\frac{1}{3}$ vol. and dilute nitric acid was formed. On
mixing the gases over mercury covered with water they condensed completely to fuming nitric acid. He remarks on the
discrepancy between the analysis and synthesis and says ordinary
nitric acid contains 'a considerable superabundance of purest air'.
If the experiment was made with common air, 16 vols. were
required instead of 4 of purest air, hence common air contains
$\frac{1}{4}$ vol. of purest air.

Lavoisier's analysis experiment gives for nitric acid 196 or 226 vols. nitrous air and 246 or 238 purest air. But since $NO = \frac{1}{2}N_2 + \frac{1}{2}O_2$, Lavoisier's results, as he corrected them, give:

$$
\begin{array}{rl}
1776\colon 196 \text{ vols. nitrous air} & = 98 \text{ nitrogen} + 98 \text{ oxygen} \\
\text{oxygen} & = \qquad\qquad 246 \\
& \overline{\qquad\qquad 344} \\
\therefore \text{ N/O by vol.} & = 98/344 = 1/3.51 \\
1779\colon 226 \text{ vols. nitrous air} & = 113 \text{ nitrogen} + 113 \text{ oxygen} \\
\text{oxygen} & = \qquad\qquad 238 \\
& \overline{\qquad\qquad 351} \\
\therefore \text{ N/O by vol.} & = 113/351 = 1/3.11
\end{array}
$$

The experiment of mixing nitrous air and oxygen gives:

$$
\begin{array}{rl}
7\frac{1}{3} - \frac{1}{3} = 7 \text{ vols. NO} & = 3\frac{1}{2} \text{ vols. nitrogen} + 3\frac{1}{2} \text{ vols. oxygen} \\
\text{oxygen} & = \qquad\qquad 4 \\
& \overline{\qquad\qquad 7\frac{1}{2}} \\
\therefore \text{ N/O by vol} & = 3\frac{1}{2}/7\frac{1}{2} = 1/2.14
\end{array}
$$

In 1783 Lavoisier (Note 52 below, page 503 of reference cited) reported that he had found that 69 parts of nitrous air combine with 40 parts of vital air over water, although there was some uncertainty in the results, which in any case fixed the proportion of nitrous air between 69 and 66.

In experiments[58] which he says were made in 1784 on the detonation of charcoal with saltpetre Lavoisier burnt $1\frac{1}{2}$ oz. of saltpetre with 1 gros 42 grains of charcoal in a brass tube and collected the gas. From this he absorbed the carbon dioxide and measured the residual nitrogen. He then decomposed the residue of potassium carbonate in the tube with acid and measured the carbon dioxide evolved. From the densities of carbon dioxide and nitrogen he calculated the weights and the weight of caustic potash in the saltpetre was calculated by difference. The result was (at 28 in. Hg barometer and 10°R):

Carbon dioxide	585.82 cu. in.	5 gros	47.143 grains
Nitrogen	161.76 cu. in.	1 gros	3.419 grains
Caustic potash		6 gros	63.438 grains

He does not seem to have taken enough carbon to have

decomposed all the nitre. He assumed that carbon dioxide contains 28 carbon and 72 oxygen, says he had shown that 40 parts of oxygen combine with 68 of nitric oxide, and took the following densities in grains per cubic inch: oxygen 0·47317, carbon dioxide 0·69500, nitrogen 0·46624.

From the weights of charcoal and saltpetre and the volumes and densities of the gases, Lavoisier calculated as the quantities of initial materials and products (potash by difference):

	cu. in.	gros	grains
Carbon		1	42.000
Oxygen	619.53	4	5.143
Nitrogen	161.73	1	3.419
Potash		6	63.438

Hence he says, 5 gros 8·562 grains of nitric acid contain 4 gros 5·143 grains of oxygen and 1 gros 3·419 grains of nitrogen.

He deduced a completely wrong composition of nitric oxide which gives as the composition of nitric acid by weight and volume:

	Weight		Volume	
Nitric oxide	Nitrogen 20.4635	32.1 %	20.7044	32.3 %
	Oxygen 43.4771	67.9 %	43.3456	67.7 %
Additional oxygen	36.0594		35.9500	
	100.0000		100.0000	
Ratio O_2:N_2	3.9		3.8	

Lavoisier states he had heard that Cavendish had found that nitric acid (acide nitreux) is composed of 7 parts of vital air (oxygen) and 3 of atmospheric mofette (nitrogen), which differed from his result, but Cavendish's experiments were made on a very small scale and could be susceptible to errors. Cavendish's published figures[57] are, in two experiments, 416 vols. nitrogen and 914 oxygen, and 1920 nitrogen and 4860 oxygen. The average is roughly that given by Lavoisier, $NO_{2.33}$ instead of the correct value $NO_{2.5}$ and is much nearer the truth than any of Lavoisier's results.

We now discuss the excerpts from Higgins. Excerpt 1 relates to the experiment with charcoal and potassium nitrate referred to in excerpt 2. From his analysis of the products, and from experiments on the proportion of nitric oxide and oxygen present in nitric acid, Lavoisier arrived at the figures for the composition of nitric oxide and of nitric acid. His ratio of NO to O_2 by weight or volume was about 1.8 to 1. As has been said, Lavoisier, like Kirwan[65] (cf. excerpt 3), believed that nitric oxide contained by weight or volume approximately two parts of oxygen to one of nitrogen. Kirwan considered the basic compound of nitrogen and oxygen as *nitrous basis* and that 100 parts of *nitrous basis* united with 22 parts of phlogiston to give nitric oxide[66]. Elsewhere[67], however, Kirwan states that nitrous air consists of *nitrous basis* united to 0·18 of its weight of phlogiston.

Though he said (excerpt 1) that Lavoisier's experiment showed that the $O_2:N_2$ ratio in nitric acid was five to one, Higgins later (excerpt 2) wrote that nitrogen was one fifth of nitric acid, so that $O_2:N_2$ was four to one[55].

There is, as has been indicated, a good deal of arithmetical confusion in excerpt 5. Thus he writes (273.234)/3 equal to 91.78 cu. in. (in place of 91·078) for what on his view was the nitrogen content of 273·234 cu. in. of nitric oxide, and, correctly, on his ideas, $(2 \times 91 \cdot 078)$ equal to 182·156 cu. in. for the corresponding oxygen content. As seen (p. 81 above) Lavoisier obtained in the experiment quoted (figures recalculated by Kirwan) 273·234 cu. in. of nitric oxide and 287·742 cu. in. of oxygen. Higgins apparently assumed that these volumes should be equal and that the larger volume was in error. He used the larger volume in his calculations and then subtracted 287·742–273·234, equal to 14.508, though carelessly he puts the difference equal to 14.512. We have then:

	cu. in. of O_2
A volume of 273.234 cu. in. of nitric oxide (Higgins's variety) contains	182.156
Add for pure oxygen obtained	287.742
Total oxygen	469.898
Subtract (287.742 – 273.234) to correct for excess of oxygen	14.508
Total oxygen	455.390
Higgins subtracted 14.512 to obtain	455.386
Five multiplied by 91.078	455.390

This is a surprising result, since nitric oxide does not contain two parts of oxygen to one of nitrogen. Indeed the use of his incorrect idea of the composition of nitric oxide vitiates Higgins's calculations, apart from the inaccuracy of Lavoisier's experiments.

It should be noted that Lavoisier's carbon (1784) and mercury (1776) experiment gave different results, and that Higgins took figures which suited him. The carbon experiment gave for the weight ratio of nitric oxide to oxygen in nitric acid 64/36, that is 1·78. Higgins would have thought the volume ratio to be about the same, since following Kirwan he believed that the densities of nitric oxide and oxygen were not greatly different (*C.V.*, p. xiv). From the mercury experiment the volume ratio came out to be approximately one to one. As Higgins considered that nitric oxide contained one third of its volume of nitrogen, this latter result gave the required five to one for the oxygen : nitrogen ratio in nitric acid.

Lavoisier in 1779 wrongly believed that the density of oxygen was 1·37 times that of nitric oxide, so that he deduced from the volume results of the mercury experiment that the weight ratio of nitric oxide to oxygen in nitric acid was 0·7. He says in relation to the carbon experiment that elsewhere in different memoirs[52] he had shown that nitric acid was the result of the combination of 40 parts of oxygen with 68 of nitric oxide. He does not comment on the 1776 experiment.

The true composition of nitric acid (nitrogen pentoxide) was first established by Berzelius[68] who found the correct composition by analysis of lead nitrate. But as he believed that nitrogen (AO) was an oxide of the hypothetical element 'ammonium' (A), he thought that nitric acid was $N(=AO)+5O$, that is $A+6O$. Later[69] he gave the formula $N+5O$. This is the same as Higgins's formula, and with modern atomic weights it is $2N+5O$.

To recapitulate, Higgins had shown that nitrous oxide contains less oxygen than nitric oxide, and he believed, though he was not clear on this, that nitric oxide with oxygen gave two further oxides which contained less oxygen than nitric acid without water. He, therefore, placed the nitrogen–oxygen compounds in the order shown. But in view of the unreliability of his experimental results, his foreshadowing of the law of multiple proportions seems to have been based on his belief in the atomic theory, rather than on experimental evidence. It is interesting to recall that Dalton also used results on the combination of nitric oxide with oxygen to show that 'oxygen may combine with a certain portion of nitrous gas or with twice that portion, but with no intermediate quantities'[47], and his experiments were approximate only. It may be said of Higgins as it has been said of Dalton that 'the framing of the atomic hypothesis may have been the antecedent, and the discovery of multiple proportions the consequence, rather than the converse'[70].

There would seem to be a case for regarding Higgins as having intuitively foreshadowed the law of multiple proportions, though as with his other work on the atomic theory he does not seem to have realised at the time the novelty of his conception. The law follows from his idea of the combination of particles and is implicit in his diagrams.

Use of Symbols. Interatomic Bonds and Forces

Higgins has a claim to be regarded as the first to use the initial letter with or without other letters of the name of elements to represent an atom in a molecular formula. It is true that Gellert[71] used letter symbols, such as cobalt, K; Bismuth, W; and denoted a calx by prefixing the symbol C, so that bismuth oxide was C.W. Again in 1787, Hassenfratz and Adet[72] designated metals by letters enclosed in circles, e.g., (Fe) (ferrum), iron; (C) (cuprum), copper; (P) (plumbum), lead; (S) (stannum) tin; (Sb) (stibium), antimony. The symbols of compounds were to some extent made up of those of their elements and the different proportions of oxygen and nitrogen in compounds of these indicated. The suggestions were favourably recommended by a committee of the 'Académie'[73] but were not accepted by chemists. Until the advent of the chemical atomic theory they lacked meaning.

The chemical symbols employed by Higgins are shown in the following table. It will be noted that he used 'I' sometimes for inflammable air (hydrogen) and sometimes for iron. His symbols not only represent atoms but also served as a shorthand notation for the elements; both uses are still employed by modern chemists. Further, he showed molecules as composed of atoms linked by 'bonds'. It is correct to interpret his diagrams in this way, since he specifically refers to the forces holding atoms in combination and attempts to evaluate these forces, as will be seen in the sequel. His notation is, therefore, a definite advance on previous systems.

Chemical Symbols used by Higgins in the 'Comparative View'

SYMBOL	ELEMENT	PAGE
C	Copper	262, 263
d, D	Dephlogisticated air = oxygen	39, 40, 42–49, 59–61, 66–70, 190–193, 262–264, 271–273
I	Inflammable air = hydrogen	45, 192, 193
I	Iron	47–49, 59, 60, 61, 70, 192, 193, 262–264
M	Mercury	272, 273
P, p*	Phlogisticated air = nitrogen	133–135 171, 172
S	Sulphur	39, 40, 43–49, 59–61, 66–70, 271, 272
V	Volatile vitrolic acid, i.e. sulphur dioxide or sulphurous acid	262–264, 273
B	'Basis' of marine acid air (HCl)†	190–193

* In writing the nitrogen oxides Higgins used a, b, c, d, e, for atoms of oxygen to distinguish between the various atoms in a molecule. Higgins employed roman capitals and lower case italic in writing out formulae.

† Like his contemporaries Higgins thought that hydrogen chloride contained oxygen united to a 'basis'.

Chemical Formulae used by Higgins in the 'Comparative View'

Higgins's Formula	Modern Formula	Page	Higgins's Formula	Modern Formula	Page
C———D	CuO	262	P———a	N_2O	171,172
C⟨D,V	$CuSO_4$	262	P⟨a,b	NO	133,172
I———D and I———d	H_2O	45,192,193	P⟨a,b,c	N_2O_3	134,171
I———D and I⟨D,d	Iron oxides	48,49,70,193	P⟨a,b,c,d	NO_2 N_2O_4	134
S———d———I	$FeSO_3$	61	P⟨a,b,c,d,e	N_2O_5	135
I,D,d,S	$FeSO_4$	48	S———d S———D	SO_2	43, 44, 46–49, 70
M———D	HgO	273	S⟨d,D S———D———d	SO_3	39, 40, 44 45, 47 – 49, 59–61, 66, 67, 271
M⟨D,V	$HgSO_4$	273	B⟨D,d	HCl	190,192,193

It is often stated (see for example, Verkade, *Proc. Chem. Soc.*, 1958, 208; Green, *J. Roy. Inst. Chem.*, 1958, *82*, 522, 524; Brown, *J. Chem. Educ.*, 1959, *36*, 109) incorrectly, that Couper (1831–92; see Alembic Club Reprint No. 21; *Ann. Chim.*, 1858, *53*, 469) in 1858 was the first to designate the bonds between atoms in chemical formulae by lines.

In addition to showing the atoms in a molecule as bonded together, Higgins also assigned arbitrary numerical values to the 'affinity' forces which he considered to act along these bonds. These values are shown below:

Affinity Forces for Oxygen

ELEMENT	AFFINITY FORCE FOR OXYGEN	Page in Comparative View
Carbon	10	16
'Basis' of marine acid	8	190, 209
Metals	7	104, 138, 190, 248
Fe	7	17, 38, 42, 47–48, 59–61, 105, 191, 273
Zn	7	38
Hg	$6\frac{3}{8}$	272, 273
Cu	$5\frac{1}{3}$	262
Sulphur	$6\frac{7}{8}$	38–40, 42–44, 48, 61, 104, 120
	>7	34 (statement obscure)
Hydrogen	$6\frac{5}{8}$	38, 39, 45, 104, 192, 193
	6	248
	4	34
Nitrogen	6*	104, 133, 171, 172, 209

* In a table of affinity forces on p. 104, Higgins gives a figure 3 for this force, but it is clear from the other pages cited that this is a mistake for 6.

Other Affinity Forces

ELEMENTS AND COMPOUNDS CONCERNED	FORCE	Page in Comparative View	ELEMENTS AND COMPOUNDS CONCERNED	FORCE	Page in Comparative View
* C and C ('aggregate' attraction)	11	17	SO_2 and Cu (in CuO)	1	262
			SO_2 and CuO	3	262
S and S ('aggregate' attraction)	4	34	SO_2 and O (in CuO)	2	262
Two molecules of sulphuric acid ('aggregate' attraction)	2	271	SO_2 and HgO	3	273
			SO_2 and Hg (in HgO)	1	273
S and H	3	34	SO_2 and O (in HgO)	2	273
S and Fe	$\frac{1}{8}$	61	Nitric acid and alkali in potassium nitrate	4	105
SO_2 and Fe	3	263			
SO_2 and iron oxide	2	48, 49	Force retaining oxygen in potassium nitrate	7	105, 120
O (in SO_2) and Fe	1	263			
Fe and Fe ('aggregate' attraction)	$6\frac{7}{8}$	17			

* Higgins means by 'aggregate' attraction that 'power which solid or less condensed bodies have of counteracting chemical union' (*C.V.*, p. 16). He seldom uses the idea. (See Black, *Lectures*, 1803, *1*, 280, in regard to the 'union of *aggregation*'.)

The arbitrary numerical values which Higgins assigned to the forces between oxygen atoms and those of other elements are approximately in the order of 'Mr Lavoisier's Table of the affinities of the Oxygenous Principle' given on p. 10 of the *Comparative View*[74]. Lavoisier's order was: basis of marine acid, carbon, zinc, iron, hydrogen, copper, mercury, sulphur[75]. As will be seen from the Affinity Table, however, Higgins was not always consistent in his assigned values. For example, his normal value for hydrogen is $6\frac{5}{8}$, but he also uses the values 6 and 4.

His method of application of the affinity values may now be considered. He assumed that nitrogen and oxygen, for example, are linked by an affinity force, in this case 6, equally possessed by the two atoms, so that each atom has 3 units. Hence nitrous oxide is written P–3——3–d or P——6——d. In nitric oxide Higgins believed that the force 3 assigned to nitrogen is divided into two units of $1\frac{1}{2}$ and he writes the molecule

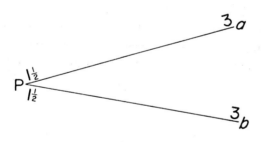

that is

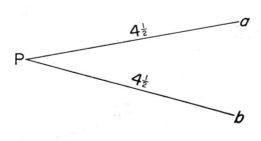

Similarly nitrogen pentoxide is

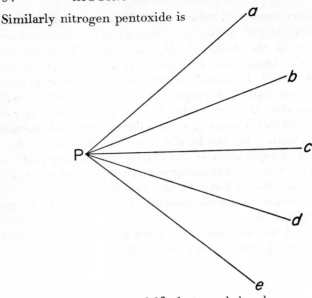

with an affinity force of $3\frac{3}{5}$ along each bond.

He went wrong in some of the calculations. For example, sulphur dioxide (or sulphurous acid) is S—$6\frac{7}{8}$—d. Sulphur trioxide or sulphuric acid he writes (*C.V.*, pp. 40, 44, 59, 61)

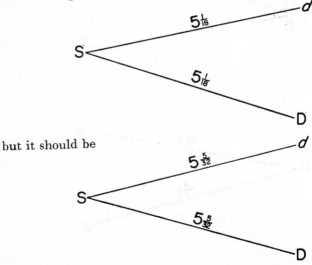

but it should be

Reaction Mechanisms

We give now three examples of Higgins's applications of his ideas on 'reaction mechanisms'. The first relates to the fact that iron gives with concentrated sulphuric acid, sulphur dioxide, while with dilute acid, hydrogen is obtained (*Comparative View*, p. 44):

'The first effort of the metal wholly deprives the particles of vitriolic acid in contact with it of their dephlogisticated air, and they instantly exert the force of $6\frac{7}{8}$ on the dephlogisticated air of the neighbouring indecomposed vitriolic acid, which can only resist with the force of $5\frac{1}{18}$: they will not take D and d from S, but D or d, whichever happens to be most contiguous to them; therefore two portions of volatile vitriolic acid are formed. In order to render this the more intelligible, let S be an ultimate particle of sulphur, recently deprived of its dephlogisticated air, and still possessed of the power of $6\frac{7}{8}$ to recover this again; and

let S$\underset{5\frac{1}{18}}{\overset{5\frac{1}{18}}{<}}\underset{D}{\overset{d}{}}$ be a particle of vitriolic acid in the vicinity of S:

will not S take D or d from S? and will not the volatile compounds S$\overset{6\frac{7}{8}}{——}d$ S$\overset{6\frac{7}{8}}{——}$D be formed? The latter will pass off in an elastic state, while the former, S$\overset{6\frac{7}{8}}{——}d$, being nigher the metallic calx, is attracted by it. As the most concentrated vitriolic acid contains a portion of water, part of this likewise is decomposed; hence arises the inflammable air. Let A be a particle of water, I and D its constituent principles; I inflammable air, and D dephlogisticated air, combined with the force of $6\frac{5}{8}$; if

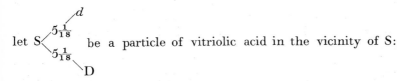

$$\text{I}\overset{6\frac{5}{8}}{——}\text{D} \qquad\qquad \text{S}\overset{d}{\underset{D}{<}}$$

A should be interposed between S, and would not S the rather deprive I of D, than wait the approach of the vitriolic molecule which is beyond its reach? particularly when the above-mentioned force of S is constantly rivetted or levelled, if I may use the expression, towards dephlogisticated air, in whatever compound, or in whatever state it meets with it, unless some other power counteracts it; and what can this be, but the union of the ultimate particles of sulphur to some other substance which attracts them more forcibly, or their attachment to one another so as to form an aggregate? neither of which circumstances interferes here. In addition to the above explanation of the interference of the small quantity of aqueous particles in concentrated vitriolic acid, I need only say, that when this acid is so diluted as to afford only inflammable air, the particles of water, by surrounding these of the acid, or by the intermixture of their more numerous surfaces, are exposed to the influence of the sulphur, the instant it is deprived of its dephlogisticated air by the metal, and thereby prevent the formation of the volatile sulphureous acid, marked S———D, while S———d, which is necessary to solution, is constantly forming by the decomposition of water. Thus the water, though it is decomposed itself, defends the vitriolic acid, whereby we obtain inflammable air in such abundance.'

The second example is interesting as showing a rudimentary idea of a transition compound. Like his contemporaries Higgins thought hydrochloric acid contained oxygen. Discussing the action of iron on hydrochloric acid he writes (p. 189 of the *Comparative View*): 'It likewise seems to me, that marine acid is composed of two principles only, viz. an unknown inflammable basis, and dephlogisticated air, intimately combined.' He expounds at length his view that a metal removes oxygen from the hypothetical base to form a calx which then unites with the acid. To overcome the difficulty created by the strong attraction postulated between the base and oxygen he suggests a kind of transition state in which the metal removes oxygen from the base while the base simultaneously abstracts oxygen from water. He says (*C.V.*, p. 192): 'To render this the more intelligible, let

I—d be a molecule of water, $B\!\!\begin{array}{c} d \\ \diagdown \\ D \end{array}$ a molecule of marine acid, and I a surface of iron; let us suppose these to be influenced with the different forces expressed by the numbers annexed to them; is it not reasonable to suppose, as soon as I, or iron, should influence d D, that B would re-act on d, or the dephlogisticated air of the water, and disengage I, or inflammable air.

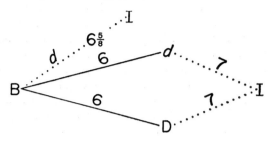

'I make no doubt but a good mathematician (for I acknowledge my own deficiency) would demonstrate this to a degree of certainty. However, although I am convinced of the truth of it myself, I would have my philosophical reader to strictly inquire into it before he either approves or disapproves of it.' The appeal to the mathematician has a modern ring.

Finally (p. 262), we have Higgins's explanation of the precipitation by metallic iron of copper from copper sulphate: 'Let C be copper, D dephlogisticated air, which (let us suppose) attract each other with the force of $2\frac{2}{3}$, (to avoid perplexity, reciprocal attraction is not considered) and let this be the calx of copper.

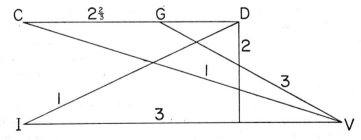

Let V, or volatile vitriolic acid, be attached to this compound with the force of 3, and let us suppose 2 of this force to proceed from the dephlogisticated air attached to the copper, and the

H

remainder, which is but 1, to be in consequence of the influence of the copper itself on the sulphur and dephlogisticated air of the volatile vitriolic acid; therefore let G be the centre of gravity of V. Let us suppose this to be the state of a neutral solution of copper in the vitriolic acid. Here the copper attracts V and D with only the force of $3\frac{2}{3}$, and C and D attract V with the force of 3. Let us again suppose I to be iron, which attracts V, or volatile vitriolic acid, with the force of 3, it cannot take it from C and D, which hold it with the force of 3; but it so counteracts the attachement of D and V to C, that it is reduced to $\frac{2}{3}$. Let us now suppose I, from its attraction to dephlogisticated air, to influence D with the force of 1: in this case C will be deprived of D and V, for the force of $3\frac{2}{3}$ must readily obey the power of 4. This, in my opinion, is what takes place in all metallic precipitations.'

Higgins is rather free with his numerical values which appear to be assigned to give the results he wants. Yet, reading what he has written, confused and involved though it be, one feels that he has some claim to be the first to assign atomic mechanisms to chemical reactions. Perhaps because his views are set out diffusely and are not apparent without careful study, Higgins has received less credit than he deserves for his chemical intuition. This, as these quotations show, went far beyond that of some of his contemporaries. Schützenberger[76] says: 'Higgins, the precursor of Dalton in the atomic theory, seems to have been more occupied than the latter concerning the forces which unite atoms to one another. He had very clear ideas on the way in which the "ultimate particles" are grouped to form compounds and on the forces which hold them together (qui les contiennent).' Schützenberger also draws attention to the text and diagram in Higgins, which 'contain an exceedingly remarkable idea on the constitution of salts'.

Berthollet's publications at the beginning of the nineteenth century had thrown doubt on the validity of representing affinities as invariable quantities capable of numerical treatment, and chemists lost interest in the matter. Dalton paid little or no attention to it, and it was not until the middle of the century that interest in it revived after the publications on mass action by Guldberg and Waage. Since this matter has an important bearing on Higgins's views on affinity and on his 'bond' diagrams, and in order that the value of his contribution to chemistry may be adequately assessed an account is given below of the views of his predecessors and contemporaries on the affinity forces operating in chemical reactions[77].

Higgins, it may be added, recognised two kinds of chemical affinity. After referring (*C.V.*, p. 72) to Austin's experiments on the decomposition of hepatic air (hydrogen sulphide) by electric sparks, Higgins says: 'That sulphur is suspended in its natural state in light inflammable air (hydrogen), may be inferred from the above experiment; but whether in its extreme division is difficult to determine; or whether it be chemically united to the inflammable air, or combined independently with its own atmospheres of fire, and mechanically mixed with this, cannot be satisfactorily proved. In my opinion it is mere solution, such as takes place between the neutral salts and water, or the alkalies and water, or sugar and water, &c. . . . It appears to me that solution, that power whereby water dissolves aerial acid, alkaline air, vitriolic acid air; and that power whereby light inflammable air dissolves sulphur and phosphorus; and likewise that power whereby all the aeriform fluids dissolve water in their elastic state; and lastly, whereby water dissolves the neutral salts, &c. without changing their properties, is occasioned by a sort of intermediate attraction, not differing from chemical attraction but in its degree of force, and not at all different from the power whereby the heavenly bodies influence one another.'

This is an anticipation of Berthollet's view[78] that solution is merely a case of weak chemical affinity, and that solutions, alloys, and glasses, are examples of compounds formed in varying proportions. As is well known, Berthollet's contention that atmospheric air is a compound of oxygen and nitrogen united by very weak affinity was disproved by Dalton on the basis of his law of partial pressures (see p. 125, below).

Use of *Affinity Diagrams and Numbers*

Affinity diagrams were used by Black[79] in his lectures from 1756 or 1757[80]. Thomson[81] says Robison[82] told him that Black's ideas were similar to those of Cullen[83]. Klaproth and Wolff[84] say that Cullen used numbers to represent affinities, as in the diagram below, but Black later abandoned this method, since it used only mechanical and not chemical conceptions. Robison[85] says Black used algebraic symbols for the attractions.

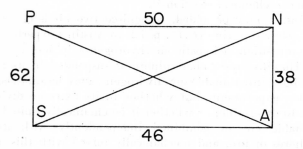

Black, like his contemporaries, thought of compounds as being formed by the combination of particles. He mentions[86] the union of a particle of vitriolic acid with a particle of fossil alkali (soda) to form a particle of Glauber's salt. But he wrote[87] that sufficient knowledge was not available to give a solid foundation to any attempt to explain the different qualities of substances by beginning from their ultimate elementary principles, and that he did not pretend to determine the ultimate elements of bodies. As R. Angus Smith[88] points out, Robison's note[89] on Black's diagrams indicates that although definite proportions was taken for granted, no general law to account for it had then been given. Since the lines drawn between the substances represent the attractions between them they foreshadow Higgins's 'bonds', but in such diagrams before Higgins there is no suggestion that the attractions are between *particles*, although, as will be seen below, this idea was well known early in the eighteenth century.

The first diagram of this type (without numerical values for affinities) seems to have been given in 1610 by Jean Beguin[90] in discussing the reaction, $3HgCl_2 + Sb_2S_3 = 3HgS + 2SbCl_3$ on heating. He speaks of the 'sympathy' of the elements rather than affinity. John Freind[91] discussed all chemical operations on the basis of varying attractions between particles, and this was elaborated into thirty 'theorems of attraction' by John Keill[92]. Freind represented the attractions by algebraic symbols and says that arbitrary numbers may be assigned to the letters, when several solutions of the equations will be possible. He also tried to take into account the diameters of the particles and the cohesive forces when they are in a solid state. G. L. Le Sage[93] gives a table of attractions of light for various substances based on refractive indices; he uses the astronomical sign of conjunction, δ, between two symbols for substances to denote the chemical attraction. Bergman[94], apparently independently of Cullen, developed diagrams of the same type in his 'Essay of Elective Attractions'[95] to show the results of double decomposition reactions—he called them tables of double elective attractions. Angus Smith[96] gives long quotations from Bergman's collected writings[97]. Smith points out that Bergman had no clear idea of the laws of composition, e.g. he thought that 100 parts of silver were reduced by 31 parts of copper in nitric acid and 30 in sulphuric acid. In the same way 100 pounds of copper in a vitriolic solution are restored to a metallic form by 146 pounds of zinc, but in a nitric acid solution, 164 pounds of zinc are wanted[98]. Had Bergman's methods of analysis been better he might have observed that the same quantities of copper and of zinc were required in each instance.

Bergman's tables contain no numerical values for affinities, but they were republished by Nicholson[99] with names instead of symbols and with numerical values for affinities taken from Guyton de Morveau (see below p. 104). Thomson[100] indicates that his belief that Cullen, Black, and Bergman taught the atomic theory was based mainly on their use of affinity diagrams discussed above. Even if they had the Newtonian view of atoms, and thought of attraction between reacting particles, they had no clear ideas in regard to the combination of atoms to form molecules with a definite composition; their interest was rather in the interaction of substances.

Affinity numbers of the type assigned by de Morveau are first given by John Elliot in 1782[101]. They were chosen so as to indicate the direction of double decomposition between pairs of salts. For example, the affinity of alkali and sulphuric acid is 9, that between silver calx (oxide) and nitric acid is 2, that between nitric acid and alkali is 8, and that between sulphuric acid and silver calx is 4. 'Since 8 and 4 is greater than 9 and 2', silver nitrate and potassium sulphate react to form potassium nitrate and silver sulphate. In 1782 Kirwan[102] sought to express affinities by numbers on the assumption that the affinity of a base for an acid is greater the greater the amount of base required to neutralise an acid, but the affinity of an acid is greater the less acid is required to neutralise a base. He determined the amounts of various bases and of various metals required to saturate 100 parts of each of the mineral acids, and exhibited the results in tables which are really tables of equivalents although Kirwan did not draw this conclusion[103]. His ideas on the subject are shown by the following extract: 'Chemical affinity or attraction is that power by which the invisible particles of different bodies intermix and unite with each other so intimately as to be inseparable by mere mechanical means. In this respect it differs from magnetic and electrical attraction. It also differs from attraction of cohesion in this, that the latter takes place between particles of almost all sorts of bodies whose surfaces are brought into immediate contact with each other; for chemical attraction does not act with that degree of indifference, but causes a body already united with another to quit that other and unite with a third, and hence it is called elective attraction. Hence attraction of cohesion often takes place between bodies that have no chemical attraction to each other; thus regulus of cobalt and bismuth have no chemical attraction to each other, for they will not unite by fusion, yet they cohere to each other so strongly, that they can be separated only by a stroke of a hammer. . . .

'The discovery of the quantity of real acid in each of the mineral acid liquors, and the proportion of real acid taken up by a given quantity of each base at the point of saturation, led me unexpectedly to what seems to be the true method of investigating the quantity of attraction which each acid bears to the several bases to which it is capable of uniting; for it was impossible not to perceive, 1st, That the quantity of real acid, necessary to saturate a given weight of each basis, is inversely as the affinity of each basis to such acid. 2ndly, That the quantity of each basis, requisite to saturate a given quantity of each acid, is directly as the affinity of such acid to each basis. Thus 100 grs. of each of the acids require for their saturation a greater quantity of fixed alkali than of calcareous earths, more of this earth than of volatile alkali, and more of this alkali than of magnesia, and more of magnesia than of earth of alum, as may be seen from the following table.

Quantities of basis taken up by 100 grs. of each of the mineral acids

	Veg. fixed alkali. Grs.	Mineral alkali. Grs.	Calcareous earth. Grs.	Volatile alkali. Grs.	Mag-nesia. Grs.	Earth of alum. Grs.
Vitriolic acid	215	165	110	90	80	75
Nitrous acid	215	165	96	87	75	65
Marine acid	215	158	89	79	71	55

'As these numbers agree with what common experience teaches us concerning the affinity of these acids with their respective bases, they may be considered as adequate expressions of the quantity of that affinity, and I shall in future use them as such. Thus the affinity of the vitriolic acid to fixed vegetable alkali, that is the force with which they unite, or tend to unite, to each other, is to the affinity with which that same acid unites to calcareous earth as 215 gr. to 110; and to that with which the nitrous acid bears to calcareous earth, as 215 gr. to 96, &c.'

Kirwan's quantitative tables, which are essentially tables of chemical equivalents, might have led him or his friend William Higgins to a table of atomic weights. It is surprising that, as Kirwan and Higgins were close friends, Kirwan, who lived to 1812, never seems to have taken any interest in an atomic theory.

De Fourcroy (1755–1809)[15] in 1784.[104] attempted to represent affinities by numbers after the manner of Elliot and Kirwan. At first he took account only of the two quiescent affinities and *one* divellent affinity, but then realised that four affinities are concerned, giving diagrams of the usual type.*

In 1784 also, a numerical example (potassium sulphate and calcium nitrate) was given by Lubbock[105]. Affinity diagrams of the usual type were given in a long article on affinity by Guyton de Morveau[106]. He criticised Fourcroy's numerical values of the affinities as being too small to take account of the large number of possible cases of reaction, and gave a new table of arbitrary numbers.

Before 1789, therefore, when Higgins published his book, the idea of attractions between particles which could be expressed by numbers, the use of lines in diagrams to represent attractions, and the assignment of numbers to represent affinities, were well known. Indeed, Newton[107] had written, 'particles attract one another by some force, which in immediate contact is exceeding strong, at small distances performs the chymical operations, and reaches not far from particles with any sensible effect'[108]. It is possible that Kirwan's publication of 1783 influenced Higgins's views. What may be claimed for Higgins are the ideas of using diagrams to show molecular structure and of the union of *more than one* particle of a second element with one particle of a first element, and the falling off of affinity in consequence in a manner which Higgins assigned in an arbitrary, and from the point of view of ordinary statics, improbable way. His assumption of NO for the formula of the lowest oxide of nitrogen, instead of N_2O is also without doubt a consequence of his way of constructing his force diagrams, since the series N_2O, NO, N_2O_3, NO_2, and N_2O_5 would have been an impossible one for him to deal with on the basis of his idea. Dalton was not hampered in this way.

It may be mentioned that the idea of 'elective' affinity persisted until well into the nineteenth century. George Pearson[109]

---

* In cases of double decomposition of the type $AB + CD = AC + BD$, 'Mr Kirwan conceives that we may trace the operation of two distinct series of affinities. The affinities tending to preserve the original compounds [those between A and B, and C and D], he terms the *quiescent affinities*; because they resist any change of composition. On the other hand the affinities, which tend to disunite the original compounds and to produce new ones [those between A and C, and B and D], he terms *divellent affinities*.' (W. Henry, *Elements of Experimental Chemistry*, 7th edit., 1815, *1*, 55.)

in a translation of the *Méthode de Nomenclature Chimique* of de Morveau, Lavoisier, Berthollet, and de Fourcroy[110], gives extensive tables of elective attractions. He notes that Cullen had devised his diagrams independently of Bergman. He dedicates the book to Kirwan and praises his magnanimity in accepting the antiphlogistic theory after championing the opposing one for so long.

There are discussions on the subject in works by William Henry[111], John Murray[112], Samuel Parkes[113], and Abraham Rees[114].

5. OTHER CLAIMS TO NOVELTY

Five observations cited by Higgins in the *Comparative View* call for examination as to novelty: (i) the reduction of nitric acid to ammonia by tin (*C.V.*, p. 309); (ii) the use of sulphurous acid for the determination of carbon in iron (*C.V.*, p. 49); (iii) the presence of bile in blood (*C.V.*, p. 162); (iv) the statement (*C.V.*, p. 13) that as iron will not rust in dry oxygen, the process involves decomposition of water, the oxygen from which attacks the metal, while the hydrogen reacts with gaseous oxygen; (v) the action of nitric oxide on chlorine (*C.V.*, p. 212).

Reduction of Nitric Acid to Ammonia

On p. 309 of the *Comparative View* Higgins claimed that in March 1785 he had observed that tin reduced nitric acid to ammonia (see p. 3 above). His uncle Dr Bryan Higgins was not impressed, but Dr Brocklesby[21] arranged for Higgins to exhibit the experiment at Sir Joseph Banks's[115] house about April 1785. Later (spring 1786), Higgins discussed the matter with Dr Austin[116], who mentions seeing the reaction at Banks's house[117] (see p. 4). Guyton de Morveau described the same experiment in the *Encyclopédie méthodique*[118]. His result is cited by de Fourcroy in the French edition of Kirwan's *Essay on Phlogiston* published in 1788[119].

The reduction of nitric acid to ammonia by a metal had been described by Priestley[120] four years before 1785, although the method he used was different from that of Higgins and Guyton de Morveau. He showed[121] that ammonia is formed slowly (after several months) when iron wire is allowed to stand in dilute copper nitrate solution. Although Austin[117] mentions Kirwan as well as Priestley, no reference to the reduction of nitric acid to ammonia seems to be contained in the text of Kirwan's *Essay on Phlogiston*. It is possible that Austin may have heard of Fourcroy's remark in the French edition, although (since it was published only in 1788) this does not seem likely.

There is no doubt that Guyton de Morveau's observation, though the exact date of this work is not known, was published before that of Higgins. If Higgins did make the experiment in 1785, as he says, he may have made it before de Morveau, but even this is uncertain, since the latter was occupied for some years in writing the articles of the *Encyclopédie*. There is no evidence that he knew anything of Higgins's experiment. The most reasonable assumption seems to be that Higgins and Guyton de Morveau made the discovery independently and that both can be given the credit of novelty.

Higgins's experiment has another interest. He later[122] referred to the second and fifth [*sic*] editions of William Henry's *Epitome of Chemistry*[123], which quoted the description in the *Comparative View* (p. 309), of the reduction of nitric acid to ammonia. This reference enabled Higgins to prove that Henry had read the *Comparative View*. Thomson[124] had written that Henry and Dalton had disclaimed seeing Higgins's book[125]. Thomson, however, was wrong. W. C. Henry[126] says he 'had carefully perused, many years ago, this volume' (i.e. the *Comparative View*), and quotes from it; he goes on to say: 'I have heard my father (William Henry) affirm, on various occasions, and to various persons, that Dalton had never seen Mr Higgins's work, till some years subsequently to the publication of the *New System*, when it was lent to him by my father.' What is said before makes it probable that this was in 1811, when William Henry says he found Dalton reading Davy's paper[127] in which Higgins is mentioned. 'He [Dalton] expressed his surprise, and asked me if I had seen Higgins's book. I told him that I had not only seen it, but quoted it, and lent him the volume.' In 1811, it is clear, Dalton was unaware of the existence of Higgins's book, and he saw it for the first time in that year.

Higgins's criticism of Henry, therefore, was based on a mis-understanding for which Thomson was responsible.

Estimation of Carbon in Iron

Higgins said little on this subject in the *Comparative View* (pp. 49, 51). He states that iron nails free from rust dissolved in sulphurous acid with formation of a black powder which burned as if it were a mixture of carbon and sulphur. He made a number of similar experiments and the results convinced him that the sulphur obtained came from the iron. He concludes, 'I have strong reason to suspect, that sulphur has more to do in the different properties of iron that we are aware of.'

In the Preface (p. x) to his *Essay on the Theory and Practice of Bleaching* Higgins writes: 'I have seen also, with great astonishment, that some experiments which I made and published, were a considerable time afterwards adduced as *new* discoveries on the continent.'

Higgins then discusses his work on the formation of 'bile' from blood (see p. 108 below). He goes on (p. xi): '*Monsieur Vanquilin (sic;* should be Vauquelin) has published as his discovery in the *Journal des Mines* (Vendémiaire, Ann. V, (1796), No. 25., p. 3), "*a new method of determining the quantity of carbon contained in steel*". See the extract from it in the *Annales de Chemie* for the year 1797 (1797, **22**, 1). This *new* method is by means of the volatile sulphurous acid, and for the discovery I will refer to my *Comparative View*, pages 49, 50 and 51, where the justice of my claim will evidently appear.

'I by no means impeach the above philosophers with plagiarism; I have too much respect for the high character they have acquired in the scientific world to suspect them of such conduct, but that it has been, at least, an oversight, must be allowed.

'. . . Amongst its [sulphurous acid's] various properties, that of dissolving iron without the *production* of hydrogen gas, at the same time that the *whole* of the carbon and sulphur contained in the iron were left behind, impressed me most, by pointing out the importance of it as a *menstruum* for the analysis of iron or steel in an easy, simple, and certain way.

'The celebrated Bergman laboured hard to analyse the different kinds of iron and steel, and made the most of the menstrua which the chymistry of his days afforded: He ascertained only the presence of those substances contained in iron; nor was it possible to find out their proportion by any means hitherto discovered, until the happy application of the sulphurous acid in that way.'

In his *Experiments and Observations on the Atomic Theory*, Higgins (p. 73) referred to what he had written in the *Comparative View* on the action of sulphurous acid on iron and wrote: 'This (sulphurous) acid is an excellent menstruum for analysing iron or steel, for the whole of the carbon they contain is left behind in this solution, which is not the case when they are dissolved in other acids. The French chemists brought this forward as a new discovery of their own, seven years after my *Comparative View* had been published. As I have taken sufficient notice of this transaction in the preface to my *Essay on Bleaching*, together with the change which nitrous acid produces on blood (see below), which Fourcroy assumed to himself, it is needless to comment of the subject here.'

Berthollet in 1789[128] showed that iron dissolves in sulphurous acid without evolution of gas. Higgins's claims go beyond the book. He discovered the solvent action of sulphurous acid on iron, but he gives no indication that the possibility of applying this reaction for analytical purposes had occurred to him, and his suggestion that Vauquelin appropriated the method from him is without foundation. As with his atomic theory he did not realise that he had come near an important discovery until this was made by another, and, as usual, he then claimed too much too late.

The Presence of Bile in Blood

On p. 162 of the *Comparative View* Higgins wrote: 'The effect of nitrous (nitric) acid on blood is very singular; and though it has not much to do with what we are upon at present, yet, hoping that any fact relating to so interesting a subject may be acceptable to my reader, I shall give as brief an account of it as I can.' He goes on to say that blood fresh from the butchers gives on digestion with nitric acid a yellow substance with the taste of bile. He adds: 'At this time I had not leisure to make any farther inquiries into this subject, being busy in assisting at a public course of chemistry, at Oxford; nor have I had since an opportunity of enjoying the pleasure I then promised myself in so interesting an investigation.' (See Part I, Note 16, p. 30.)

In the Preface to his *Essay on the Theory and Practice of Bleaching* (p. x) Higgins wrote: '. . . *Monsieur Fourcroy* published in the year 1791 (See *Medecin* [*sic*] *eclairé par les sciences phisiques Tom. 2d. pag.* 321. *No* xi), as a new discovery, the presence of bile in the blood; or rather, the conversion of some of the principles of the blood into a substance resembling bile: This I had done some years before him by the mediation of the nitrous (nitric) acid. For the truth of what I assert, see pages 162 and 163 of my *Comparative View* published in the year 1789.'

Fourcroy's publication mentioned by Higgins is not available but Fourcroy and Vauquelin in 1790 (not 1791)[129] claimed to have proved the presence of bile in ox-blood. They mixed it with a third of its volume of water and coagulated it by heat. They separated the coagulum and evaporated the clear liquid, when it became like bile in colour, smell, and taste. They say nothing about heating blood with nitric acid.

Higgins's experiment on the presence of bile in blood is mentioned, without giving his name, by Klaproth and Wolff[130]. Fourcroy and Vauquelin's evaporation experiment was contradicted by Parmentier and Déyeux[131] but Déyeux later[132] found it to work with blood from a bilious subject (*le sang bilieux*). Higgins's reference to Fourcroy as having published his experiment without giving him credit may also include a paper by Fourcroy and Vauquelin[133] in which they heated flesh and also blood with nitric acid and obtained a yellow bitter solution giving on evaporation a detonating product which they call 'hydro-carbure d'azote suroxigéné', which would presumably be picric acid. They obtained the same product with indigo which does give picric acid (cf. Woulfe below).

It is possible, therefore, that the yellow bitter substance obtained by Higgins was picric acid, which Woulfe[134] had obtained from indigo and nitric acid. J. M. Hermann[135] prepared it again in the same way without mentioning Woulfe, and the preparation was, as stated, given again by Fourcroy and Vauquelin[136]. In 1799 Welter[137] obtained a yellow soluble bitter substance, which he called *amer*, together with oxalic acid, by oxidising silk with nitric acid. The yellow insoluble product of oxidation of flesh with nitric acid he thought was a compound of *amer* with another new substance.

Gmelin[138], who does not refer to Woulfe or Higgins, but mentions Fourcroy and Vauquelin (1805) and Welter, says of picric acid: 'whether it is contained in the yellow bitter substance into which albumin, fibrin, the crystalline lens, casein, and gluten, are converted by nitric acid, remains to be determined.'

To sum up, Higgins would seem to have made his observation, for what it was worth, independently of other workers.

The Rusting of Iron

The idea that the rusting of iron is brought about by oxygen supplied by water, and that the hydrogen formed then combines with atmospheric oxygen to reform water is usually attributed to Mrs Fulhame in her book on the Phlogiston theory[139] which was published in 1794[140]. But Higgins in the *Comparative View* (p. 13) had written years before: 'Iron moistened with water, and confined by mercury, will yield inflammable air. Iron, treated in the same manner, and confined with dephlogisticated air, will produce no inflammable air: but the air will be diminished. Iron will yield no inflammable air if it be confined in very dry dephlogisticated air, neither will the air be diminished, nor will the iron tarnish in any length of time. Hence it appears, that iron has no effect on air in a common temperature, but that it is the water which is decomposed, and that the dephlogisticated air and inflammable air unite at the very instant of its liberation, and re-compose water.'

In the Preface (p. xxv) to his *Essay on Bleaching* to which reference has already been made, Higgins commented on Mrs Fulhame's book: 'About four years ago, a very ingenious pamphlet [*sic*] appeared in the name of a Mrs Fulhame, in which this doctrine of mine respecting the decomposition and recomposition of water has been adduced and extended to every species of oxygenation, and even to the deoxydation of metals in every degree of heat. I did not think myself warranted when I had written, and much less so now, upon a more mature deliberation, to apply it in that general way.

'Had this fair author read my book, and indeed I suppose she did not, (having quoted every other treatise upon the subject,) no doubt she would have been candid enough to do me the justice of excepting *me* from the rest of my co-operators in science, when she told them they erred for having overlooked this modification of their doctrine, and also when she adduced it as an original idea of her own.'

And on p. xxx we have: 'I now beg leave to assure Mrs F. before we part, that I read her book with great pleasure, and heartily wish her laudable example may be followed by the rest of her sex; particularly by those who possess talents and means for making chemical experiments.'

Finally in a footnote on p. 53 of his *Atomic Theory* Higgins refers again to Mrs Fulhame: 'A very ingenious treatise on this kind of affinity was published by Mrs Fulham [*sic*] about fifteen years ago, wherein she erroneously attempts to explain the phenomenon of combustion on the same principle, and boasts very much of her discovery, having met nothing like it in the works of Lavoisier, Fourcroy, Kirwan, &c. at the same time that she cautiously omitted mentioning the work from which she borrowed her ideas.'

There seems little doubt as to Higgins's priority on the occurrence of water as an intermediate in the rusting of iron. This is perhaps the most important of the stray ideas occurring in the *Comparative View*. It is improbable that Mrs Fulhame had taken any ideas from Higgins's book, and there is every reason to suppose that she and Higgins put forward the theory independently[141].

The Action of Nitric Oxide on Chlorine

Higgins found that dry chlorine and nitric oxide do not react (*C.V.*, 212): 'I think the dephlogisticated marine air retains its dephlogisticated air with nearly as great force as the nitrous air

attracts it; for when the airs are perfectly dry, and mixed over
mercury, no decomposition seems to take place until water is
introduced.' This experiment was much later repeated by John
Davy in his controversy with John Murray, since the latter had
said that chlorine contains oxygen because it produces red fumes
when mixed with nitric oxide. Murray had used moist gases[142].
Higgins does not seem to have claimed this discovery.

Notes to Part II

1. See Partington, *Nature*, 1955, *176*, 8. For the writing of the *Comparative View* see Higgins, *Phil. Mag.*, 1816, *48*, 363; 1819, *53*, 401; *Atomic Theory*, 1814, p. 7.
2. Review of Higgins's *Atomic Theory* (*Annals of Philosophy*, 1814, *4*, 52). See also Article on 'Theory, Atomic, in Chemistry' in Dr A. Rees's *Cyclopaedia* (1819, *35*) and comments on this article, which must have been available before 1819, by Higgins in *Phil. Mag.*, 1818, *51*, 161; (see Part III, note 24, p. 142) Thomas Thomson, M.D. (1773–1852), first Regius Professor of Chemistry in the University of Glasgow, was responsible for bringing Dalton's atomic theory to the notice of the scientific world. He strongly opposed Higgins's claim to have anticipated Dalton. For an account of Thomson's life see Partington, *Annals of Science*, 1949, *6*, 115; *An Eighteenth Century Lectureship in Chemistry*, Glasgow, 1950, p. 176.
3. *Monthly Review*, 1789, *81*, 197; *Analytical Review*, 1789, *4*, 177; *English Review*, 1790, *15*, 188; *Critical Review*, 1790, *70*, 545. B. C. Nangle (*The Monthly Review* (1749–89), Oxford University Press, 1934) from data in the editorial files of the *Monthly Review* now in the Bodleian Library gives (p. 123) the author of the review of Higgins's book as, probably, A. Chisholme of whom nothing is known. He reviewed works in chemistry, mineralogy, and aerostatics.
4. *Monthly Review*, 1800, *31*, 442. There is no mention of Higgins in 'Observations on Mr Dalton's Theory of Chemical Composition' by Ewart in the *Annals of Philosophy*, 1815, *6*, 371.
5. *Monthly Review*, 1817, *82*, 379. (See also note 6 below.) The volume in the National Library (Dublin), which originally was in the library of the Royal Dublin Society, has marginal polemical notes on the review almost certainly written by Higgins.
6. *Philosophical Magazine*, 1816, *48*, 363; see also *ibid.*, 1819, *53*, 401. James Watt, M.D., of Glasgow, in a letter entitled *On the Introduction of the Antiphlogistic System into Great Britain* (*Annals of Philosophy*, 1817, *9*, 407), refers to this paper and states that he is not interested in the discovery of the atomic theory, but believes Higgins is not the one who overthrew the phlogiston theory in Great Britain. He attended lectures given by Dr Irvine of the University of Glasgow in the winter of 1786–87 in which phlogiston was discussed, and the theory of combustion advanced. Irvine also stated that Black had adopted the same views. Watt points out that Higgins's book had not been heard of until recently by many readers of chemical works. He considers Higgins to be a distinguished chemist, but that as far as the overthrow of phlogiston is concerned he claims more than his due. (See note 9 below.)

   William Irvine, M.D. (1743–87), was Professor of Chemistry at Glasgow (1770–87). He assisted Black in experiments on steam.

7. *Essay on Bleaching*, 1799, Preface, p. ix (see note 4 above).

8. *Chemistry through the Eighteenth Century*, Partington, *Philosophical Magazine Commemoration Number*, 1948, 63.

9. Professor James Kendall in a presidential address to the Royal Society of Edinburgh (7 July 1952; *Proc. Roy. Soc. Edinburgh*, 1952, *63*, 346; see also p. 385) describes the first volume of the *Proc. Chem. Soc.* of the *University of Edinburgh* discovered in 1947 in the archives of the Royal Irish Academy by the Very Rev. Dr P. J. McLaughlin (see note 139 below). The contents confirm the view (see note 11 below) that Black was an early advocate of Lavoisier's theory of combustion, since a number of his students held it in 1785–86. Higgins was incorrect in suggesting (*Phil. Mag.*, 1819, *53*, 401) that Black was converted by the *Comparative View*. Kendall (*Endeavour*, 1944, *3*, 119) says that Professor T. C. Hope (1766–1844) promulgated publicly the doctrines of Lavoisier in the winter of 1787–88 to his classes in the University of Glasgow (see note 15 below).

10. Richard Lubbock (1759–1808) studied at the University of Edinburgh from 1781 to 1784. After graduating M.D. he practised as a physician at Norwich. (For a detailed study of Lubbock's views see Partington and McKie, *Annals of Science*, 1938, *3*, 356.)

11. *Dissertatio de principio sorbile*, Edinburgh, 1784. This work shows that one of the first chemists to adopt Lavoisier's ideas must have been Black who taught them before 1784. (See Partington, *Short History of Chemistry*, 3rd ed., 1957, 134; cf. Read, in *An Eighteenth Century Lectureship in Chemistry* (ed. A. Kent), Glasgow, 1950, 89). *The Dictionary of National Biography* says that George Pearson (1751–1828), physician and chemist, was one of the first Englishmen to accept the antiphlogiston theory. He did much to spread this theory by translating (1794, 1799) the *Nomenclature Chimique*, 1787, into English.

12. Partington, *Annals of Science*, 1939, *4*, 272. Sullivan (*Dublin Quart. J. Medical Science*, 1849, *8*, 465) states that William Higgins might have been the first chemist in Great Britain to adopt the antiphlogistic theory.

13. Partington, note 12, p. 269.

14. See Reilly and O'Flynn, *Isis*, 1930, *13*, 298.

15. De Morveau (see note 106 below), *Encycl. Méth.*, *Chymie*, 1796 (*7*), iii, 560; de Fourcroy (see Smeaton, *Endeavour*, 1959, *18*, 70). *Élemens d'Histoire Naturelle et de Chimie*, 1793 edition, vol. 1, p. xi. See also Hoefer, *Histoire de la Chimie*, Paris 1869, ii, 544. De Morveau, de Fourcroy, and Pearson (trans. *Nomenclature Chim.*, 1799, p. 19) also quote a letter written in 1790 by Black to Lavoisier stating that he was teaching the new theory to his pupils. De Morveau refers to Kirwan and Black as 'English Chemists'.

16. Lorenz Crell's *Chemische Annalen*, 1791, i, 425; see also 1791, ii, 348. In regard to the amazement produced by Kirwan's recantation, see *ibid.*, ii, 430. See also Partington and McKie, *Annals of Science*, 1938, *3*, 3. The copies of Crell's *Annalen* in the library of the Royal Irish Academy belonged to Kirwan.

17. *Phil. Mag.*, 1819, *53*, 401; see also 1816, *48*, 363.

18. Higgins (*C.V.*, p. xi, footnote) states that he thought Cavendish had adopted the antiphlogistic theory until a good part of the volume had been printed.
19. *Annals of Philosophy*, 1814, *4*, 54. Higgins denied this statement in the *Phil. Mag.*, 1816, *48*, 365. He believed Black recanted after Kirwan.
20. Lavoisier said this in 1787. See *Oeuvres*, 1842, *5*, 361.
21. See Part I, note 22, p. 33.
22. The authors' thanks are due to Dr D. C. Martin, Assistant Secretary of the Royal Society, for his help with these references. Dr Martin kindly supplied extracts from the *Journal Book of the Royal Society* for the Meeting of 17 April 1788.
23. *Phil. Trans.*, 1814, *104*, 508.
24. Cavendish also observed this. See Partington, *Short History of Chemistry*, 3rd ed., 1957, 138 ff.
25. Kirwan, *Essay on Phlogiston*, 1787, 28. Kirwan says that, following Berthollet, he believed that sulphurous acid was sulphuric acid holding sulphur in solution (see note 34 below).
26. Kirwan believed that hydrogen and oxygen gave water when exposed to red heat, but that at a lower temperature fixed air (carbon dioxide) was formed (*Essay on Phlogiston*, 1787, 26).
27. The effect of volatility had been clearly given by Mayow in his *Tractatus quinque medico-physici* (Oxford, 1674). See Partington, *Short History of Chemistry*, 3rd ed., 1957, p. 84.
28. Kirwan, *Essay on Phlogiston*, 1787, 23, Lavoisier, *Oeuvres*, 1862, *2*, 551.
29. Higgins is here taking for granted an ancient view, discussed by his uncle, Bryan Higgins, that the ultimate particles of a gas are stationary and are kept apart by atmospheres of fire or heat, later called 'caloric' by Lavoisier (see Part III, p. 124). The complex ideas involved, which are described in detail by Partington and McKie (*Annals of Science*, 1938, *3*, 337; see also Partington, *Bulletin of the British Society for the History of Science*, 1951, *1*, 133), were developed by Bryan Higgins in his *Syllabus of Discourses and Experiments* (in the library of the University of Manchester; see note 53, Part I, p. 36) in 1775, two years before Lavoisier discussed similar views. Dalton also believed in caloric. (See *New System of Chemical Philosophy*, 1808, Part 1, 187, etc.) For a history of the development of the idea of caloric see Dingle, *The Scientific Adventure* (London, 1952, *passim*).
30. See quotation from *C.V.*, p. 16 (p. 72 of the text).
31. See under 'Law of Gaseous Volumes' (p. 75 of text). Higgins in the *Comparative View* used 'molicules', corrected in the 'Errata' to 'molecules', in the sense of ultimate particles of compounds. His uncle Bryan Higgins used the word similarly in his *Experiments and Observations relating to Acetous Acid*, etc., published in 1786. The use of the word to indicate groups of atoms goes back to Gassendi (1592–1655). See Part III, p. 123, and Partington, *Annals of Science*, 1939, *4*, 262.
32. In the same volume (p. 144 f) Higgins cites experiments to show that nitric oxide contains equal volumes of nitrogen and oxygen, but he adheres to his original view that the molecular formula is NO_2, stating that a measure of oxygen gas contains twice as many ultimate particles as an equal volume of nitrogen. He restated these views in *Phil. Mag.*, 1816, *48*, 408, and 1817, *49*, 246; see note 48 below.

33. It may be noted Higgins's friend Austin (*C.V.*, p. 312; see Part I, note 25, p. 23) stated (*Phil. Trans.*, 1788, 379) that as the specific gravity of hydrogen is 'eleven times less' than that of nitrogen, the 'distances' of the particles are in the ratio of $\sqrt[3]{11}$ to 1; he assumed that the particles involved were equal in weight. He accepted Bryan Higgins's view regarding atoms as surrounded by atmospheres of 'fire'.

34. As early as 1777, Lavoisier (*Oeuvres*, 1862, *2*, 198) concluded that volatile 'sulfureux' acid is a vitriolic acid partially deprived of oxygen. No result justifying Higgins's statement on the composition of sulphuric acid has been traced. The composition of sulphuric anhydride as 42 sulphur to 58 oxygen (instead of 40 and 60) was first correctly determined by J. B. Richter, *Ueber die neuern Gegenstände der Chymie*, Breslau, Hirschberg, and Lissa, 1795, *5*, 121 f; Dalton, *New System*, 1810, *2*, 393, 399, was the first to attain correct views on the composition of the oxides of sulphur.

35. *Phil. Mag.*, 1816, *48*, 363, 408; 1817, *49*, 245.

36. 5th edition, 1815, Vol. 1, Part 2.

37. *Annals of Philosophy*, 1813, *2*, 455; see also *Phil. Mag.*, 1818, *51*, 168.

38. *Phil. Trans.*, 1814, 5; *Ann. Chim.*, 1814, *90*, 138.

39. *Phil. Mag.*, 1817, *49*, 245. See note.

40. This is hardly true. Dalton wrote in 1808. Gay-Lussac's paper was read to the Société d'Arcueil on 31 December 1808, and published in *Mém. d'Arcueil*, 1809, ii, 207. See Partington, *Nature*, 1956, *178*, 8.

41. *Phil Mag.*, 1816, *48*, 408.

42. Partington, *Short History of Chemistry*, 3rd ed., 1957, 209; *Nature*, 1956, *178*, 8.

43. Smith, *Memoirs of the Literary and Philosophical Society of Manchester*, 2nd Series, 1856, *13*, 184; Partington, *Annals of Science*, 1939, *4*, 274.

44. Partington, *Short History of Chemistry*, 3rd ed., 1957, 166. Higgins's ideas, discussed above (p. 72) under 'Composition of Molecules', that sulphur dioxide or sulphurous acid is SO, and sulphuric acid, SO_2 (*C.V.*, pp. 36 and 37), are in accordance with his belief in that law.

45. Scheele, *Chemische Abhandlung von der Luft und dem Feuer*, 1777, para. 27; English translation by J. R. Forster, London, 1780, p. 30; French translation by Dietrich, Paris, 1781, p. 78 (a supplement published in 1785 contains notes by Kirwan); *Collected Papers of Carl Wilhelm Scheele*, transl. by Dobbin, London, 1931, p. 103. See Scott, *J. Chem. Educ.*, 1952, *29*, 360.

46. Higgins's arguments on pp. 14 and 84 of the *Comparative View* are, as often, obscure.

47. See Partington, *Short History of Chemistry*, 3rd ed., 1957, 104, 115, 171. Vague ideas were current in Higgins's time on the different coloured 'nitrous acids' obtained by Priestley by keeping nitric oxide in contact with nitric acid (see Kirwan, *Essay on Phlogiston*, 1787, 37). Lavoisier (*Traité élémentaire de Chimie*, published 1789; *Oeuvres*, 1864, *1*, 64) says that less than three parts of oxygen to one of nitrogen give a red fuming acid called nitrous acid. Four parts of oxygen and one of nitrogen give a colourless acid, nitric acid.

48. *Phil. Mag.*, 1817, *49*, 241. Dalton's paper was published in the *Annals of Philosophy*, 1817, *9*, 186; see also *ibid.*, 1817, *10*, 38, 83. Higgins, when he wrote his *Atomic Theory* in 1814, was faced with the difficulty that in

the *Comparative View* he had assumed each oxide of nitrogen, other than nitrous oxide with the volume composition of which he had not specifically dealt, contained twice the volume of oxygen found later to be present. He surmounted this difficulty by assuming (*Atomic Theory*, p. 146) that the 'particle number' of oxygen was twice that of nitrogen and not equal to it as stated in the *Comparative View*.

49. *Annals of Philosophy*, 1817, *10*, 38.

50. Roscoe and Harden, *A New View of the Origin of Dalton's Atomic Theory*, 1896, 31 f, 46.

51. Dalton, *New System of Chemical Philosophy*, 1808, *1*, 219.

52. See also Lavoisier, *Oeuvres*, 1862, *2*, 129, 503; cf. Partington, *Annals of Science*, 1953, *9*, 56; Roscoe and Harden, *A New View of the Origin of Dalton's Atomic Theory*, 1896, 337.

53. *Ann. Chim.*, 1816, *1*, 394.

54. *Ann. Chim.*, 1816, *2*, 317.

55. *Atomic Theory*, 1814, 109. Higgins suggested that Lavoisier might have used 'pale nitrous acid'.

56. Higgins was in advance of Dalton in taking nitric acid as NO_5.

57. *Phil. Trans.*, 1785, *75*, 372 (read 2 June 1785).

58. *Oeuvres* 1892, *5*, 605; from the 'Récueil des Mémoires sur la Formation & la Fabrication du Salpetre', in *Memoires par divers Savants*, 1786, *11*, 625.

59. *Essay on Phlogiston*, 1787, 56.

60. *Oeuvres*, 1892, *5*, 605.

61. *Essay on Phlogiston*, 1787, 55.

62. *Essay on Phlogiston*, 1787, 62.

63. Kirwan led Higgins astray here. The figure is nearer 1003. For old French weights and measures see *Encycl. Brit.*, 14th ed., 1929, *15*, 137.

64. This citation by Higgins ('Par' presumably is 'Paris') is to Lavoisier, *Mémoirs de l'Académie Royale des Sciences*, 1776 (published 1779), 671–680. Page 670 is therefore wrong. Kirwan (*Essay on Phlogiston*, 1787, 62) gives p. 673. See also *Oeuvres*, 1862, *2*, 129; Partington, *Short History of Chemistry*, 3rd ed., 1957, 127. In *Annals of Science*, 1953, *9*, 96, Partington shows that Lavoisier's Memoir was published in a preliminary form in 1776.

65. *Essay on Phlogiston*, 1787, pp. 36, 37, 59, 69.

66. *loc. cit.*, pp. 36, 37, 38.

67. *loc. cit.*, p. 59.

68. *Ann. Physik.*, 1812, *40*, 162–208.

69. *Ann. Physik.*, 1814, *46*, 131–175.

70. See Partington on the 'Origin of Dalton's Atomic Theory' in *A Short History of Chemistry*, 3rd ed., 1957, 170; *Scientia*, July 1955.

71. *Anfangsgründe zur metallurgischen Chemie*, Leipzig, 1776, i, 172, 231; the first edition of this book was published in 1750.

72. See de Morveau, Lavoisier, Berthollet, and de Fourcroy, *Méthode de Nomenclature chimique*, Paris, 1787; Winderlich, *J. Chem. Educ.*, 1953, *30*, 58; *Symbols and Formulae in Chemistry*, Caven and Cranston, London, 1928.

73. *Rapport sur les noveaux charactères chimiques*, Lavoisier, *Oeuvres*, 1892, *5*, 365.

74. This was first pointed out by Reilly and MacSweeney, *Sci. Proc. Roy. Dublin Soc.*, 1929, *19*, 139.

75. *Mém. Acad. Roy. Sci.*, 1782, 530; *Oeuvres*, 1862, *2*, 546.

76. In Wurtz, *Dictionnaire de Chimie*, Paris, 1869, *1*, 75–76; in the article 'Affinité', pp. 69–83.

77. A good account of the development of views on affinity is given by Ostwald, *Lehrbuch der allgemeinen Chemie*, Leipzig, 1911, Vol II, Part 2, *Verwandtschaftslehre*, who fails to mention Higgins.

78. Higgins refers to Berthollet's views and asserts his own priority in regard to the distinction between 'weak and strong affinity' in *Phil. Mag.*, 1817, *49*, 243.

79. An account of Joseph Black and his work is given by Read in *Joseph Black, M.D., Eighteenth Century Lectureship in Chemistry*, Glasgow, 1950.

80. *Lectures on the Elements of Chemistry*, ed. Robison, Edinburgh, 1803, *1*, 258, 279, 465, 544.

81. *Annals of Philosophy*, 1814, *3*, 334.

82. John Robison (1739–1805) was lecturer in chemistry in Glasgow (1766) and professor of natural philosophy in Edinburgh (1773). See *Dict. Nat. Biog.*

83. J. Thomson, *An Account of the life etc. of William Cullen*, Edinburgh and London, 1859, *1*, 570; Black, *Lectures on Chemistry*, ed. Robison, Edinburgh, 1803, *1*, 545. William Cullen (1710–90) was Black's predecessor at Glasgow and Edinburgh. Cullen published nothing on the atomic theory (cf. Wightman, *Annals of Science*, 1955, *11*, 154).

84. *Chymisches Wörterbuch*, Berlin, 1810, *5*, 297–334, article on affinity.

85. Black, *Lectures*, 1803, *1*, 466.

86. *Lectures*, 1803, *1*, 280.

87. *Lectures*, 1803, *1*, 343, 344.

88. *Mem. Lit. Phil. Soc. Manchester*, 1856, *13*, 146.

89. *Lectures*, 1803, *1*, 544–546.

90. T. S. Patterson, *Annals of Science*, 1937, *2*, 243.

91. *Praelectiones Chymicae*, London, 1709, based on lectures in Oxford in 1704 (see *Dict. Nat. Biog.*).

92. *Phil. Trans.*, 1708, *26*, 97; Keill was also at Oxford.

93. *Essai de Chymie méchanique*. Couronné en 1758 par l'Académie de Rouen; no place, 50 f.

94. Sir Torbern Olof Bergman (1735–84), professor at Uppsala, contributed much to inorganic analysis, but is best remembered for his work on affinity.

95. *Nova Acta Regiae Societatis Scientiarum Upsaliensis*, 1775, *2*, 159; the set in the Royal Irish Academy belonged to Kirwan. A translation of the essay was published by Thomas Beddoes in 1785. (See *Dict. Nat. Biog.*, and Part I, note 39, p. 35.) On a French translation, see Smeaton, *Ambix*, 1959, 7, 47.

96. Note 88, pp. 148–157.

97. *Opuscula Physica et Chemica*, Vols. 1 to 6, 1779–90.

98. Smith, note 88, p. 151.

99. *Dictionary of Chemistry*, 1795, 1, 176–187; 1808 edition; article on attraction. (The pages are not numbered.)

100. Thomson, *Annals of Philosophy*, 1814, *3*, 329.

101. *Elements of the Branches of Natural Philosophy connected with Medicine*,

1782, 143, and plate IV; on John Elliot, see Partington and McKie, *Annals of Science*, 1938, *3*, 337, (350).

102. *Phil. Trans.*, 1783, *73*, 15 (read in 1782); see Angus Smith, note 88, p. 158.

103. Partington, *Short History of Chemistry*, 3rd ed., 1957, p. 161; Angus Smith, note 88, p. 159.

104. *Mémoires et Observations de Chimie*, 1784, 308, 438; *Elémens d'Histoire Naturelle et de Chimie*, 1789, *1*, 64; *2*, 91. See *Ann. de Chim.*, 1789, *1*, 244.

105. *Dissertatio de principio sorbile*, Edinburgh, 1784, 39. See notes 10 and 11 above.

106. *Encycl. Méth. Chymie, Pharmacie, et Metallurgie*, 1786, *1*, 548. See Hassenfratz, *Annales de Chimie*, 1790, 7, 39. (Hassenfratz was an editor of the *Annales de Chimie* about 1790).

Guyton de Morveau (1737–1816) collaborated in the production of *Méthode de Nomenclature Chimique* in which the names of chemical substances were altered to bring them into line with Lavoisier's antiphlogistic theory (see note 11 above). He first used the word *radical* in the modern sense in 1785 (*Nouv. Mem. Acad. Dijon*, 1785, *1*, 90; *Obs. sur la Physique*, 1786, *28*, 205). See also Angus Smith, note 88, p. 157, and Partington and McKie, *Annals of Science*, 1937, *2*, 388.

107. *Opticks*, 1730, Query 31, p. 364.

108. Quoted from Partington, *Short History of Chemistry*, 3rd ed., 1957, 166.

109. See note 11 above.

110. p. 105 of the 1799 edition of Pearson's translation.

111. *Elements of Experimental Chemistry*, 11th ed., 1829, *1*, 28. See note 123 below.

112. *Elements of Chemistry*, 6th ed., 1828, *1*, 22.

113. *Catechism of Chemistry*, 1837, p. 52.

114. *Cyclopaedia*; article on *affinity* in Vol. 1 (1819).

115. See Part I, p. 2.

116. See Part I, p. 3.

117. *Phil. Trans.*, 1788, *78*, 379; *Ann. Chim.*, 1789, *2*, 260. Austin says the experiment was made at Sir Joseph Banks's house 'some years ago'; see Part I, p. 2.

118. *Encycl. Méth.*, 1786 (published in 1788), i, 756.

119. p. 272; see also Fourcroy, *Encycl. Méth.*, 1796, iii, 575.

120. *Experiments and Observations on the Different Kinds of Air*, 1790, *1*, 398.

121. *Experiments and Observations Relating to Various Branches of Natural Philosophy*, Birmingham, 1781, *2*, 301 ('Of an unexpected appearance of volatile alkali'); reprinted in *Experiments and Observations of Different Kinds of Air*, Birmingham, 1790, *2*, 41.

122. *Phil. Mag.*, 1816, *48*, 416.

123. William Henry (1774–1836) is best remembered for his discovery of the law of the solubility of gases in water at different pressures (1803). The first edition of his *Epitome of Chemistry* was published in 1801. The second edition (1801 also) quotes (p. 65) the *Comparative View* p. 300 in place of p. 309 for Higgins's reduction experiment. This error was repeated in the 3rd edition (1805, p. 163), and in the 4th (1806, p. 156). The Epitome was then expanded and issued as the *Elements of Experimental Chemistry*. The page continued to be incorrectly quoted, e.g. in

the 6th edition (1810, *1*, 422), the 7th (1815, *1*, 375), the 9th (1823, *1*, 403) the 10th (1826, *1*, 413), and the 11th and last (1829, *1*, 432). The first reference to the reaction as having been discovered 'some years ago' becomes 'many years ago' in the 11th edition. Henry mentions Higgins by name and refers to his book, so that no objection can be made against him. The first edition of the *Epitome* was not available to the authors.

Mr K. G. D. Cave (Assistant Librarian, Christie Library, University of Manchester) wrote as follows (17 January 1956): 'We possess a copy of the first edition, apparently Henry's own copy, with his additions and corrections for the second edition. There are xvi preliminary pages and 216 of text, the latter being interleaved with blank pages for notes. The preface is subscribed "Manchester, March 9th. 1801." '

On 24 January 1956, Mr Cave wrote: 'On p. 64 of the first edition of Henry, there is the same attribution to Higgins of the discovery of the "mutual relation of ammonia and of the compounds of azote" but the precise reference, which appears as a footnote in the second edition, is not given in the first. The exact words of the footnote are written out in Henry's hand on the blank page opposite for inclusion in the new edition, but there is no other annotation on this page. Our copy of the second edition also is interleaved and annotated by the author; but there is no note here either to shed any further light on this point.

'We still have the second edition of Higgins's work, dated 1791, to which W. C. Henry (see note 126 below) alludes. There are pencilled notes, mostly rather illegible now, on pp. 4, 5, 6, 11, 19, 27, and 30 but nothing on p. 309 which is the one referred to by the elder Henry.

'The end flyleaf also has pencilled notes on both sides, the recto being headed "Facts which might be considered anticipations of the atomic theory," followed by half a dozen page references to the book. The writing is very like that of the annotations in the elder Henry's interleaved copy of the "Epitome", but is in pencil not ink. It is not Dalton's, to judge from the facsimile in W. C. Henry's "Life". I had almost concluded it to be the elder Henry's when I noticed on p. 75 of W. C. Henry's "Life" the extracts he gives from Higgins "as the most striking anticipations . . . of atomic views". The page reference for these extracts are some of those given in the flyleaf notes so it seems plain that these pencilled notes are by the younger Henry not the elder.'

The authors' thanks are due to Mr Cave for his valuable assistance.

124. *Annals of Philosophy*, 1814, *4*, 54.
125. Higgins, who was careless about references, gives p. 64 for the second edition of the *Epitome* in place of p. 65 (see note 123 above) and appears to have confused the 5th and the 3rd editions.
126. *Memoirs of the Life and Scientific Researches of John Dalton*, 1854, 75–79.
127. *Phil. Trans.*, 1811, 16 (footnote).
128. *Ann. Chim.*, 1789, *2*, 54.
129. *Ann. Chim.*, 1790, *6*, 177 (181).
130. *Chemisches Wörterbuch*, Berlin, 1807, *1*, 471.
131. *J. de Physique*, Nivoise, An II (1793–94), *44*, 372 (388).
132. *Mém. div. Sav. Acad. Paris*, 1805, *1*, 136.
133. *Ann. Chim.*, Messidor, An XIII (1805), *55*, 303; *Mém. de l'Inst.*, Paris, 1806, *6*, 531, 544.

134. *Phil. Trans.*, 1771, *61*, 114.
135. *Observations sur la Physique*, 1788, *32*, 361.
136. *Ann. Chim.*, 1805, *55*, 303.
137. *Ann. Chim.*, 1798–99 (Nivoise, An VII), *29*, 301; he says the work was done in the École Poletechnique under Guyton de Morveau in Fructidor, An III, i.e. 1795 (August–September).
138. *Handbook of Chemistry* (tr. Watts), 1857, *11*, 211.
139. Mrs Fulhame's book is entitled *An Essay on Combustion, with a view to a New Art of Dying [sic] and Painting wherein the Phlogistic and Antiphlogistic Hypothesis are proved erroneous* (London, 1794, pp. xiii +182). There is an extract of the book in *Ann. de Chimie*, 1798, *26*, 58. The two copies in the library of the Royal Irish Academy were presented by Mrs Fulhame to the Academy and to Kirwan respectively. Mrs Fulhame is a mysterious figure in the history of chemistry; little is known of her beyond her book. The entry (13/12/1794) in the Register at Stationers' Hall gives her Christian name as Elizabeth (information kindly supplied by the Honorary Archivist, Mr S. Hodgson). She believed water was essential for oxidation and reduction.

She mentions in the preface that the idea of making cloths of gold, silver, and other metals, occurred to her in 1780, and that, after some time she realised the idea by experiment. She suspended her idea of publication until October 1793, when 'an illustrious friend of science . . . offered to have a memoir on the subject presented to the Royal Society; but different incidents dissuaded me from that mode of publication'. She is otherwise noteworthy in attributing, in her book (p. 180), the female sex to the phoenix, normally regarded as sexless.

Mrs Fulhame was elected before 1798 a corresponding member of the Chemical Society of Philadelphia, which was founded in 1792 by James Woodhouse and was the oldest chemical society in the world save that founded by Black's students in Edinburgh in 1785. (See note 9, p. 114 above; see also *Endeavour*, 1958, *17*, 59). Details of this Society are given by Miles, *Chymia*, 1950, *3*, 95; *Bulletin of the History of Medicine*, 1956, *30*, 469; Hepburn, *J. Franklin Institute*, 1956, *261*, 527; E. F. Smith, *Chemistry in America*, New York, 1914, 35. We are indebted to Dr J. S. Hepburn of the Franklin Institute, Philadelphia, for information about the Society which flourished up to about 1810.

An American edition of Mrs Fulhame's book was published in 1810 in Philadelphia by James Humphreys. A special preface was written for the edition which states that Mrs Fulhame was elected an honorary member on the merit of her book. It is more likely from other records that she was a corresponding member.

E. F. Smith, *Chemistry in Old Philadelphia*, Philadelphia, 1919, p. 95, says that the American lawyer and chemist Thomas Cooper (1759–1840), was probably the author of the preface. Cooper who was born in London and educated at Oxford had a most interesting career. He went with James Watt as a democratic envoy to Paris in 1792; later he emigrated to America. He practised as a lawyer in Pennsylvania and afterwards was Professor of Chemistry in the University of Pennsylvania and in other colleges. He eventually became President of South Carolina College. An educationalist and a political philosopher, he was described by President John Adams as 'a learned, ingenious, scientific, and talented

madcap'. (See *Encycl. Brit.*, 14th ed., 1929, *6*, 381; *Dict. Nat. Biog.*)
Mrs Fulhame refers in the Preface to her book to Dr Fulhame. Dr F. N. L. Poynter, Librarian of the Wellcome Historical Medical Library, informed us that a Thomas Fulhame was listed as the author of an Edinburgh M.D. dissertation of 1784. In this connection Miss Jean M. Simpson, Reference Assistant in the Edinburgh University Library, writes (19 October 1956): 'Thomas Fulhame, M.A., Hibernus—as he is described in the matriculation register—matriculated in medical subjects in the years 1779–1784. He graduated in 1784 with a thesis "De Febre Puerperarum". On the title page of this thesis, he is once more described as M.A., Hibernus, with the designation, Societ. Phys. Edin. Soc. Hon. et Praeses Annus. I have confirmed that he was President of the Edinburgh Physical Society (later, the Royal Physical Society of Edinburgh) in the years 1783–4, as he appears in a list of former presidents in *Laws of the Royal Physical Society*, *Edin.*, 1819, but I am afraid that I cannot discover where he obtained his Arts degree—it was certainly not at Edinburgh, and he does not seem to appear in any of the Scottish University Registers of Graduates.'

In connection with the adjective 'Hibernus', it will be noted that as stated above, two copies of Mrs Fulhame's book are in the library of the Royal Irish Academy. No indication has been obtained that Dr Fulhame lived in Dublin.

140. cf. Mellor and Russell, *J. Chem. Soc.*, 1902, *81*, 1272; Mellor, *J. Phys. Chem.*, 1903, 7, 557; *Treatise on Inorganic and Physical Chemistry*, London, 1924, *5*, 812.

141. J. W. Smith in *The Effects of Moisture on Chemical and Physical Changes*, London, 1929, pp. 8, 85, 138, discusses Higgins's theory of the effect of water in reactions and concludes that he anticipated Mrs Fulhame.

142. See *Roy. Soc. Catalogue of Scientific Papers*, 1868, *2*, 175; 1870, *4*, 556.

Part III

HIGGINS AND DALTON

THE ATOMIC THEORY originated in Greece about 450 B.C.[1]. It postulated indivisible atoms and an extended vacuum. This theory, proposed by Leukippos and Demokritos, was modified about 300 B.C. by Epikouros who added weight to the properties of atoms, supposing that they fall perpendicularly through space but from time to time swerve from some unknown cause and collide, forming aggregates, from which material bodies are composed. Although atoms are indivisible they are composed of different numbers and arrangements of smaller parts, giving rise to atoms of different kinds. Atoms have hooks or branches, by which they interlock to form aggregates.

This old Greek atomism was well known in antiquity and, by way of Lucretius, in the middle ages. In the seventeenth century extensive use was made of it by Bodin, Gorlaeus, Sennert, and Magnenus, but the effective revival of the atomic theory is due to Gassendi (1592–1655), who (as the Arabs had done before and Newton was to do later) assumed that atoms were created by God in such a way as to be most useful to man. From Gassendi the theory became known to Boyle, and from Boyle to Newton, whose well-known statement in the *Opticks* is taken almost literally from Gassendi. Newton, however, added a new feature, viz. attractive forces between atoms which cause them to unite, instead of the old interlocking mechanism.

Newton (1687) showed that if it is assumed that the atoms of air (which he regarded as an element) are at rest and repel one another with a force inversely proportional to the distance, air will obey Boyle's law. Although Bernoulli (1738) gave a kinetic explanation, supposing the pressure to be due to moving particles between which no force acts, this view was not generally favoured and Newton's was preferred.

123

When gases different from air were discovered, and it was shown that air is a mixture of two gases, and that the gases ammonia and hydrochloric acid combine to form a solid, some modification of Newton's theory was required. This was done by Bryan Higgins. He published four books, from which his atomic theory may be collected[2]: (1) *A Syllabus of Chemical and Philosophical Enquiries* (1775) (undated; also reprinted in (2)); (2) *A Philosophical Essay concerning Light*, 1776 (in its present form incomplete); (3) *Experiments and Observations relating to Acetous Acid*, etc., 1786; (4) *Minutes of a Society for Philosophical Experiments and Conversations*, 1795 (see pp. 32, 57 above). Bryan Higgins opened a School of Practical Chemistry in Greek Street, Soho, in July 1774, where he gave lectures and demonstrations. The substance of these is contained in (1) and (4). The latter includes some important material and was translated into German in 1803; it is quoted as an authority in the older editions of Gmelin's *Handbook*. Priestley attended the lectures and purchased some chemicals from Higgins. In (2) Higgins refers to Priestley's discovery of gases as 'conceits', and he had claimed in conversation that he had anticipated Priestley in the discovery of some gases. Priestley published a pamphlet of eighty-six pages, *Philosophical Empiricism: containing Remarks on a Charge of Plagiarism respecting Dr H——S*, 1775, in which he says that he had told Higgins about the discoveries which the latter claimed, and had shown him the experiments.

Bryan Higgins made the assumption that the material particles in gases are hard and accurately or nearly globular. They attract one another by forces depending on the distance d according to the law $1/d^n$, where n is a constant, and also depending on polarity. The particles in gases are surrounded by repelling atmospheres of fire (see Part II, note 29, p. 115). Combination in definite proportions, which Bryan Higgins calls 'saturation' (a name later used by William Higgins), is not a distinct or primary law of nature, but is an effect of the attractive and repulsive forces operating in opposition, and for it to occur it is necessary that the atmospheres of fire surrounding the particles should be broken or blended. He gives diagrams showing the combination of gaseous ammonia and hydrochloric acid, and

for the formation of inflammable air by the combination of one
particle of an acid and elastic fluid with one particle of phlogiston.
Since he knew that equal volumes of ammonia and hydrochloric
acid gas combine he may have had some idea that the number
of particles in a gas is related to the volume in some simple
manner, although his statements on this point are very vague.
He considered only combination of one particle of one gas A
with one particle of another gas B to form a compound particle
A + B, and made use of the phlogiston theory.

It is seen that the theory differed from that of William
Higgins, who assumed that particles could combine in different
ratios, A + B, A + 2B . . . A + 5B, and the nature of the attractive
force was also different. It is probable, however, that William
Higgins got his first ideas of his theory from Bryan Higgins.

The origin and content of Dalton's atomic theory and its
relation to earlier and later theories have been elucidated by the
studies of Roscoe and Harden[3] and of Meldrum[4]. To understand its origin, something must be known of Dalton himself.
John Dalton (1766–1844) was born of Quaker parents in a small
Cumberland village. Largely self-taught, he became a school-
master in Kendal in 1781. He took up the study of meteorology
and in 1793 published *Meteorological Observations and Essays*,
a book which contains the germs of his later discoveries: in it he
said that the water vapour in the atmosphere is mixed with, and
not chemically combined with or dissolved in, the other gases
(see p. 99 above). In the same year he became a mathematical
tutor in New College, Manchester, resigning in 1799 and afterwards supporting himself by giving private tuition and by
chemical work. He had a small private laboratory with simple
apparatus. In ordinary quantitative analysis, in which he had no
training, his work was no more, and sometimes less, accurate than
that of his contemporaries, but in the much more difficult
subject of gas analysis he obtained correct and accurate results.
Some of his later quantitative determinations of the equivalents
of metals are surprisingly good. It is an error to suppose that he
was a coarse and inaccurate experimenter.

Dalton[5] took from Newton the theory that the particles of
gases are self-repulsive, and from Lavoisier that the repulsion is

due to self-repulsive particles of caloric or the matter of heat combined with the material particles (as Bryan Higgins had assumed). These were accepted views at the time (see note 29, p. 115). In the years 1799–1801 Dalton published experimental investigations which established his scientific reputation. In 1816 he became corresponding member of the Academy of Sciences in Paris and in 1830 one of its eight foreign associates: he became F.R.S. in 1826 and in 1832 he received the honorary degrees of D.C.L. of Oxford and LL.D. of Edinburgh. In 1833 he began to receive a pension from the Government. He died suddenly in 1844 and was buried in Manchester with civic honours. He was greatly liked and respected by his contemporaries, who recognised his love of truth and great originality. When Dalton announced his atomic theory he was well known for his other fundamental work, and if he had done no more than this, his would still be an honoured name in science.

In Dalton's time atmospheric air was thought by many chemists (including Davy) to be a chemical compound of oxygen and nitrogen. Dalton himself discovered that two gases would mix by diffusion and he asserted that it was not necessary to assume that this was the result of weak chemical affinity. The state of the water vapour in the atmosphere was also not well understood, and it was much discussed whether the water existed as a true gas, or whether it was dissolved in the air like sugar in water, as a result of attraction or weak chemical affinity (see p. 125 above). All these obscure questions were answered, and the whole subject of the mixing of gases and vapours cleared up, by Dalton's researches and speculations. It is difficult for a modern reader, unfamiliar with the state of the subject when Dalton began his work, to form a just conception of the great advances in knowledge which are due to him, since most of the ideas on mixed gases which now come to mind originated with Dalton and were unknown before him.

In 1801 Dalton stated his law of partial pressures in the form that in a mixture of gases the particles of any one gas repel one another but not the particles of any other gases. This view was found difficult to accept at the time. Early in 1803 he described experiments on the mixing of gases by diffusion, and soon after he concluded that the particles of different gases (including the envelope of heat) are spherical and of different sizes; if the repulsive force is due to heat, particles of different sizes pressing against one another cannot be in equilibrium in gases, and mixing or diffusion will ensue. Although Meldrum thought that Dalton had two physical atomic theories, one assuming that the particles of different gases are of the same size, proposed in 1801, and a second, assuming that they are of different sizes, proposed in 1804, the statement that the particles of different gases are different in size occurs in Dalton's note-book under the date 6 September 1803, when the first table of atomic weights, or what Meldrum called the chemical theory, also appeared. This entry in Dalton's note-book, made on his birthday, contains, implicitly or explicitly, the following statements:

1. Atoms are indivisible and incapable of being created or destroyed.

2. All the atoms of a given element are identical and have the same invariable weight.

3. The smallest particles of gases are surrounded by spherical elastic envelopes of heat.

4. The atoms of different elements have different weights.

5. A particle of a compound is formed from a fixed number of atoms of its component elements (law of fixed proportions).

6. The weight of a compound particle is the sum of the weights of its constituent atoms.

7. If more than one compound of two elements is known, the numbers of atoms of either element in two compound particles are in the ratio of whole numbers (law of multiple proportions).

8. The weight of an atom of an element is the same in all its compounds (law of reciprocal proportions).

9. If only one compound of two kinds of atoms A and B is known, it is, unless there is some reason to the contrary, $A + B$. If there is more than one compound, one is $A + B$ and the other $2A + B$ or $A + 2B$, and so on. On 12 October 1803, Dalton recognised that nitrous anhydride is $2N + 3O$, but he regarded this as a binary compound of higher order, viz. $(NO) + (NO_2)$.

10. If the numbers of atoms m and n of two elements in a

particle of a compound mA + nB are assumed, the relative weights of the atoms A and B can be calculated from the ratio of the weights mA/nB of the elements found by analysis. Dalton chose the atomic weight of hydrogen as unity and gave the weights of other atoms on this basis.

11. Equal volumes of different gases at the same temperature and pressure cannot contain the same number of particles, since water vapour, the particle of which must contain at least one atom of oxygen, is lighter than oxygen gas.

These statements contain the whole content of Dalton's chemical atomic theory; they were arrived at completely at one and the same time, and they remained unchanged in all Dalton's later publications. It will be appreciated that Dalton's atomic theory is different from the modern chemical atomic theory, and it will also be clear that the modern theory rests on Dalton's as a foundation. In calculating atomic weights according to statement (10), Dalton used analyses by famous chemists such as Lavoisier, Chenevix, Fourcroy and Thenard, and not his own experimental results, and the errors in the numbers were not his. He soon found that the results of other chemists were contradictory, and he said that he proposed to publish only what he could, as far as possible, confirm by experiment, since he had been misled by the results of others. This perfectly correct attitude has been misinterpreted[6] as conceit on Dalton's part.

How did Dalton arrive at the central idea of his theory, that atoms of different elements have different weights? In spite of much research, a reply to this question cannot be given with certainty. Dalton himself gave different answers, some of which must be incorrect. One of his statements, viz. that the theory was a result of his speculations on mixed gases, seems likely to be true. He said these led him to suppose that the particles of different gases are different in size, and from this he hit on the idea that they are different in weight.

At the end of a paper on the solubility of gases read on 21 October 1803 to the Manchester Literary and Philosophical Society, Dalton gave a table of atomic weights without saying how they had been calculated. The paper was printed in 1805, and the table then contained some additions, including marsh gas and ethylene, and oxides of nitrogen. In August 1804, Thomas Thomson visited Dalton in Manchester and found him analysing marsh gas and ethylene. The results showed that, for a given weight of carbon, marsh gas contains just twice as much hydrogen as ethylene, and Thomson afterwards said that Dalton invented the atomic theory to explain this multiple proportion. The theory had, however been arrived at in 1803. Dalton's experiments on oxides of nitrogen, also showing multiple proportion, are given as additions to a paper read in 1802 but not printed until 1805; they had been made in October to November 1803, after the table of atomic weights had been written, although inconclusive experiments on the same lines are recorded in March and April 1803, and on 4 August 1803 Dalton recorded that 'oxygen joins to nit. gas sometimes 1·7 to 1, and at other times 3·4 to 1', which is a case of the law of multiple proportions. Hence the origin of the theory on the basis of these experiments cannot be ruled out.

In 1807, Thomson gave the first printed account of Dalton's atomic theory in his *System of Chemistry*, Dalton's own brief statement of it being contained in the first volume of his *New System of Chemical Philosophy* published in 1808. In this, after some general statements about atoms, Dalton points out that the relative weights of atoms may be calculated from the composition of compounds if the number of atoms of each element in a particle of a compound is known or assumed. The statements made in the book include those, (1)–(11), given above, and no more. In his later publications Dalton changed the values of the atomic weights somewhat, but they had all been found by the same methods. Even in the last volume of his *New System* (1827) Dalton made no advance on his empirical rules.

Dalton in 1803 thought [(11) above] that equal volumes of gases need not contain equal numbers of particles, since steam, the particles of which must contain at least one atom of oxygen, is lighter than oxygen gas. He does not seem to have entertained the idea that the particles of elementary gases are not single atoms but contain two or more atoms. Avogadro in 1811 showed that this assumption, with the hypothesis that equal volumes of

K

all gases, elementary or compound, contain the same number of particles (molecules; the name had been used by Gassendi and by Bryan Higgins) at the same temperature and pressure, will explain all the difficulties such as that raised by Dalton. Unfortunately, Avogadro's publication was mostly disregarded until Cannizzaro drew attention to it in 1859 and showed how it could be used to find both molecular and atomic weights. It was the combination of Dalton's and Avogadro's theories by Cannizzaro which led to the modern form of the chemical atomic theory.

In addition to his atomic theory, Dalton made important contributions to physics and chemistry both before and after he proposed the theory. He discovered the law of the equal expansion of gases by heat independently of Gay-Lussac, the law of partial pressures, and the correct view of the state of water vapour in the atmosphere. He investigated the diffusion of gases and the conduction of heat in liquids, and his experiments on the combustion of hydrocarbons (1805) are fundamental. His discovery of a gas isomeric with ethylene (1820) was confirmed by Faraday. In 1793 his observations on the aurora borealis led him to suspect that it depends on the magnetic field of the earth, and that the atmosphere might contain a paramagnetic gas, a theory developed by Faraday (1851) after the discovery of the paramagnetism of oxygen. Dalton's experiments on the volumes of solutions (1840) were extended by Joule and Playfair and showed that certain salts do not increase the volume of water when dissolved in it. Dalton used a method of determining vapour densities (1819) similar to that used later by Dumas (1826). He showed by experiment (1837) that the composition of the atmosphere at altitudes of 3000, 9600 and 15,000 ft. is practically constant; the slight variations in composition at high altitudes are much less than would be expected from the different densities of oxygen and nitrogen, and this he explained as due to the agitation of the atmosphere by currents and counter-currents, a theory recently proposed again[7].

In comparing the atomic theories of Higgins and Dalton it is necessary, as was said above, to divest one's mind completely of the familiar modern aspects of the chemical atomic theory, and to attend closely to what Higgins and Dalton say themselves. If this is done, it seems to be beyond dispute that the two theories differ in important respects. Dalton's emphasis is on the *weights* of the atoms. He assumed that the chemical elements have atoms which differ in weight and that it is possible to arrive at the relative weights of the atoms from the composition of compounds by weight. His methods of doing this were faulty and often gave incorrect results, but the principle is correct and it is the main feature of Dalton's chemical atomic theory.

It might seem to us that if it is assumed that the particle of water contains one atom of hydrogen and one atom of oxygen, and it is known that eight parts by weight of oxygen combine with one part by weight of hydrogen, it follows at once that the oxygen atom is eight times the weight of the hydrogen atom. This is not necessarily the case, and we have a statement to this effect from one of the most ingenious theorists of Dalton's time, who in boldness of speculation and wideness of view was hardly second to Dalton himself.

Grotthuss[8] in 1805 had represented a molecule of water as composed of an atom of oxygen and an atom of hydrogen, using circular symbols practically the same as Dalton's, and in 1807 he formulated it as containing one atom of hydrogen and two of oxygen. Grotthuss knew the ratio of the combining weights of oxygen and hydrogen. Yet in 1818 he said: 'It is remarkable how near I was to Dalton's discovery relating to the weights of atoms. The diagrams in Dalton's *System* are exactly the same as those I had given much earlier. I admit, however, that the beautiful and difficult idea of determining the relative weights of the atoms from the composition of bodies had not occurred to me.' (See pp. 137, 138 below.)

The first reference to Higgins in relation to Dalton seems to have been made in a Bakerian Lecture to the Royal Society in 1810 by Davy, who had lectured to the Royal Dublin Society in that year (see Part I, p. 20) and probably received an account of his work from Higgins himself. Davy says[9]:

'In my last communication to the Society, I have quoted Mr Dalton as the original Author of the hypothesis, that water consists of 1 particle of oxygen, and 1 of hydrogen; but I have since found that this opinion is advanced, in a work published in 1789—*A Comparative View of the Phlogistic and Antiphlogistic Theories*, by William Higgins. In this elaborate and ingenious performance, Mr Higgins has developed many happy sketches of the manner in which (on the corpuscular hypothesis) the particles or molecules of bodies may be conceived to combine; and some of his views, though formed at this early period of investigation, appear to me to be more defensible, assuming his data, than any which have since been advanced; for instance, he considered nitrous gas (nitric oxide, NO) as composed of two particles of oxygen, and one of nitrogen.' (Dalton had, correctly as it happens, assumed that it consists of one particle of oxygen and one of nitrogen).

Davy goes on to criticise with some asperity many results of his 'learned friend' Dalton, and says he felt 'obliged to dissent from most of them, and to protest against the interpretations that he has been pleased to make of my experiments'. This, however, refers to Dalton's idea that the alkali metals are hydrides of the alkalis, and Davy from an early period (before the publication of the atomic theory) had a high opinion of Dalton.

In 1812 Davy[10] said:

'Mr Higgins is, I believe, the first person who conceived that when gasses combine in more than one proportion, all the proportions of the same element were equal; and he founded this idea, which was made public in 1789, on the corpuscular hypothesis, that bodies combine particle with particle, or one with two, or three, or a greater number of particles. Mr Dalton, about 1802, adopting a similar hypothesis, apparently without the knowledge of what Mr Higgins had written, extended his views to compounds in general.'

In 1825, in an obituary notice of Higgins, Davy[11] said:

'. . . He brought forward no new experiments and endeavoured to establish a loose kind of dynamic hypothesis. . . . It is impossible not to regret that he did not establish principles which belong to the highest department of chemistry, and that he suffered so fertile and promising a field of science to be entirely cultivated by others; for though possessed of great means of improving chemistry, he did little or nothing during the last thirty years of his life.'

In presenting the Royal Medal to Dalton in 1826 Davy, then President of the Royal Society, said[12] that many ideas of William Higgins had been anticipated by Bryan Higgins in 1786 and, as these were known to William, 'it is difficult not to allow the merits of prior conception, as well as of very ingenious illustration, to the elder writer'. Dalton, says Davy, was probably unacquainted with the works of Higgins and Richter, or 'at least he never refers to them', and 'whoever will consider the ingenious and independent turn of his mind, and the original tone prevailing in all his views and speculations will hardly accuse him [Dalton] of wilful plagiarism'.

In 1813 Thomas Thomson[13] agreed that Higgins's book was meritorious; 'it states some striking facts respecting the gases, and anticipated Gay-Lussac's theory of volumes', but Dalton 'first generalised the doctrine, and thought of determining the weight of the atoms of bodies'. John Nash, in a paper[14] entitled 'The Discovery of the Atomic Theory claimed for Mr Higgins', which was most likely inspired by Higgins, criticised Thomson's paper. Nash refers to pages 15, 37, and especially 80–81 of the *Comparative View*.

Thomson[15] in a reply to Nash repeated that Dalton was the first to generalise the atomic theory and to think of determining the weights of atoms. Higgins could not have done this since the only analyses of metallic oxides available to him were probably those of Bergman, interpreted in terms of the antiphlogistic theory by Lavoisier about 1785[16]. (Many compositions of metallic oxides had, however been given by Wenzel in 1777[17].) These figures (quoted in part by Higgins on p. 268 of the *Comparative View*) were, Thomson says, insufficient to form the basis of an atomic theory. Higgins based his ideas chiefly on volumetric results obtained with compounds of oxygen, hydrogen, nitrogen and sulphur. Thomson says he had possessed Higgins's book 'since the year 1798 and had perused it carefully; yet I did not find anything in it which suggested to me the atomic theory. That a small hint would have been sufficient I think pretty clear from this, that I was forcible struck with Mr Dalton's

statement in 1804, though it did not fill half an octavo page.'
Thomson thought the discussions on pages 36, 37, 81, and 132 of
the *Comparative View* show that Higgins 'had no idea of the
atomic theory when he wrote his book'.

In a review of Higgins's book of 1814, Thomson[18] says the
Comparative View was unknown in Edinburgh and London
until Davy drew attention to it. Thomson denied that 'there is
the slightest allusion to the weight of a single elementary atom'
in it, or that there is 'the slightest reason to induce us to believe
that the idea of ascertaining the weights of those atoms so much
as entered into the conception of the writer'.

Gaultier de Claubry[19] in a review of Higgins's *Atomic Theory*
(1814) in the *Journal de Physique* considered Higgins's priority
in regard to the discovery of the atomic theory to be incontest-
able. The translator (W.B.) of the French paper is even more
strongly in favour of Higgins, referring to Thomson as unfair
and unjust. Like Higgins himself the translator lays great stress
on the relative forces of attraction between ultimate particles.

W. C. Henry[20], after giving a summary of the *Comparative
View*, in which he had 'carefully perused many passages',
concluded that Higgins supposed the atoms to be equal in weight.
He refers to Higgins's claim in 1814, in which he 'charges
Dalton, if not directly, yet by implication, with plagiarism
(pp. 9, 10, 17, 164, &c.)', and thought that, 'as the question of
the originality of Dalton's doctrines may be raised by the future
historian of Science, I deem it important to perpetuate here the
oral and written testimony in my possession[21]. I have heard my
father (William Henry, the personal friend of Dalton) affirm, on
various occasions, and to various persons, that Dalton had never
seen Mr Higgins's work, till some years subsequently to the
publication of the *New System*, when it was lent to him by my
father. I have also found among my father's papers the following
memorandum of a conversation with Mr P. Clare, respecting
Mr Dalton, dated February 26, 1833:

   ' "Mr Clare recollects that many years ago . . . he was invited
to breakfast at Mr Ewart's with Leslie, who was then passing
through the town (Manchester). The professor proposed a walk,
during which Mr Leslie told Dalton that Davy, in a paper in the

Philosophical Transactions, had denied Dalton's claim to the atomic theory and had set up one for Higgins. This was new to Mr Dalton. . . . It must then have been after this time that calling on Mr Dalton, I [William Henry] found him in the act of reading the note of Davy's paper in the *Phil. Trans.*, 1811, p. 15[9]. He expressed his surprise and asked me if I had seen Higgins's book. I told him that I had not only seen it, but quoted it[22], and lent him the volume." '

W. C. Henry goes on to say (what Dalton himself also said) that Dalton never devoted much time to reading but 'his was essentially a self-reliant and productive nature'. As far as we are aware, this statement by Henry is the only one available on which an opinion of Dalton's independence of Higgins can safely be based. All the statements that Dalton read, or even knew of the existence of, the *Comparative View* before he arrived at his atomic theory in September 1803, when closely examined, are found to rest on no material facts or documentary evidence apart from statements by Higgins[23]. No useful purpose would, therefore, be served in going over the numerous references which can be found to the Higgins–Dalton controversy. It will be sufficient to quote two accounts which appeared soon after Higgins made his claim in 1814, and the opinion of Kopp, who always wrote with care and without prejudice.

The anonymous article[24] on 'Theory, Atomic, in Chemistry', in Ree's *Cyclopaedia*, which (like the rest of the work) is unpaged, says:

'The most decided language used in any chemical work before the discoveries of Mr John Dalton, giving any idea that the doses are limited by distinct atoms, will be found in a work by Mr Higgins, entitled "A Comparative View of the Phlogistic and Antiphlogistic Theories." The work was primarily written to combat the phlogiston theory and as an answer to Kirwan's *Essay on Phlogiston*. It used diagrams and numbers as estimates of affinities.' These numbers 'served his purpose much more than the consideration of the proportions being caused by distinct atoms; and the language which would induce the belief that he had such a conception of the nature of elementary matter occurs only in a very few parts of his work'. A brief but fair summary is given, including the compositions of the oxides of nitrogen and a remark that Higgins supposed that sulphuretted hydrogen contains 9 parts of sulphur and 5 of hydrogen, the sulphur being merely dissolved and not combined. The compositions of the oxides of nitrogen 'are very remarkable, as they agree with the conclusions in the present time, and give strong proof of Mr Higgins's genius at the time he wrote.

'He does not, however, lay any stress upon these remarks, and was not probably aware that they would be confirmed by future research. We are induced to think so, from the manner in which he expresses himself in other parts of the work, in which he frequently speaks of the absorption of small portions of oxygen, and bodies having a small portion of oxygen more than they can retain. This vague manner of speaking, and others which we do not immediately recollect, is sufficient to shew that Mr Higgins had no fixed notions of the cause of definite proportions.'

The article in the *Analytical Review* (see Part II, p. 113) soon after Higgins's book was published, and quoted by him, 'gives him the highest praise for the able manner in which he has refuted the doctrine of phlogiston, but does not even hint at his diagrams of ultimate particles'. If Higgins could show from the data in his book that inferences similar to those drawn by Dalton could be derived from it, then 'he will be entitled to share in the merit of the discovery of the atomic theory. We say share with him, for we are firmly convinced that Mr Dalton had never read Mr Higgins's book previous to the publication of his own work.' It is emphasised that Dalton's views, more firmly based than Higgins's, did not command general assent until they had been established by independent experiments, so that it is hardly surprising that Higgins's, which could hardly be said to be founded on any relevant experiments at all, were generally neglected. In 1820, W. J. MacNeven[25] (a countryman of Higgins) said that 'Mr Higgins . . . made a near approach to the atomic theory', but MacNeven thought that Dalton was its true author.

Higgins[26] in 1819 refers to a statement in the *Comparative View* (p. 37; quoted in Part II, Section on the 'Composition of Molecules'; see p. 73 above).

'As 2 cubic inches of light inflammable air require but 1 of

dephlogisticated air to condense them, we must suppose that
they contain equal numbers of divisions, and that the difference
of their specific gravity depends chiefly on the size of their
ultimate particles'. He says these words can bear the following
interpretation:

'Although a cubic inch of oxygen gas is fourteen times heavier
(some make it more) than a cubic inch of hydrogen gas; yet, as
there are but half the number of particles in the latter that the
former contains, the particles of oxygen can be no more than
seven times heavier.'

In 1814 (*Atomic Theory*, 1814, p. 12) Higgins said: 'We have
every reason to suppose that the ultimate particles of every
substance in nature possess the same specific gravity and that
the difference in the weight of metals depends upon the distance
of their respective ultimate particles from each other.' In a
footnote he says: 'This I have shewn to be the case in respect of
some gases.—See pages 14, 15, of my *Comparative View*.' In
the last, he accounts for the different densities of gases by assuming that their particles are at different distances from one
another.

Kopp[27], who refers to the two editions of the *Comparative
View* as well as to the summaries by Henry (see Part II, note 126)
and R. Angus Smith, and hence (since in his later writings he
always says when he was unable to see an original) may be
presumed to have read it (see Part II, note 88), gives the following opinion. He thought that Higgins obtained the numbers of
elementary particles in a compound particle simply from the
ratios of the absolute weights, the weights of the atoms being
assumed equal. In sulphur dioxide 1 part by weight of sulphur is
combined with 1 part by weight of oxygen and the formula is
$S + O$. In sulphuric acid it is combined with 2 parts of oxygen and
the formula is $S + 2O$. In nitric oxide 1 part by weight of nitrogen
is (Higgins thought) combined with 2 parts by weight of oxygen
and the formula is $N + 2O$. In nitric acid 1 part of nitrogen is
combined with 5 parts of oxygen and the formula is $N + 5O$. In
nitrous oxide, containing less oxygen, the ratio is 1 to 1 and the
formula is $N + O$. The compounds intermediate between nitric
oxide and nitric acid were assumed to be $N + 3O$ and $N + 4O$, and

there was at that time no real evidence that there were just two of them. Since Higgins knew the composition of water by weight and assumed it to be $H + O$, 'it cannot be said that Higgins in general assumed that the weights of the smallest particles of different bodies which he regarded as undecomposable were equal in weight'[28]. We have shown above (p. 131), by reference to Grotthuss, that this conclusion is not warranted.

Kopp's statement about the composition of sulphur dioxide seems to be based on the statement ($C.V.$, p. 36) by Higgins that sulphur dioxide is formed from equal weights of sulphur and oxygen, and that the specific gravity of sulphur dioxide is twice that of oxygen, from which he concluded that 'the ultimate particles of sulphur and dephlogisticated air contain equal quantities of solid matter', and that in sulphur dioxide 'a single ultimate particle of sulphur is intimately united only to a single particle of dephlogisticated air'. It would seem that Kopp had not understood Higgins's argument (see Part II, Section on the 'Composition of Molecules', p. 72).

Kopp says that Higgins's views were partly in agreement with what was known later, but were proposed only incidentally and for a few compounds and were not a general atomic theory applicable to all compounds. Only after Dalton's theory was published did Higgins present his claim. His mode of expression is indefinite and his views on the composition of gases by *weight* were *later* said to refer to composition by *volume*, so that they were regarded as having anticipated Gay-Lussac's law of volumes. For sulphur and nitrogen compounds, Kopp thought, Higgins in 1789 was referring to weight ratios (see p. 71) and did not believe that equal volumes of different gases under similar conditions contain equal numbers of smallest particles.

The name 'specific gravity' for what we call the weight of a particle, and not the density of the matter composing it, was used by Cicero[29]. Thomson, in his first account of Dalton's atomic theory[30], spoke of the 'density' of an atom when he meant the atomic weight, and Dalton afterwards[31] criticised this, saying that it implied that 'all atoms are *of the same size*, and differ only in *density*; but he has since very properly discontinued the use of the phrase'. In his first note on the atomic theory (1803) Dalton used the old name 'specific gravity' for the weights of atoms[32] and he may have used this name in his conversation with Thomson in Manchester in the autumn of 1804. Thomson probably felt that the name was inappropriate and substituted 'density'. It will be noticed that Higgins and Dalton used 'specific gravity' in relation to atoms in different ways, which suggests that their views were independent.

The old atomists Demokritos and Epikouros apparently both assumed that the matter of all atoms is the same. The first seems to have supposed that the *mass* is proportional to the volume of the quantity of matter contained in the atom; the second, that this is true of the *weight*[33]. In speaking of atoms, Newton[34] refers to 'Particles of Matter of several Sizes and Figures, and in several Proportions to Space, and perhaps of different Densities and Forces', which may mean that the weights can be different, although it can mean almost anything.

Dalton's theory was developed on an experimental basis and was put forward systematically and logically, and with great clearness. After a short period of hesitation it was accepted and used by practically all chemists; some, such as Thomson and Berzelius, accepted it from the first. It made a great change in chemistry, which became a more quantitative science; the formula and composition of a compound could be predicted before it was prepared, and new insight into the nature of chemical reactions was given.

It would be unjust to Dalton to claim too much for Higgins. Higgins was a remarkably original thinker who applied the atomic theory to chemical problems in much greater detail than anyone before him, including Bryan Higgins, from whom he received the initial ideas. He deduced molecular formulae for water, the oxides of nitrogen and sulphur, and the composition of hydrogen sulphide, and he clearly recognised the law of multiple proportions. He used molecular diagrams with linear bonds linking atoms which were represented by symbols, in some cases the initial letters of the names of the elements, and these were superior to Dalton's symbols. He had a notion that there is a simple ratio law for the numbers of particles in equal volumes of gases under the same external conditions. His views on reaction mechanisms were novel and remarkable for their time; they show real chemical insight and in some respects foreshadow later developments.

Higgins, unfortunately, was an obscure writer who did not take the trouble to make his meaning clear, and as a result his book made no impression on his contemporaries. He, and not they, must be held responsible for their neglect of his ideas. He does not set out his postulates systematically, and for him in 1789 the atomic theory was only one weapon which could be used against the doctrine of phlogiston, which we must realise was then still flourishing. He showed that Lavoisier's teachings, combined where necessary with atomic ideas, gave a rational explanation of some chemical phenomena. Higgins nowhere indicates that he considered his atomic theory as important, or even fundamentally novel, in itself. In some respects he was in advance of his time; if he had thought out his ideas systematically and pursued the line he opened out in 1789, he could have advanced chemical theory in a notable way. As it was, he allowed twenty-five years to elapse, and Dalton's theory to appear, before he sought to promulgate his earlier ideas. He then claimed more for himself than he was entitled to, and his unjustified statements about Dalton must have antagonised those with no prejudice but with knowledge of the facts of the case. Higgins's cause has never been furthered by claiming too much for him and granting too little to Dalton, and in our account we have tried to do full justice to both. Higgins has an honourable place in the history of chemical theory but he does not stand on the same level as Dalton.

Notes to Part III

1. Partington, *Annals of Science*, 1939, *4*, 245–282, where detailed references to the atomic theory up to Dalton's time are given and the question as to the independent origination of an atomic theory in India is discussed.
2. See Part I, notes 1, 2, 4, 5, 15, and 53, and Appendix to Part I. George Fordyce (1736–1802), who began an annual course of lectures on chemistry in London in 1759, referred to 'chemical attraction which combines the smallest integral particles of one body with the smallest integral particles of another body so as to form an integral particle of a substance different from either'. He goes on to say that 'one integral particle of one body may unite with one or two particles of another body'. This is in a Ms. of notes of Fordyce's lectures of 1784–85 and the statement that more than one particle of one body may unite with one particle of another precedes William Higgins's publication in 1789. How long before 1784 Fordyce had been teaching this we cannot say.
3. H. E. Roscoe and A. Harden, *A New View of the Origin of Dalton's Atomic Theory*, 1896; see also *idem*, *Z. phys. Chem.*, 1897, *22*, 241; *Phil. Mag.*, 1897, *43*, 153; W. W. H. Gee, H. F. Coward, and A. Harden, *Mem. Manchester Lit. and Phil. Soc.*, 1914–15, *59*, no. 12; H. F. Coward, *J. Chem. Education*, 1927, *4*, 22.
4. A. N. Meldrum, *Chem. News*, 1910, *102*, 1; *Mem. Manchester Lit. and Phil. Soc.*, 1910, *54*, no. 7; 1910–11, *55*, nos. 3, 4, 5, and 6; on B. and W. Higgins, *idem*, *New Ireland Review*, 1909–10, *32*, 275, 350.
5. For Dalton's atomic theory see Partington, ref. 1; L. K. Nash, *Isis*, 1956, *47*, 101–116.
6. Paneth and Soddy, *Nature*, 1950, *166*, 799; 1951, *167*, 735; cf. Partington, *ibid.*, 1951, *167*, 120, 735.
7. Paneth, *Nature*, 1937, *127*, 347.
8. Grotthuss, *Schweiggers J. Chemie*, 1818, *20*, 225 (269); Ostwald's *Klossiker*, no. 152, p. 92. Grotthuss's first paper was published in Rome in 1805 and in *Annales de Chimie*, 1806, *58*, 54, and his second in *Annales de Chimie*, 1807, *63*, 5; *Nicholson's J.*, 1811, *28*, 112. The figures of the water molecules in first paper are $\oplus\ominus$ and in the second paper $\odot$. $h\odot$ (i.e. HO$_2$).
9. Bakerian Lecture, 15 November 1810; *Phil. Trans.*, 1811, *101*, 1 (15); *Works*, 1840, *5*, 326. Meldrum, *Mem. Manchester Lit. and Phil. Soc.*, 1911, *55*, no. 22, thought Dalton's paper written on 19 December 1810, *Nicholson's Journ.*, 1811, *28*, 81, was a reply to Davy, but this is unlikely.
10. *Elements of Chemical Philosophy*, 1812, 107; *Works*, 1840, *4*, 78.
11. *Works*, 1840, *7*, 75–76.
12. *Works*, 1840, *7*, 95.
13. *Annals of Philosophy*, 1813, *2*, 445.
14. *Phil. Mag.*, 1814, *43*, 54.
15. *Annals of Philosophy*, 1814, *3*, 329–338.

16. Experiments on the precipitation of one metal by another, *Mém. Acad. R. Sci.*, 1782 (1785), 512 (presented in December 1783); *Oeuvres*, *2*, 528–545.

17. *Lehre von der Verwandschaft der Körper*, Dresden, 1777 (republished with new title-page in 1782); these are summarised by Walden, *Mass, Zahl und Gewicht in der Chemie der Vergangenheit, Sammlung chemischer und chemischtechnisher Vorträge*, ed. Ahrens, Stuttgart, 1931, Neue Folge, Heft *8*, 84–87.

18. *Annals of Philosophy*, 1814, *4*, 52–66.

19. *Journal de Physique*, 1817, *84*, 393; W. B. in *Phil. Mag.*, 1817, *50*, 406 (abstract). Perhaps William Babington, or W. T. Brande.

20. *Memoirs of the Life and Scientific Researches of John Dalton*, 1854, 78; see Part II, notes 123 and 127, pp. 119, 120.

21. The later writers on Higgins have mostly ignored this.

22. See pp. 106, 119 for this.

23. See note 6 above.

24. Although the title-page of the volume of Ree's *Cyclopaedia* which we quote is dated 1819, the fact that Higgins replied to the article in 1818 indicates that the work was probably published in parts, the title-pages being issued afterwards for binding, as was the case in many other large works; see Part II, note 2, p. 113.

25. *Annals of Philosophy*, 1820, *16*, 195.

26. *Phil. Mag.*, 1819, *53*, 408–409; see p. 44 above.

27. *Die Entwickelung der Chemie in der neueren Zeit*, Munich, 1873, 282–285. Roscoe and Schorlemmer, *A Treatise on Chemistry*, 5th (last) ed., 1920, *1*, 35, say: 'For whilst all previous upholders of an atomic theory, including even Higgins, had supposed that the relative weights of the atoms of the different elements are the same, Dalton at once declared that the atoms of the different elements are not of the same weight.' In his earlier *Geschichte der Chemie*, 1844, *2*, 388, 390, Kopp gave a concise but good summary of Higgins's views and those of Dalton, but did not say that Higgins thought the atoms all equal in weight. Kopp refers to the *Comparative View* itself, as well as to the summaries of Henry and R. Angus Smith.

28. Meldrum, *Mem. Manchester Lit. and Phil. Soc.*, 1910, *55*, no. 4, referred to Higgins's statement, *Comparative View*, 275, that 100 grains of tin can combine with 7½ or 15 grains of oxygen (the correct figures are 13·4 and 26·8), hence (says Meldrum) the atom of the metal was supposed to be much heavier than one atom or even two of oxygen. This is the only statement in the whole book which suggests that the atoms of some *metals* may be heavier than the atoms of non-metals.

29. *De Fato*, § 11; ed. Müller, Leipzig, 1890, 261.

30. *System of Chemistry*, 1807, *3*, 425.

31. *Annals of Philosophy*, 1814, *3*, 175. (See p. 44 above.)

32. Roscoe and Harden, *A New View of the Origin of Dalton's Atomic Theory*, 1896, 27.

33. See note 1 above.

34. *Opticks*, 1717, Query 31, pp. 375–379. That the atoms of different bodies differ in *weight* is quite clearly stated by Gassendi. Dalton's significant contribution was a method of finding the relative weights from the gravimetric compositions of chemical compounds.

William Higgins Index

L

to his 'Society for Philosophical
Experiments and Conversations
(*q.v.*), 33; not William's father,
33; adopts Lavoisier's views,
36; subscribers to his 'Society',
37; his example to William, 39;
account of his family, 49;
reference to account of his
life, 51, 52, 141; may have
studied under Cullen at Edinburgh, 51, probably not in
Russia, 52; a friend of Boswell
and Johnson, 52; attacked by
Priestley, 51, 52, 124; his
writings, 52, 53; other chemical
work, 53; his will, 54; his
granddaughter, Eleanor Stephens, 55; near relatives, 58;
references to his atomic theory,
62; not influenced by William,
63; reference by William to his
ideas, 64; his views on molecules, 77; not impressed by
William's experiments, 105;
his views on caloric, 115, 116,
126; account of his atomic
theory, 124, 125; his school of
chemistry, 124; use of the term
'molecule', 130; referred to by
Davy, 133; gave William ideas
on atomic theory, 139. *see*
Beddoes, Berkenhout; Conway;
Cooke; Cullen; Davy; Priestley;
see Greek St., Soho, Lincoln's
Inn

Higgins, Captain Charles, 22, 49,
53, 54, 58, 59

Higgins, Charlotte, *see* Golding

Higgins, Dr John, 29

Higgins, Dr Patrick, 29

Higgins, Dr Thomas, 2, 29, 34,
49-51, 54, 57, 58

Higgins, elder brother of William,
49, 53, 58

Higgins, Eleanor, *née* Dillon, 49

Higgins, Emma Julia,

see Peel

Higgins family, 1, 2, 28, 29
see Appendix to Part I

Higgins, James, 50

Higgins, Jane, *née* Welland, 49

Higgins, Mary, *see* Harmon

Higgins, Mary Jane Josephine
O'Connor,
see von Haeseler

Higgins, William, birth and transfer to London, 2; lecture
assistant to Professor at Oxford,
2; work for Bryan Higgins, 2,
3; exhibits experiment on reduction of nitric acid, 3; knew
Dr Brocklesby, 3; mineralogical
excursion through England, 3;
work with Dr Caulet, 3.

Goes to Oxford, 3; in contact
with Dr Austin, 3; matriculates
at Magdalen Hall, 3; migrates
to Pembroke College, 3; knew
Drs Wall and Haworth, 4;
'operates' at Oxford, 4; leaves
Oxford and returns to London,
4; association with Beddoes, 4;
reads paper at Royal Society, 5;
experimental work for 'Comparative View', 5; discards phlogiston theory, 5; analysis of
'nitre' for Wall, 5; quarrels
with Bryan Higgins, 5; publication and price of 'Comparative View', 5, 6; application to
committee of Privy Council, 6

Applies to Apothecaries' Hall,
7; appointed to Apothecaries'
Hall, 7; lodged in 'small back
room', 8; work for the Hall, 8;
examines sample of water, 8,
9; complains of interruption to
his work, 9; criticised by Directors, 9; his post retrenched, 10;
importunes for salary, 10; admitted Honorary Member of
Apothecaries' Hall, 11

M

Correlation between *William Higgins* and *Comparative View*

William Higgins	*Comparative View*
Page	Page
92	16, 17, 34, 48, 49, 61, 105, 120, 262, 263, 271
93	10
94	40, 44, 59, 61
95	44
96	189, 192
97	262
99	72
105	13, 49, 162, 212, 309
106	309
107	49, 50, 51
108	162
109	162, 163
110	13
111	212
115	xi, 16, 317 (Errata)
116	14, 36, 37, 84, 312
119	300, 309
120	4-6, 11, 19, 27, 30, 309
133	15, 37, 80-81, 268
134	36, 37, 81, 132
136	37
137	14, 15
138	36
142	275

Correlation between *Comparative View* and *William Higgins*

Comparative View	*William Higgins*
Title Page	Page
Preface	
Page	37
iv	65
v	65
xi	33, 61, 115
xii	29
xiii	36, 66
xiv	78, 87
Text	
Page	
2	67
4	120
5	120
6	68
7	68
8	70
10	93
11	120
13	71, 73, 105, 110
14	71, 76, 78, 116, 137
15	72, 133, 137
16	72, 91, 92, 115
17	91, 92
18	68
19	120
27	120
30	120
32	69
33	69
34	91, 92
35	69
36	72, 73, 76, 116, 134, 138
37	73, 76, 116, 133, 134, 136
38	91

Comparative View Text Page	William Higgins Page
39	89-91
40	89, 90, 91, 94
42	89, 91
43	89-91
44	89-91, 94, 95
45	89-91
46	89, 90
47	89-91
48	89-92
49	89, 90, 92, 105, 107
50	107
51	107
59	89-91, 94
60	89-91
61	89-92, 94
62	33
66	89, 90
67	89, 90
68	89
69	89
70	89, 90
71	33
72	33, 73, 99
73	33, 73
74-76	33
77	33, 73
78	33, 74, 77
79	33
80	33, 74, 76, 133
81	73, 74, 77, 133, 134
82	79
83	80
84	78, 116
91	33, 66
92 ff	68
104	91
105	80, 91, 92
106	80
107	80
120	65, 69, 91, 92
131	65
132	71, 76-78, 81, 134
133	77, 89-91

Comparative View Text Page	William Higgins Page
134	89, 90
135	89, 90
138	91
143	81
155	81
162	105, 108, 109
163	109
164	30, 35, 65, 77, 78
165	78
166	78
171	77, 89-91
172	89-91
173	65
176	5, 35, 66
177	35, 36
178	66
179	77
189	96
190	89-91
191	81, 89, 91
192	89-91, 96
193	89-91
197	77
209	91
212	105, 111
219	69
225	69
227	70
228	70
231	70
237	70
248	91
249	33
262	89-92, 97
263	89, 92
264	89
268	133
271	89, 90, 92
272	89, 91
273	89-92
275	142
281	64
283	5, 36

Comparative View Text Page	*William Higgins* Page
284-316	63
300	35, 119
304	36
309	30, 33, 105, 106, 119, 120
310	30, 33
311	33
312	3, 4, 33, 35, 116
313	4, 33, 35
317 (Errata)	115

Comparative View Index*

* Not in the original; compiled by the authors.

A

COMPARATIVE VIEW

OF THE

PHLOGISTIC AND ANTIPHLOGISTIC

THEORIES.

WITH INDUCTIONS.

TO WHICH IS ANNEXED,

AN

ANALYSIS OF THE HUMAN CALCULUS,

WITH OBSERVATIONS ON ITS ORIGIN, &c.

BY WILLIAM HIGGINS,

OF PEMBROKE COLLEGE, OXFORD.

THE SECOND EDITION.

EST QUODAM PRODIRE TENUS, SI NON DATUR ULTRA.
HOR

LONDON:

PRINTED FOR J. MURRAY, NO. 32, FLEET-STREET.

MDCCXCI.

ERRATA.

Page | Line
2, | 12 from top, after lastly, *insert* a full point
3, | 17, *dele* mixture of
11, | 25, *read* molecules, and so elsewhere
15, | 16, *dele* full point, and *insert* a semicolon
15, | three last lines, *read* Or do a dense and a rare atmosphere promote their chemical union by easily blending and suffering them to approach nearer?
16, | 7, *for* these *read* them
16, | 8, *for* with *read* from
20, | 16, *for* may *read* might
44, | 13, *for* indecomposed *read* undecomposed
46, | 20, *dele* that is
59, | 24, *for* dilute *read* diluted
83, | 7, *dele* only
114, | 16, *dele* 2-10ths, and *insert* $\frac{4}{10}$
129, | 14, *dele* comma
129, | 15, *for* to *read* with
144, | 10 from bottom, *for* loses *read* lost
154, | 11, *dele* full point, and *insert* a semicolon
169, | ult. *insert* $\frac{1}{3}$
188, | 5 from bottom, *insert* a comma after *it*
207, | 2 from bottom, *dele* comma, and *insert* a full point
226, | 3 from bottom, *for* barites *read* barytes.

CONTENTS.

INTRODUC-

INTRODUCTION.

O N comparing the prefent ftate of chemical knowledge with that which
prevailed twelve years fince, I truft that
every true friend of philofophy will
join me in contemplating with pleafure
the rapid improvements which, even
during that fhort period, have been
made in this noble fcience. And, provided the prefent ardent fpirit of inquiry continues to diffufe itfelf, it muft
fhortly ripen chemiftry into fuch perfection, as will contribute more to the

welfare

welfare and happinefs of mankind in general, than can at prefent be imagined.

He who firft made glafs, or extracted a metal from its ore, knew not the value of his difcovery ; nor did he forefee the benefits that would arife to mankind from it. So many chemical facts lately difcovered, though feemingly of fmall importance, may, hereafter, prove of the greateft utility. For inftance, the difcoveries of the phofphoric acid in bones, and of the conftituent principles of volatile alkali, feem as yet of no great confequence : but I venture to predict, that when phyfic is refcued from its prefent obfcurity, thefe will be equal to any that have hitherto been made. The utility of many facts may depend upon the difcovery of a fingle one, which may throw light upon, and connect the whole. Hence, we find the ne-

4

— ceffity

ceffity of well underftanding and ar-
ranging fuch facts as we have in our
poffeffion, and likewife of increafing
their number as much as poffible; but
in order to do this with facility and
pleafure, and alfo to profit by them, it
is neceffary that we become perfectly
acquainted with the true theory of chemiftry, for falfe hypothefes can only
tend to confufe and lead us further
aftray from the paths of truth, which
alone ought to be the object and pur-
fuit of true philofophy.

Nature has but one way of perform-
ing her different operations, therefore
we may juftly fuppofe that there is but
one true mode of accounting for them,
and confequently either the phlogiftic
or antiphlogiftic theory muft be falfe.

Des Cartes's vortical fluid appeared
very plaufible, and was generally received, until the immortal Newton, by
his profound reafoning, pointed out

its

its inconſiſtency. Des Cartes grounded his hypotheſis upon one phenomenon; the motion of the different planets from weſt to eaſt. In like manner, Becher and Stahl founded their doctrine upon the phenomenon of combuſtion only.

Conſidering the knowledge they had in their days of the conſtituent principles of bodies, their hypotheſis was very ingenious, although, in my opinion, as ill founded as that of Des Cartes. Speculative reaſoning muſt ever fall to the ground when put to the teſt of experiment; ſuch has been the fate of the Carteſian philoſophy.

Although Lavoiſier has not been as yet ſo ſucceſsful as the great opponent of Des Cartes, yet he and his cotemporaries ſeem to promiſe, by their exertions, as ſure and as laſting a theory as the Newtonian: even this has been oppoſed: why then ſhould we be ſurpriſed that the antiphlogiſtic doctrine
ſhould

fhould meet with its opponents alfo ?
Notions early imbibed will not be
readily exchanged for new ones; the
flow but fure hand of time alone can
difpel thofe clouds which never fail
to eclipfe truth at her early appearance.

The prefent controverfy amongft philofophers depends upon the following
queftions: 1ft, Whether water be or
be not compofed of dephlogifticated
and light inflammable air? 2dly, Whether or no the condenfation of dephlogifticated air, or its union to different
bodies, does not depend upon one
principle, common to all combuftible
bodies ? Or, in other words, whether
or no all bodies which burn or calcine, fuch as fulphur, phofphorus, charcoal, oils, metals, phlogifticated air, &c.
contain the matter of light inflammable air as one of their conftituent principles? One fhould fuppofe if thefe
fubftances were compofed of two prin-

a 4   ciples,

ciples, namely, a peculiar bafis, and the matter of light inflammable air or phlogifton, that it would be poffible to refolve them into thefe principles, more efpecially when we confider the great attraction of the matter of light inflammable air to fire; but the maintainers of phlogifton have not as yet been able to do this: therefore the only ground they have to build their hypothefis upon is, that thefe bodies unite to dephlogifticated air; then, according to their philofophy, dephlogifticated air has the property of uniting but to one fubftance in nature, except fire. If the above fubftances were fimples, or even compounds, but deftitute of the matter of light inflammable air, or phlogifton, the antiphlogiftians cannot do any more than they have done already; for if fulphur were refolved into its conftituent principles, and if thefe were

two

two airs, or more condenfed bodies, different from any other with which we are at prefent acquainted, the phlogiftians might ftill fay that they contained phlogifton (or the matter of light inflammable air), if they even were the moft fimple bodies in nature, provided they had the property of uniting to dephlogifticated air. Then the antiphlogiftians, in order to eftablifh their doctrine, it feems, muft prove the non-exiftence of that fubftance in bodies, whofe prefence as one of their conftituent principles has never yet been proved. On this difficulty the phlogiftic theory feems to reft.

Hence it appears that this doctrine, which has been generally received throughout Europe, almoft the laft half century, ftill ftands in need of being fubftantiated; and alfo that the joint efforts of the firft philofophers of the prefent age cannot fix their favourite doctrine upon a more

firm

firm bafis than the celebrated Stahl had done in his obfcure days.

Thus feeing upon what principles the phlogiftians and antiphlogiftians maintained their different doctrines, and the impoffibility of perfuading us by experiments alone, from what only exifts in our imagination, fo prone we are to reconcile every phenomenon we fee to our manner of thinking, I was obliged to have recourfe to a mode of reafoning rather novel in chemiftry. I have confidered phlogifton as a fubftance chemically united to bodies in a folid ftate, and then inquired into the nature of fuch compounds, and whether the different phenomena in chemiftry were confiftently explicable on fuch principles. Again, I have endeavoured to find whether the fame phenomena were as explicable by fuppofing the different bodies which unite to dephlogifticated air to attract it, independent of a common principle or phlogifton ; by

which

which means I have been enabled to make a fair comparifon, and to draw, according to my judgment, juft conclufions. If I have appeared more inclined one way than another, it is what the evidence of my fenfes and the love of truth compelled me to. I have not altogether depended upon the affertion of other philofophers, for I have frequently repeated almoft the whole of the different experiments quoted in the following fections; otherwife I fhould not prefume to offer my opinion to the public, knowing how differently we often judge of what is ever fo well defcribed to us, when we fee it. In treating of the acids, I was obliged to have frequent recourfe to the metals; for, in the prefent knowledge of chemiftry, it is impoffible to inquire into the nature and conftitution of the one, without the affiftance of the other. I have alfo been obliged to introduce feveral diagrams, in order to render what I meant to convey

the

the more intelligible; and indeed I thought it the fureſt mode of reaſoning, and the moſt effectual means to come at truth *.

I hope it will appear, that I have not taken pains to ſelect facts in order to caſt the ſcale in favour of the antiphlogiſtic doctrine; for, as truth was my object, I conſidered all facts equally efficacious in bringing her to light; therefore I made uſe of ſuch as firſt occurred to me, and I thought were conſiſtent with, and applicable to, the ſubject; in ſhort, I preferred thoſe that have been adduced in favour of the phlogiſtic theory; particularly ſuch as have been advanced by Mr. Kirwan, in his Eſſay on Phlogiſton, a work which I have frequently alluded to, as being intended to ſubvert the antiphlogiſtic doctrine.

* The diagrams, placed at the margin, are very frequently to be read at the end of the firſt ſhort line, as part of the ſentence, otherwiſe the ſenſe will appear very obſcure.

Although

Although I adopted the antiphlogiftic theory four years ago, and although every phenomenon which occurred to me fince, tended to confirm the truth of that doctrine; yet, when I confidered the number of able philofophers, namely, Cavendifh *, Prieftley, Kirwan, Black, Higgins, &c. who perfifted in the old doctrine, I began to waver in my principles, and my defire to minutely inquire into both doctrines daily increafed; but knowing how inadequate I was to fo arduous a tafk, and likewife how many there were who might have performed it fo much better than myfelf, it was fome time before I could fummon refolution enough to begin; but my attachment to the fcience at length overcame every other confideration.

If my efforts fhould, in this enlightened age, be too feeble to do much good, I

* I thought Mr. Cavendifh had lately adopted the antiphlogiftic theory, until a good part of this volume had been printed, as appears in the firft fection page the 4th.

hope

hope at leaſt that they will not be productive of evil. I have written with conviction and without prejudice (otherwiſe
it would be natural to ſuppoſe, that I
would join my countrymen in defence
of that doctrine in which I have had my
early inſtructions in chemiſtry *).

If I ſhould be ſo unfortunate as to reaſon upon wrong principles, the ſooner I
am contradicted the better pleaſed I ſhall
be; but if my arguments and inductions
be juſt, if I even ſhould meet with cen-
ſure, it cannot laſt long; time, the parent
of truth, will operate in my favour.

I fear I ſtand in need of much indulgence in both the ſtyle, and in the many
overſights reſpecting the correction of
the preſs, a taſk with which I have been
totally unacquainted until the printing of
theſe ſheets commenced; and indeed I
had an occaſion to abſent myſelf part of

* I am indebted to Dr. Higgins for my firſt inſtructions
in chemiſtry, who is a phlogiſtian.

the

the time, and the perſon who officiated for me was wholly ignorant of the ſubject, and equally as ignorant as myſelf with reſpect to the buſineſs of the preſs.

I have annexed an Analyſis of the Human Calculus, which I hope will be acceptable as well to my medical as chemical readers. I was the more induced to publiſh it, as being delivered in to the Royal Society in the year 1787, and read at one of their ſpring meetings in the year 1788.

I have given an exact and true detail of the manner in which I have treated it; in order to give thoſe who were better acquainted with chemiſtry than myſelf an opportunity of pointing out my errors, and to facilitate the labours of leſs experienced chemiſts, who may wiſh to proſecute the ſame ſubject; for, without mutual information, chemiſtry, as well as all other ſciences, could never make any great progreſs.

As

As I have made my calculations according to Mr. Kirwan's table, being, in my
opinion, the moſt accurate of any that has
as yet appeared, I thought proper to
inſert it here, knowing that ſome of my
readers will often have an occaſion to refer to it ; I have alſo added the heavy
inflammable air, as I conſider it a ſubſtance quite different from the light inflammable air.

*Mr. Kirwan's table of the abſolute weight of
100 cubic inches of different kinds of air,
and their proportions to common air.*

100 Cubic Inches.	gr.	Proportion to common Air.
Common air,	31	1000
Dephlogiſticated,	34	1103
Phlogiſticated,	30	985
Nitrous,	37	1194
Vitriolic,	70, 215	2265
Fixed,	46, 5	1500
Hepatic,	34, 286	1106
Alkaline,	18, 16	600
Light Inflammable,	2, 613	84, 3,
Heavy inflammable,	34	1103

A

COMPARATIVE VIEW, &c.

SECTION I.

Of the Compofition and Decompofition of Water.

ALTHOUGH Mr. Lavoifier had fhewn the Decompofition of Water, in the year 1781, by a variety of ingenious and accurate experiments, as will appear in the fequel of this work; yet, his hypothefis was not received by any other philofopher; nor was he convinced himfelf, until the year 1784, when Mr. Cavendifh removed all doubts, by uniting light inflammable air and dephlogifticated air, and fhewing that the refulting compound was water.

B

Thus

Thus having proved by fynthefis what the former philofopher fufpected from analyfis, the doctrine of Water was univerfally embraced by all the philofophers in Europe.

It undoubtedly is one of the moft interefting difcoveries that ever was made in Chemiftry. 1. It enables us to account for feveral very important phenomena, which appeared before very myfterious. 2. It throws light upon vegetation, and the means whereby nature fupplies the conftant wafte of our atmofphere. Laftly, It has thrown great light on the different ftages of fermentation, which was not in the leaft underftood before.

Some philofophers have lately fufpected that water has never been either compofed or decompofed in any of our proceffes. Mr. Kirwan fuppofes that water is formed by the union of inflammable air and dephlogifticated air only, when one or both are expofed to a red heat; but that in a lower heat they form fixable air *. Mr. Lavoifier is of opinion, that one hundred parts of water contain eighty-feven of dephlogifticated air, and thirteen of light inflammable air, which is nearly feven to one.

According to Dr. Prieftley's eftimation of the weight of both airs, it is but five to one.

* Effay on Phlogifton, p. 26.

I

However,

However, from the variety of circumſtances that may change the real ſpecific gravity of theſe airs, I think we ſhall be nearer to truth if we ſay ſix to one, provided the airs be very pure. Two to one by meaſure appear to be the exact proportion.

Dr. Prieſtley ſuppoſes that the water produced by the condenſation of inflammable air and dephlogiſticated air, is only what was ſuſpended and attached to them in their elaſtic ſtate, and that their reſpective gravitating particles form a different compound, namely, Nitrous Acid. To aſcertain this, he confined his mixture of airs with dry fixed alkali over mercury, in order to abſtract from it as much water as poſſible.

Having thus prepared his ~~mixture of~~ airs, he found, after exploding them, that the product of water fell far ſhort of the weight of both airs; and he obſerved a denſe vapour after every exploſion, which ſoon condenſed, and adhered in a ſolid ſtate to the ſides of the veſſel, which he afterwards found to be the Nitrous Acid*. Though I do not doubt this indefatigable philoſopher's facts, yet, I beg leave to differ from him in his concluſions. I think the facts he adduces are not

* Phil. Tranſ. 1788.

only

only infufficient to ground his hypothefis upon, but do not in the leaft tend to contradict Mr. Cavendifh's doctrine of Water and Nitrous Acid. Let us fuppofe four ounce meafures of the mixed airs to produce, by inflammation, in their ordinary ftate one grain of water, and the fame bulk of air, by expofure to lime or alkali, to be deprived of half a grain, and that, after condenfation, the quantity of water produced not to exceed half a grain ; are we to conclude from thence that water had not been formed ? Befides, we are to confider that the fpecific gravity of air is altered in proportion to the quantity of water abftracted from it. Therefore, an accurate weight of both airs fhould be afcertained after they are deprived of their water, before we conclude that the weight of the water produced falls fo much fhort of the weight of the airs employed.

That nitrous acid is often formed I have frequently experienced ; but that it feparates from the moifture produced, and, in a folid ftate, is what I could never obferve nor fufpect, confidering the attraction of nitrous acid for water. I frequently inflamed feveral cubic inches of light inflammable and dephlogifticated air, and never obferved, by the niceft teft, the prefence of an acid, when the airs worked

worked upon were pure, and when the inflammable air prevailed. But when I reverfed the proportion, I always obtained nitrous acid in a fingle charge. When the
dephlogifticated contained one-eighth phlogifticated air, I obtained nitrous acid in great
abundance. Hence I infer, if we could procure dephlogifticated air entirely free from
phlogifticated, that not a particle of any fort
of acid would be produced. If nitrous acid
fhould refult from an union of light inflammable and dephlogifticated air, why is not
this formed during the flow combuftion of a
ftream of inflammable air in dephlogifticated
air ? I condenfed, as fhall be hereafter defcribed, half a gallon of dephlogifticated air
by the continual flame of light inflammable
air, and I could not detect the fmalleft veftige
of any fort of acid. Then, I afk, what becomes of the airs ? they muft form fome compound ; for, from the quantity of fire difengaged, it is evident that a chemical union
takes place. The difference in refult between this procefs and that in which we ufe
the electric fpark may be eafily accounted
for. The intenfe heat produced in the latter
procefs by the general and inftantaneous inflammation of both airs, together with that
of the electric fpark, promotes an union be-

B 3   tween

tween a portion of the dephlogisticated air and the phlogistic, which is always present in the purest respirable air. Whereas the languid combustion in the former experiment is insufficient to cause such an union. Why is not nitrous acid formed during the combustion of ether or strong spirit of wine, when the quantity of fixable air formed could never employ the whole of the dephlogisticated air expended, as evidently appears by the formation of fixable air by the electric spark? These circumstances, in addition to the many instances we have of the decomposition of water by calcination, fermentation, and vegetation, are sufficient to remove all my doubts respecting its constituent principles. That all elastic fluids hold a considerable quantity of water in solution, is well known to every body; but we are not to infer from thence, that water is a necessary ingredient in them, and that it is chemically united to the real gravitating matter of the different airs, particularly when we can extract the most part of it from them. Therefore, I do not see why we should say with Dr. Priestley, that inflammable air consists of inflammable air and water. We may as well say, that silicious earth (as water is separable from it) is silicious earth and water, or that sulphur is sul-

phur

phur and water, and fo with all other known fubftances.

If the greater part of dephlogifticated air be water, and if iron be calcined in confequence of its union to water, as Dr. Prieftley fuppofes, I would afk, Why is not inflammable air produced during the calcination of iron in dephlogifticated air, as well as when calcined by the fteam of water? For the Doctor fays, " But from the preceding experiments it appears, that by far the greateft part of the weight of dephlogifticated air is water; and the fmall quantity of acid that is in it may well be fuppofed to be employed in forming the fixed air, which is always found in the procefs of calcination." By this it is evident, that the Doctor does not allow the entry of dephlogifticated air into the calces of iron; and, according to himfelf, there was only the thirteenth of an ounce meafure found in the refiduum of feven ounce meafures of dephlogifticated air abforbed by iron*. Now feven ounce meafures of dephlogifticated air are fufficient to form five, or at leaft four and a half ounce meafures of fixable air. Therefore, I would afk, what becomes of this dephlogifticated air, or why was not nitrous acid formed?

* Vol. vi. p. 120.

SECTION II.

Of the Composition of Acids.

IT is to Mr. Lavoisier that we are chiefly indebted for our present knowledge of the constituent principles of the different acids; though it is true Dr. Priestley made the first advances towards it. It was by means chiefly of these substances that theoretical chemistry has made so rapid a progress these last ten years : so that we may very well say they have been the keys of philosophical chemistry. Mr. Lavoisier has shewn that dephlogisticated air is one of the constituent principles of all acids, and therefore called it the oxygenous principle, or the principle of acidity.

But yet we find that it is capable of uniting to bodies without possessing this character. Hence it appears doubtful to which of the principles we are to attribute this singular property. The different acid bases are sulphur, phlogisticated air, phosphorus, the matter of charcoal, regulus of arsenic, and the unknown basis of marine acid. Various are the opinions of the phlogistians respecting the nature of the union of dephlogisticated

air

air to the above bafes, though they all agree
that they contain phlogifton. Some of thefe
gentlemen fuppofe that the different bafes are
faturated with phlogifton, which uniting to
dephlogifticated air, forms water, at the fame
time that another portion of dephlogifticated
air combines with the bafis, and conftitutes
the acid. Others fuppofe that thefe bafes
contain all the principles of their refpective
acids faturated, or as if it were enveloped by
phlogifton; and that the air only feparates
this phlogifton by its fuperior attraction,
whereby the occult acid is liberated.

Mr. Kirwan fuppofes that the dephlogifticated air unites to phlogifton, and forms
fixable air, which, by combining with the
bafis, conftitutes the acid. Thus he thinks
that fixable air is the principle of acidity, and
enters into the conftitution of all acids. I
fhall endeavour to point out, in the following
pages, the neceffity of this laft philofopher's
doctrine towards the fupport of the phlogiftic
theory, and likewife his grounds for adopting
fuch an hypothefis. Undoubtedly the doctrine of fixable air will enable phlogifton to
ftand its ground much longer than it otherwife would; for, it may be adopted where
the other phlogiftic doctrines are found infufficient; and again, in their turn, thefe
may

may be introduced to explain such phenomena as are inexplicable in the former doctrine. Thus, by the mutual affiftance of thefe different hypothefes, the phlogiftians, by fhifting their ground, may remain for fome time in the field.

The antiphlogiftians are of opinion, that fulphur, phofphorus, &c. are, according to our prefent knowledge of chemiftry, fimple bodies, which, when united to dephlogifticated air, conftitute their refpective acids. Thus the antiphlogiftians confider all acids to confift of two principles only; one peculiar to each.

Mr. Lavoifier's Table of the affinities of the Oxygenous Principle. Mem. Par. 1782, p. 535.

Bafes.	Refulting Compounds.
Bafis of marine acid.	Dephlogifticated marine acid.
Reg. of man.	
Charcoal.	Fixed air.
Zinc.	Calx of zinc.
Iron.	Calx of iron.
Sulphur.	
Inflammable principle.	Water.
Nickle.	Calx of nickle.
Lead.	Calx of lead.
Tin.	Calx of tin.

Phof-

Phofphorus.	Fhofphorous acid.
Copper.	Calx of copper.
Bifmuth.	Calx of bifmuth.
Regulus of antimony.	Calx of antimony.
Mercury.	Calx of mercury.
Silver.	Calx of filver.
Regulus of arfenic.	Calx of arfenic.
Sugar.	Acid of fugar.
Sulphur.	Acid of vitriol.
Nitrous air.	Acid of nitre.
Principle of heat.	Dephlogifticated air.
Gold.	Calx of gold.

Smoaking marine acid.

Nitrous acid.

Black calx of manganefe.

Mr. Kirwan objects to the foregoing table.
1. Becaufe he fuppofes charcoal, according
to its precedency, fhould decompofe water, in
a boiling heat at leaft, confidering that iron,
which is placed lower, will produce inflammable air under the fame circumftances. But
the nature of charcoal fhould be firft confidered. Though its aggregate attraction appears weaker than that of iron, from its facility
of pulverization ; yet when reduced into powder, or fmall molicules, its ultimate particles
may cohere with greater force. The frangibility of charcoal is in a great meafure owing
to the number of minute cavities which inter-
fect

fect its texture, from the expulsion of the succulent part of the wood. Independent of the aggregate attraction, which certainly counteracts
chemical union more than we are aware of,
I think the ultimate particles of charcoal are
surrounded with some repelling fluid, which
defends them from the action of air and water; and the same may be said with respect
to spirit of wine, ether, and oil: for they all
have greater affinity to dephlogisticated air
than phosphorus, which combines with it in
the common temperature of the atmosphere.
This, whether it be the electric fluid, common
fire, or some other fluid, with which we are
not acquainted, deserves attention. Nitrous
air will rush into union with dephlogisticated
air in any temperature, and yet sugar will
not, though it deprives it of its dephlogisticated air. Pure calcareous earth, perfectly
dried, will not attract marine acid air; and
yet water, to which it has less affinity, will
condense it, and enable it to unite to this.
Light inflammable air and dephlogisticated
air will not combine in their ordinary state
but by the help of fire, either the electric, or
a common spark; yet they will unite very
readily when one or both are partially condensed. Thus nitrous air, which, as shall
hereafter appear, is composed of dephlogisticated

cated air and phlogiftic only, will condenfe hepatic gas. Hepatic gas, as I fhall endeavour to fhew in the fequel, is light inflammable air in its full extent, holding fulphur in folution. The fulphur is precipitated, and the refiduum is dephlogifticated nitrous air. Here a portion of the dephlogifticated air of the nitrous combines with the inflammable air of the hepatic gas, and forms water. It cannot be faid that this takes place in confequence of a double affinity. Phlogifticated air is with difficulty united to dephlogifticated air, though it attracts it with greater force than nitrous air. Iron moiftened with water, and confined by mercury, will yield inflammable air. Iron, treated in the fame manner, and confined with dephlogifticated air, will produce no inflammable air : but the air will be diminifhed. Iron will yield no inflammable air if it be confiued in very dry dephlogifticated air, neither will the air be diminifhed, nor will the iron tarnifh in any length of time. Hence it appears, that iron has no effect on air in a common temperature, but that it is the water which is decompofed, and that the dephlogifticated air and inflammable air unite at the very inftant of its liberation, and re-compofe water. Thefe are difficult to be accounted for. All that

that we can fay of them is, that a certain degree of condenfation facilitates their union ;
but this conveys no idea of the true caufe.
It may be faid, that water condenfes marine
air in confequence of its capacity for fire.
But why phofphorus, and not oils, or fugar ?
or, why nitrous air, and not phlogifticated,
unite to dephlogifticated, in a common temperature ? Or, again, why iron takes the oxygenous principle from water in preference to
that in its aërial ftate, when the light inflammable air difengaged condenfes it, is, in my
opinion, very little underftood.

It is true, all this may be juftly attributed
to fire, which, from its attraction to bodies,
counteracts their chemical union to one
another : but, from the following confiderations, I think fome other power muft interfere. It is generally allowed, and juftly, that
nitrous air confifts of dephlogifticated air and
phlogiftic in the proportion of two of the former to one of the latter. The fuppofition of its
containing phlogifton, I hope, will hereafter
appear to be erroneous ; therefore every ultimate particle of phlogifticated air muft be
united to two of dephlogifticated air ; and
thefe molicules combined with fire conftitute
nitrous air. Now if every of thefe molicules
were furrounded with an atmofphere of fire
equal

equal in fize only to thofe of dephlogifticated air, 100 cubic inches of nitrous air fhould weigh 98,535 grains ; whereas, according to Kirwan, they weigh but 37 grains. Hence, we may juftly conclude, that the gravitating particles of nitrous air are thrice the diftance from each other that the ultimate particles of dephlogifticated are in the fame temperature, and of courfe their atmofpheres of fire muft be in fize proportionable ; or elfe fome other repelling fluid muft interpofe. The fize of the repelling atmofpheres of nitrous air thus confidered, and likewife the weaker attraction of the molicules of this air to dephlogifticated air than that of the ultimate particles of phlogiftic in their fimple ftate. It is furprifing to me, with how much more facility the former unites to dephlogifticated air than the latter. The decompofition of nitrous air, by the light inflammable air of the hepatic gas, is equally extraordinary, confidering, as I faid before, that the inflammable air is not in a condenfed ftate; and, therefore, combined with its natural portion of fire. Do atmofpheres of equal denfity favour the union of their refpective gravitating particles ? Or, do a denfe and a rare atmofphere, by eafily blending, promote their chemical union by fuffering them to approach

proach nearer? Or does the electric fluid interfere?

From the foregoing confiderations, it feems to me that the attractive forces of bodies are not to be eftimated by the facility of compounding, but rather by the difficulty of decompounding thefe again. Therefore, I beg leave to differ with Mr. Kirwan in his objections (page 24) to Mr. Lavoifier's Table of Affinities, until he adduces more fubftantial reafoning.

I think fulphur fhould be placed before light inflammable air, and manganefe before charcoal, for reafons which will hereafter appear. Therefore, without making any alteration in Mr. Lavoifier's Table, I took the liberty of having thefe placed between both columns. In order to be the more explicit, I fhall ufe the term aggregate attraction alone, in explaining that power which folid or lefs condenfed bodies have of counteracting chemical union. Though, as I have obferved above, I fufpect fome other force to co-operate with this: but I fhall not prefume to defcribe to others what I do not well underftand myfelf. Thus, let us fuppofe charcoal to attract dephlogifticated air with the force of ten, and contrary powers, which I fhall call

the

the aggregate attraction, to refift this with the force of eleven. Let us likewife fuppofe iron to attract dephlogifticated air with the force of feven, and its aggregate attraction to counteract this with the force of fix and feven-eighths. It would require greater heat to unite the two former than the two latter, though they have by far the greater affinity to one another. But when once the fcale is caft in favour of the former, the rapidity of their union ought to be greater than that of the latter; which is really the cafe.

C   SECTION

SECTION III.

On the Vitriolic Acid.

MR. Kirwan is of opinion, that fulphur confifts of a bafis, or a radical principle, which, when faturated with phlogifton, conftitutes fulphur, but with fixed air vitriolic acid; and when combined partly with the one and partly with the other, volatile fulphureous acid *.

Let us for a moment allow fulphur to be what Mr. Kirwan fuppofes, that is, a certain bafis faturated with phlogifton, and which, when expofed to dephlogifticated air, with due application of heat will unite to it, exhibit the phenomenon of combuftion, and produce vitriolic acid. I afk Mr. Kirwan, What takes place in this procefs? He of courfe will fay, that the dephlogifticated air unites to the phlogifton of the fulphur, and forms fixable air, which re-unites to the radical bafis, and conftitutes the acid.

According to Mr. Kirwan himfelf, water ought to refult from an union of dephlogifticated air and phlogifton during the combuf-

* Effay on Phlogifton, p. 28.

tion

tion of fulphur, confidering that this cannot take place but in a red heat; therefore it appears to me, that his doctrine is a little contradicted in this procefs.

Other phlogiftians, on the contrary, will fay, that a portion of the dephlogifticated air unites to the phlogifton of the fulphur, and forms water, while another part unites to the bafis of fulphur, and conftitutes the vitriolic acid. I muft confefs, in this one circumftance, this laft hypothefis appears to me to be the moft rational and moft flattering mode of fupporting this imaginary theory.

Mr. Kirwan muft acknowledge, that light inflammable air and dephlogifticated air conftitute water; and, in his opinion, light inflammable air is pure phlogifton combined with fire, but when united to metals, the bafis of fulphur, &c. that it is in a concrete ftate. Fixed air has never been known to refult from an union of dephlogifticated air and light inflammable air in its pure ftate. I condenfed upwards of one hundred cubic inches of dephlogifticated air by the combuftion of light inflammable air in a jar inverted over lime water. The inflammable air was produced from iron entirely free from ruft, and the vitriolic acid ufed was highly concentrated, and afterwards diluted with three times its bulk

C 2   of

of water. The inflammation of both airs took place during the extrication of the inflammable air, which paffed through a copper tube feven inches long, with a bulb in the middle, which contained a fmall quantity of foap lees, both to retain any fixable air that may be feparated from the iron, and likewife any vitriolic acid that may be mechanically forced up. The combuftion was carried on at the extremity of this tube in a continual flame, and water trickled down the fides of the jar during the whole procefs; but not a particle of fixable air could I deteſt. I repeated the fame experiment over diftilled water, which I carefully boiled in order to expel any fixable air it ~~may~~ contain, and could not deteſt the fmalleft veftige of any acid. When thefe airs are combined by the electric fpark, no fixable air is produced. During the deflagration of zinc in dephlogifticated air, no fixable air is produced, provided they be both pure. All philofophers agree that fixable air is an acid; then I afk, What are its conftituent principles? Mr. Kirwan will no doubt fay, Dephlogifticated air and phlogifton. Again, I afk, what the conftituent parts of water are? He will fay, as above, Dephlogifticated air and phlogifton. That is to fay, they are the fame things, but differently modified.
Let

Let us confider how widely different thefe two fubftances are in their properties, and we fhall find that no modification could make this vaft difference.

Fixed air will unite to different bodies, and change their phyfical and chemical qualities; even it will unite to water, according to Mr. Kirwan, its fecond felf, and make a vaft alteration in its properties. Allowing then, as I faid before (and which is but a temporary indulgence), fulphur to be what the phlogiftians fuppofe, a certain bafis and phlogifton, where are the materials for fixed air? for, from what has been obferved, it cannot be fuppofed that phlogifton, either in its aerial or denfe ftate, will form fixable air. What anfwer can Mr. Kirwan make to this, though I allow him phlogifton? In my opinion, he muft give up his fixed air, and fay, with other phlogiftians, that vitriolic acid is formed by an union of dephlogifticated air to the bafis of fulphur, and that the phlogifton flies off; or adopt a more modern, and indeed the ftrongeft argument in favour of phlogifton, the formation of water. I expofed near fixty grains or more of highly concentrated vitriolic acid and light inflammable air to heat fufficient to convert the whole into volatile fulphureous acid: the

C 3

procefs

procefs was carried on with a gradual heat,
to prevent the diftillation of the acid until decompofed. The refiduum contained volatile
vitriolic acid and light inflammable air, but
not a particle of fixable air. If fixable air
were one of the conftituent principles of vitriolic acid, and if this again were compofed
of light inflammable air, or phlogifton, and
dephlogifticated air ; whether the inflammable air united to the bafis of the fulphur, or
whether it deprived the original phlogifton
of the fulphur of its dephlogifticated air, fixable air ought to be produced : for the above
procefs has been, according to Mr. Kirwan,
very favourable to the formation of fixable
air*. When ftrong vitriolic acid was reduced to the fame ftate by iron filings, fixable air was produced in very fmall proportion;
which fhews, that the fixable air did not refult from an union of dephlogifticated air and
light inflammable air, but muft come from
plumbago, or from fome other impurity in
the iron. If very pure alum be heated to
ignition, it will yield dephlogifticated air
and volatile fulphureous acid, but no fixable
air. Mr. Kirwan will undoubtedly explain
it thus, *viz.* That the bafis of the fulphur de-

* Effay on Phlogifton, p. 26.

prives

prives the fixed air of its phlogifton, and that its dephlogifticated air is difengaged, at the fame time that the volatile fulphureous acid retains a fufficient quantity of fixable air and phlogifton to keep it in an intermediate ftate.

Here then the bafis of fulphur feems to have greater affinity to phlogifton, than de-phlogifticated air has, or than it has to both dephlogifticated air and phlogifton united; which even the phlogiftians themfelves will not allow. If it fhould be urged, that this decompofition is in confequence of the at-traction of the different fluids for fire, light inflammable air fhould be produced; or, ac-cording to Mr. Kirwan, the fixable air fhould be converted into water, confidering the de-gree of heat neceffary for the procefs, and the bafis of fulphur difengaged in its fimple ftate.

Water could not be decompofed in this procefs. For, admitting the moft plaufible phlogiftic hypothefis, that of the union of dephlogifticated air to the bafis of fulphur, while another part forms water, by combin-ing with its phlogifton, a double decompofition muft take place, viz. the bafis of the fulphur muft give up its dephlogifticated air in confe-quence only of the mediation of fire; the wa-

ter

ter then muſt be decompoſed in conſequence of
the attraction of the baſis of ſulphur for phlogiſton being ſuperior to that of dephlogiſticated
air. Is it likely that the baſis of ſulphur ſhould
give up its dephlogiſticated air ſo readily, at
the ſame time that it unites to a ſubſtance of
equal volatility, and to which it has leſs attraction ? The dephlogiſticated air of the water alone muſt be ſufficient to prevent ſuch an
union. Sulphur gives up its phlogiſton (if
uniting to dephlogiſticated air be ſuch) in any
degree of heat above ignition. Its phlogiſton will even take a portion of their dephlogiſticated air from metallic calces, notwith-
ſtanding two contrary powers, according to
the phlogiſtic doctrine, oppoſe the union :
for, if ſulphur were a compound of phlogiſton
and a certain baſis, how could its phlogiſton
take dephlogiſticated air from the phlogiſton
of the metal ? Is not here phlogiſton to oppoſe phlogiſton ?

The phlogiſtians conſider metallic ſubſtances to be compoſed of certain baſes and
phlogiſton ; allowing this, and likewiſe vitriolic acid, to be compoſed of three principles,
phlogiſton, the baſis of ſulphur, and dephlogiſticated air ; and the phlogiſton and dephlogiſticated air to be in the form of fixable
air intimately united to the baſis of ſulphur ;
and

and likewife the metallic bafis to attract its
phlogifton with great force, as indeed it muft,
when the ftrongeft heat cannot part them,
notwithftanding the volatility of phlogifton.
In this cafe, how can metals decompofe vitriolic acid? for it cannot be fuppofed that the
dephlogifticated air already united to phlogifton will quit it, to unite to the phlogifton
of the metal: even the attraction of the
bafis of fulphur for both tends to render this
improbable, as does likewife the attraction
that muft fubfift on the other fide between
phlogifton and its metallic bafis. It may be
faid, that the fixable air of the vitriolic acid
unites to the metallic bafis, at the fame time
that its phlogifton either paffes off in an aerial
ftate, or unites to the bafis of the fulphur.
If fo, the metallic bafis muft have greater attraction to phlogifton and dephlogifticated
air jointly, than to phlogifton alone; therefore, it muft part with its phlogifton to unite
to fixable air. If this fhould be the cafe, phlogifton in an aeriform ftate, or light inflammable air, could not deprive the metallic bafis of
its fixable air, even in the ftrongeft heat; nor
could it take dephlogifticated air from the metallic bafis and its phlogifton; though it is true
fire may weaken their union, and thereby enable
the dephlogifticated air to quit the phlogifton

of

of the metal, to unite to the difengaged phlogifton.   Is it likely that this fhould take place,
efpecially when it appears that phlogifton and
dephlogifticated air united will expel phlogifton from metals ? Is it reafonable to fuppofe, that phlogifton will take dephlogifticated air from phlogifton, when the advantage and difadvantage of heat muft be the
fame to both ?

Let us now confider the other phlogiftic
hypothefis, that of the formation of water by
the union of phlogifton and dephlogifticated
air, while another portion of dephlogifticate
air unites to the bafis of fulphur, and forms
vitriolic acid.   Diluted vitriolic acid will calcine iron in any temperature, and light inflammable air is produced, which, in the opinion of the phlogiftians, is the phlogifton of
the metal combined with fire.   What does
the metallic bafis unite with in preference to
its phlogifton ? If it only unites to that portion of dephlogifticated air attached to the
bafis of fulphur, then this bafis might be obtained in its purity. Befides, if only dephlogifticated air united to the metals during folution, inflammable air would not be produced;
for this is never obtained during calcination
in dephlogifticated air.   The bafis of fulphur and its dephlogifticated air very likely

2   unite

unite to the metallic bafis, and expel its phlogifton. But then, if this were the cafe, pure alkali, or calcareous earth, would precipitate the bafis of iron in its pure ftate ; a circumftance which has never yet taken place ; for the precipitate is heavier than the iron, and it contains dephlogifticated air enough to faturate or condenfe the inflammable air extricated during the folution. Whence comes this dephlogifticated air ? Not from the vitriolic acid ; for it is not decompofed, as evidently appears from Mr. Lavoifier's experiment, who found that a folution of vitriol of iron required as much alkali to faturate it, as the fame quantity of acid in its fimple ftate. I have repeated this experiment, and found it to be fo. Hence, I think the phlogiftians muft have recourfe to water to enable them to attempt an explanation of the folution and calcination of metals in the vitriolic acid ; and, in my opinion, they will then approach nearer to truth than before. Does the water itfelf unite to the metallic bafis, and expel its phlogifton ? The phlogiftians muft fay it does, or allow the decompofition of water, which they are unwilling to do. . If water alone were the chief agent in the calcination, as Mr. Kirwan himfelf

obferves,

obferves*, it would calcine iron with as much facility in its purity, as when mixed with vitriolic acid. Here, then, the metal is deprived of its phlogifton, and its bafis united to dephlogifticated air: the acid is not decompofed, and the phlogiftians will not allow the decompofition of water; and from what has been faid above, the union of water itfelf is inadmiffible; therefore, they muft allow water to be decompofed. Does the dephlogifticated air of the water unite to the phlogifton of the metal, and let go its own phlogifton? Dephlogifticated air, as already obferved, can hardly be fuppofed to quit one principle to unite to another of the fame fort, which muft be already intimately united to the metallic bafis. Let us add to this, the attraction that muft fubfift between the principles of water.

The phlogiftians, if they even muft allow the decompofition of water, may ftill have recourfe to one more mode of argument in fupport of their almoft wrecked hypothefis; which appears to be but a plaufible evafion of truth, and which is, that the metallic bafis and its phlogifton attract dephlogifticated air jointly, with greater force than either feparately; and in confequence thereof, that the phlogifton of the water muft yield its dephlogifticated

* Effay on Phlogifton, p. 99.

air

air to a fuperior force. Indeed, if this were the truth, we could not well account for the reduction of metallic calces by inflammable air in the ftrongeft heat, when we fuppofe phlogifton to oppofe phlogifton, and likewife when we confider the attraction of the metallic bafis for both; which muft be very confiderable, when almoft all the metallic calces will not yield either in the ftrongeft heat, notwithftanding their volatility and attraction for fire. It is true, fire may weaken the union of phlogifton and dephlogifticated air to the metallic bafis, but not fo materially as to enable phlogifton to expel them both. In fhort, the phlogiftic theory, taken in the moft partial point of view, prefents to me fuch numberlefs inconfiftencies, that I fhould imagine its obfcurity alone has prevented its fall long before this time.

Water will not apparently act upon iron in the common temperature of the atmofphere; but, diluted vitriolic acid will rapidly diffolve it, and inflammable air will be produced. This evidently fhews, that the acid takes an active part in the calcination; and, from what has been already faid, it ftill is found to contain all its principles. Whence, then, does the iron receive its dephlogifticated air? or, let the phlogiftians explain, in their

their doctrine, how the acid acts in this procefs. If highly concentrated vitriolic acid be ufed, very little inflammable air is obtained, but chiefly volatile fulphureous acid; and if heat be ufed for a confiderable time, fulphur will be formed.

Let the phlogiftians account, in their doctrine, for fo material a difference in thefe two proceffes from the mere prefence of water. I think they have remaining but one method of accounting for the latter; which is, that the bafis of fulphur gives up its dephlogifticated air to the iron, at the fame time that the iron yields its phlogifton to the bafis of fulphur.

If this were the cafe, the fame circumftance fhould take place in diluted vitriolic acid: befides, if the metal fhould exchange phlogifton for dephlogifticated air only, turbith mineral could not be reduced by the mere expulfion of it, provided phlogifton be a neceffary principle in the conftitution of metals. I think thefe facts tend ftrongly to prove the delufion of the phlogiftic theory; for let us trace it which way we will, though it may flatter us in a few circumftances, it will lead us into a wildernefs, where we lofe fight of that concatenation of nature which

the

the adverſe doctrine enables us to inveſtigate without interruption.

What is the ſtrongeſt proof of the exiſtence of phlogiſton in bodies? Inflammation when expoſed to heat in atmoſpheric air. Is not the fire given out by the condenſed air? Does dephlogiſticated air unite to any ſub-ſtance but to that which contains phlogiſton? According to the phlogiſtic theory, it does not. Is it inconſiſtent with the natural courſe of things, to ſuppoſe, that there are bodies which do not contain a particle of light inflammable air, and whoſe attraction for dephlogiſticated air may be ſuch as to combine with it (under favourable circum-ſtances) ſo as to diſengage its fire, denſe enough to exhibit the phenomenon of com-buſtion?

If the condenſation of dephlogiſticated air by the different bodies which yield flame and light were occaſioned by the ſame principle common to them all, too great inertneſs would prevail between thoſe bodies which contain dephlogiſticated air, and thoſe that are ſuppoſed to contain phlogiſton; for phlo-giſton muſt counteract phlogiſton, and there-by preſerve a neutrality ſufficient to reſiſt numberleſs operations, as well conducted on the

the large scale of nature as in our elaboratories.

Though we have not hitherto been able to decompose pure calcareous, argillaceous, siliceous, barytic and magnesian earths, or fixed vegetable and mineral alkalies, yet we suspect them to be compounds. Indeed, the very circumstance attending the increase of calcareous earth in the animal kingdom, is a strong instance of its being a compound, as likewise is that of fixed vegetable and mineral alkalies in the vegetable kingdom : but until we resolve these into their constituent principles, we must consider them as simple substances, and not attribute their different properties to one common principle. I think I may presume to say, that sulphur, phosphorus, phlogisticated air, and metals, are as simple bodies as the earths, and that we know as little of their origin or constituent principles.

The latter will unite to dephlogisticated air, but some with more facility than others, and present during the union nearly the same phenomena. But are we to infer from thence, that the same principle is common to them all, when the resulting compounds are quite different ? The former (two excepted) will unite to acids, and present like phenomena;

mena ; and may we not infer from this, with as great probability of truth, that the fame principle which promotes a chemical union between the acid and any of thefe, is common to all, and which we may call the alkalinate principle ? Is not this laft as rational an hypothefis as that of the principle of inflammability ? There are as ftrong grounds for the one as for the other.

If fteam be paffed over fufed fulphur, light inflammable air will be obtained, as Dr. Prieftley has obferved. From whence does this air come ? The phlogiftians will undoubtedly fay that it is difengaged from the fulphur. If fo, the bafis of fulphur attracts water with greater force than it does phlogifton ; but will water and the bafis of fulphur form vitriolic acid ? By no means ; though volatile fulphureous acid is formed in this procefs, which actually requires dephlogifticated air for its conftitution ; a clear proof that water muft be decompofed. I fhould like to know how the phlogiftians can account for this decompofition. Let us fuppofe fulphur to be a compound of a certain bafis and phlogifton, and water to be compofed of dephlogifticated air and phlogifton : would the dephlogifticated air of the water quit its own phlogifton, to unite to the

D   phlogifton

phlogifton of the fulphur? Unlefs fome other
power co-operated, and what can this be?
The bafis of fulphur unites to dephlogifticated air, and forms a compound in itfelf.
Therefore it cannot be fuppofed that it could
give any affiftance to its phlogifton, which
unites to the fame principle, and forms a
feparate compound : on the contrary, we
fhould expect that their mutual attraction to
one another fhould prevent the decompofition of water. Let us fuppofe dephlogifticated air to attract light inflammable air with
the force of 4, and the bafis of fulphur to
attract phlogifton or concrete inflammable
air with the force of 3, and its aggregate
attraction to be equal to one more, which
muft be nearly the proportion, confidering
that fulphur will not unite to dephlogifticated air in the common temperature of the
atmofphere, but requires fire to remove its
aggregate attraction. In this cafe water muft
be decompofed in confequence of the attraction of the bafis of fulphur alone for
dephlogifticated air, which muft be more
than equal to the contrary powers already
mentioned (making an allowance for the attraction of aggregation), that is, it muft exceed 7 to fubdue them. The fame ftate-
men may be obferved with refpect to the

7   calcination

calcination of metals by water, if we fuppofe thefe to contain phlogifton.

A good many more facts might be urged
on this fubject; but in my opinion enough
has been adduced to convince an impartial
reader, that all the phenomena above recited
are only explicable by entirely leaving out
phlogifton, and fuppofing fulphur to be a
fimple fubftance, whofe ultimate particles attract dephlogifticated air with forces inherent in themfelves, independent of phlogifton
or concrete inflammable air, as an alkali does
an acid, or gold and tin mercury; and likewife fuppofing the combuftion of fulphur to
be as fimple a procefs as that of light inflammable air; that is, that there is no de-
phlogiftication or formation of water during
the union of the oxygenous principle to fulphur, as containing not a particle of light
inflammable air in its conftitution. I have
often combined fulphur rendered perfectly
dry, and dephlogifticated air likewife, deprived
of its water by fufed marine felenite in large
proportion over mercury, and could never
obferve that water was produced. Indeed
it may be faid, that the volatile fulphurous
acid, which is always the refult of this procefs, may re-diffolve it; but this is not very

likely,

likely, when a fmall portion of water will deprive it of its elafticity.

According to Mr. Kirwan, 100 grains of fulphur require 143 grains of dephlogifticated air to convert them into volatile vitriolic acid; but they require much more in order to become perfect vitriolic acid. Highly concentrated vitriolic acid contains 2 parts of dephlogifticated air, and 1 of fulphur, exclufive of water.

One hundred and forty-three grains of dephlogifticated air contain 41 of water, for lime will abftract 26 grains from it, and the remainder cannot be feparated from it in its aerial ftate; therefore 100 grains of fulphur, making an allowance for water, require 100 or 102 of the real gravitating matter of dephlogifticated air to form volatile vitriolic acid; and as volatile vitriolic acid is very little fhort of double the fpecific gravity of dephlogifticated air, we may conclude, that the ultimate particles of fulphur and dephlogifticated air, contain equal quantities of folid matter; for dephlogifticated air fuffers no confiderable contraction by uniting to fulphur in the proportion merely neceffary for the formation of volatile vitriolic acid. Hence we may conclude, that, in volatile vitriolic acid, a fingle ultimate particle of ful

phur

phur is intimately united only to a fingle particle of dephlogifticated air; and that, in perfect vitriolic acid, every fingle particle of fulphur is united to 2 of dephlogifticated air, being the quantity neceffary to faturation.

As 2 cubic inches of light inflammable air require but 1 of dephlogifticated air to condenfe them, we muft fuppofe that they contain equal number of divifions, and that the difference of their fpecific gravity depends chiefly on the fize of their ultimate particles; or we muft fuppofe that the ultimate particles of light inflammable air require 2 or 3, or more, of dephlogifticated air to faturate them. If this latter were the cafe, we might produce water in an intermediate ftate, as well as the vitriolic or the nitrous acid, which appears to be impoffible; for in whatever proportion we mix our airs, or under whatfoever circumftance we combine them, the refult is invariably the fame. This likewife may be obferved with refpect to the decompofition of water. Hence we may juftly conclude, that water is compofed of molicules formed by the union of a fingle particle of dephlogifticated air to an ultimate particle of light inflammable air, and that they are incapable of

uniting

uniting to a third particle of either of their conftituent principles. The above notions of water and vitriolic acid being ftrictly kept in view, let us now proceed to enquire into the nature of fulphur and vitriolic acid, and their various effects on different bodies in the antiphlogiftic doctrine.

It has been already obferved, that metals attract dephlogifticated air with greater force than fulphur, and that fulphur attracts it with greater force than light inflammable air. It has likewife been obferved, that vitriolic acid and water, mixed in a certain proportion, will calcine metals with greater facility than concentrated vitriolic acid, and that water will have very little effect on metals in a common temperature. Thefe facts, though they may appear contradictory in themfelves when flightly confidered, may be accounted for on the following principles, and are, in my opinion, inexplicable by any other means whatever.

Let us fuppofe iron or zinc to attract dephlogifticated air with the force of 7, fulphur to attract it with the force of $6\frac{7}{8}$, and light inflammable air with the force of $6\frac{3}{4}$. Let us again fuppofe thefe to be the utmoft forces that can fubfift between particle and particle. That is to fay, in water dephlo-
giftigated

gifticated air is retained with the above force, and likewife in volatile vitriolic acid, with the force already mentioned. It is unne-ceffary to introduce here the aggregate at-traction which frequently preferves a neu-trality between bodies, as, for inftance, be-tween water and zinc, or water and iron. Stating the attractive forces in the above proportion, which I am led to believe is juft, from facts already obferved, we fhould ima-gine that iron or zinc would calcine in water with greater facility than in vitriolic acid ; and if fome other circumftance did not inter-fere, it muft be the cafe. This the follow-ing will in fome degree illuftrate.

Let S be a particle of fulphur, *d* a par-ticle of dephlogifticated air, which it attracts with the force of $6\frac{7}{8}$, and let the compound be volatile fulphureous acid; here the tie between S and *d* is greater by $\frac{2}{8}$, than that between the conftituent principles of water, which is but $6\frac{5}{8}$. As the attraction of bodies is mutual, let us fuppofe S to poffefs one-half of this force, which is $3\frac{7}{16}$, and

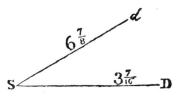

this to be its utmoft exertion, and likewife *d* to poffefs the other half, which is $3\frac{7}{16}$ more,

which

which will unite them with the above-mentioned force. Let us fuppofe another particle of dephlogifticated air D to have a tendency to unite to S, with the force of $3\frac{7}{16}$, in order to form perfect vitriolic acid: to receive D, S muft relax its attraction for *d* one-half. That is, the force of $3\frac{7}{16}$ will be divided and directed in two different points, which will reduce the attachment of dephlogifticated air and fulphur in perfect vitriolic acid to $5\frac{1}{18}$.

In order to more perfectly underftand this, let S be fulphur, *d* D two different particles of dephlogifticated air united to it, with the different forces annexed to them. If D were taken away, S and *d* would attract one another with the

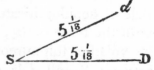

force of $6\frac{7}{5}$, and when again reftored would reduce this force to $5\frac{1}{18}$, and fo alternately. This feems to be a general law. Mild, fixed, vegetable alkali will part with a portion of its fixable air in a moderate degree of heat, but requires a very intenfe heat to expel the whole. In like manner vitriolated tartar will confolidate a portion of water during its cryftallization; in this ftate it will melt in a degree of heat below ignition, and

part

part with its water of fufion, and confolidate
in the fame degree of heat. If the mafs be
ignited, it will again fufe, and continue part-
ing with water for fome time ; and when
the whole is expelled, though the fire be on
the increafe, it will again confolidate, and
require a much ftronger heat to fufe it over
again. Here we fee that, in proportion as
the alkali is deprived of a part of its fixed
air, its power of retaining the remainder is
redoubled, and that of the vitriolated tartar
for water ; for in the firft fufion it parts
with a portion of its water very readily, but
during the fecond fufion it parts with the
remainder with difficulty. Here we find,
notwithftanding the volatility of water, the
force of attraction fubfifting between it and
the falt retains it until it is red hot ; and how
great thefe powers muft be, when we confider
the mechanical force neceffary to keep water
in a condenfed ftate, when fimply expofed
to the fame degree of heat ! I fhall forbear
mentioning feveral other circumftances of
the like nature : let it fuffice to fay, that this
explains the neceffity of raifing the fire
towards the end of all chemical proceffes.

The true ftate of water and vitriolic acid
being confidered, when thefe fluids are mixed
in different proportion, and then iron or
zinc

zinc introduced, what are we to expect will take place? Undoubtedly the following decompositions. The iron will attack the dephlogisticated air of the vitriolic acid with the force of 7, which resists but with the force of $5\frac{1}{3}$, in preference to the dephlogisticated air of the water, which resists with the force of $6\frac{1}{3}$. We are not to suppose that the metal will attract d, in preference to D, but that it will influence them both equally alike; more especially when it presents surfaces enough. The sulphur being thus despoiled of its dephlogisticated air, but still preserving its extreme division, exerts the force of $6\frac{1}{3}$ on the dephlogisticated air of the water, which it readily gains as meeting but with the resistance of $6\frac{1}{3}$, while the inflammable air is disengaged. The phlogistians may object to this by saying, that sulphur will not decompose water in the temperature of the above process. I will join them in this opinion; but be it recollected that fused sulphur, as already observed, will decompose water when brought in contact with it in the state of steam; and what promotes a decomposition here, but the interposition of fire between the ultimate particles of the sulphur, whereby its aggregate attraction is removed? But, if

this

this does not interfere in a low temperature, which is the cafe after the decompofition of vitriolic acid by metals, the decompofition of water will take place the eafier ; for, though fire removes the chief obftacle to the decompofition, it interferes a little itfelf. The ultimate particles of fulphur, when deprived of their dephlogifticated air, cannot recover more of this from the water, than is neceffary to the formation of volatile vitriolic acid, fee S___$6\frac{7}{4}$___d, which being re-attracted by the calcined metal, acts as a folvent.

If concentrated vitriolic acid be ufed, the application of heat is neceffary, and very little inflammable air is produced ; but chiefly volatile vitriolic acid. The ufe of fire here is to remove the aggregate influence of the vitriolic acid, as well as to weaken that of the iron ; both which circumftances favour the new union, or, as properly fpeaking, facilitate the decompofition. When water is mixed with the vitriolic acid, it interpofes itfelf between its fluggifh particles, which puts them beyond the fphere of their mutual influence ; and thereby, though it is attracted by the vitriolic acid, anfwers the fame purpofe that

fire

fire does; fo that the folution goes on rapidly without the application of heat.

The volatile vitriolic acid difengaged, and the fmall quantity of inflammable air produced, when concentrated vitriolic acid is ufed, may, I think, be very fatisfactorily accounted for in the following manner.

The firft effort of the metal wholly deprives the particles of vitriolic acid in contact with it of their dephlogifticated air, and they inftantly exert the force of $6\frac{7}{8}$ on the dephlogifticated air of the neighbouring *un*decompofed vitriolic acid, which can only refift with the force of $5\frac{1}{15}$: they will not take D and d from S, but D or d, whichever happens to be moft contiguous to them; therefore two portions of volatile vitriolic acid are formed. In order to render this the more intelligible, let S be an ultimate particle of fulphur, recently deprived of its dephlogifticated air, and ftill poffeffed of the power of $6\frac{7}{8}$ to recover this again; and let

$$S \underset{5\frac{1}{8}}{\overset{5\frac{1}{8}}{\diagup}} \overset{d}{\underset{D}{}}$$

be a particle of vitriolic acid in the vicinity of S: will not S take D or d from S? and will not the volatile compounds S___$6\frac{7}{8}$___d S___$6\frac{7}{8}$___D be formed? The latter will pafs off in an elaftic ftate, while the former, S___$6\frac{7}{8}$___d, being nigher the

metallic

metallic calx, is attracted by it. As the moft
concentrated vitriolic acid contains a portion of water, part of this likewife is decompofed; hence arifes the inflammable air.
Let A be a particle of water, I and D its
conftituent principles; I
inflammable air, and D
dephlogifticated air, com-
bined with the force of $6\frac{5}{8}$; if A fhould be in-
terpofed between S, and
would not S the rather
deprive I of D, than
wait the approach of
the vitriolic molicule which is beyond its
reach? particularly when the above-mentioned force of S is conftantly rivetted or
levelled, if I may ufe the expreffion, towards
dephlogifticated air, in whatever compound,
or in whatever ftate it meets with it, unlefs
fome other power counteracts it; and what
can this be, but the union of the ultimate
particles of fulphur to fome other fubftance
which attracts them more forcibly, or their
own attachment to one another fo as to form
an aggregate? neither of which circumftances
interferes here. In addition to the above
explanation of the interference of the fmall
quantity of aqueous particles in concentrated
vitriolic acid, I need only fay, that when
the

this acid is fo diluted as to afford only inflammable air, the particles of water, by fur-
rounding thefe of the acid, or by the intermixture of their more numerous furfaces,
are expofed to the influence of the fulphur,
the inftant it is deprived of its dephlogifticated air by the metal, and thereby prevent
the formation of the volatile fulphureous
acid, marked S———D, while S———d,
which is neceffary to folution, is conftantly
forming by the decompofition of water.
Thus the water, though it is decompofed
itfelf, defends the vitriolic acid, whereby we
obtain inflammable air in fuch abundance.

From what has been faid refpecting the
folution of metals in diluted vitriolic acid,
we find that ⅓ more dephlogifticated air
fhould be contained in the metallic folution,
than is neceffary to the formation of perfect
vitriolic acid. That is, it contains that portion which the fulphur takes from the water,
in addition to the quantity originally contained in the vitriolic acid; which the following circumftances tend to corroborate.

Fixed vegetable alkali will decompofe a
folution of vitriol of iron, and form vitriolated tartar, at the fame time that the
iron is difengaged of a dirty bluifh colour,
combined only with about ⅓ the portion of
dephlo-

dephlogifticated air neceffary for its thorough
calcination. It could not receive this dephlogifticated air from the vitriolic acid, for this
is united to the alkali in its perfect ftate. See

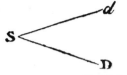 otherwife we fhould
have a compound re-
fulting from an union
of the alkali to S———d,
which is called the fulphurous falt of Stahl.

If a faturated folution of martial vitriol be
expofed to dephlogifticated air, a yellowifh
calx is depofited, and in time nearly the
entire of the iron is brought to this ftate.
I frequently examined different calces of
this fort well wafhed with hot water, and
found that fome contained vitriolic acid, and
that others did not. If the folution be expofed to the air for a confiderable time, it
acquires an acid tafte by the liberation of a
portion of the vitriolic acid. Fixable air will
likewife decompofe this martial folution, as
fhall hereafter appear. Perfect vitriolic acid
will have no effect on the perfect calx of
iron, but volatile fulphurous acid will partially diffolve it.

Thefe facts feem to correfpond, and I
think may be thus accounted for. Let I be
iron; D dephlogifticated air united with the
force of 7; let us fuppofe D to be the
quantity

quantity neceſſary to ſaturate I, ſo as to form a perfect calx; let S be ſulphur, *d* dephlogiſticated air attached with the force of 6⅞. Let us ſuppoſe S to have a tendency to unite to more dephlogiſticated air; and let us likewiſe ſuppoſe, which is

I————7————D

2

d————6⅞————S

well known to be the caſe, a ſmall attraction to exiſt between S and I. Let us ſtate the whole ſum of theſe forces between S, D, and I, to be 2; which power, though it will not ſeparate I from D, or *d* from *S*, yet is ſufficient to combine I————D to S————*d* when in contact, and when no other power is to counteract it.

If the vitriolic ſolution above conſidered be expoſed to dephlogiſticated air, the following decompoſition will take place, *viz.* another particle of dephlogiſticated air will unite to S, which will counteract the attraction of I————D for S————*d*; therefore the ſeparate compounds I————D and

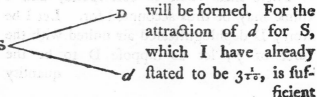

will be formed. For the attraction of *d* for S, which I have already ſtated to be $3\frac{1}{10}$, is ſufficient

ficient to fubdue the power of 2, which united
I——D and S——d. In order to prove
this more fully, let the calx of iron I——D
and perfect vitriolic acid
be mixed; they will not
unite; for I being fatu-
rated with D, can have no
effect on d D; and S in like manner being
faturated with d D, can have no effect on D.
We are to confider the particles of dephlogifticated air D D d to have no fenfible attraction for one another; and likewife the
attraction of d D to S to be fuch as to more
than counteract the attraction of S to I.
For though S may be deprived of d D by
a force not much fuperior to $5\frac{1}{18}$, yet it
would require more than the force of $10\frac{1}{36}$,
to feparate S from d D, provided the latter
were not influenced. Hence arife feveral
very important phenomena in chemiftry,
which arrangement forbids me to introduce
here; and which, from their being little
confidered, gave birth to the phlogiftic
theory.

I introduced fome iron nails, free from
ruft, into ftrong volatile vitriolic acid; when
it ftood for a few minutes, it acquired a
milky appearance, and the folution went on
without ebullition or extrication of air. On

E   ftanding

ſtanding for a few hours, the ſolution acquired a darkiſh colour, and a black powder
was precipitated. This powder, when collected and waſhed, put on red hot iron,
burned partly like ſulphur, and partly like
charcoal duſt, and the incombuſtible reſiduum was of a purpliſh colour. The filtered
ſolution was perfectly neutralized, and free
from the leaſt ſulphurous pungency. Its
taſte was ſtrongly chalybeat, but not ſo diſagreeable as that of the ſolution of iron in the
perfect vitriolic acid, or in any of the mineral acids.

Nitrous acid dropped into the ſolution
inſtantly produced a cloudineſs, which immediately diſappeared without ebullition,
though volatile ſulphureous acid was diſengaged in its utmoſt degree of pungency. The vitriolic, marine, and acetous acids decompoſed
this ſolution, but cauſed no turbidneſs, nor
was any inflammable air produced *.

In order to know whether the ſulphur

---

* I would beg leave to recommend a trial of this
preparation of iron in diſorders that require the uſe of
chalybeates ; but as this preſumption is rather founded
on theory, I ſhall not take the liberty of ſaying any thing
particular in its favour, until experience enables me to
urge it with confidence.

was

was difengaged from the volatile fulphureous acid or the iron, I poured marine acid on the fame nails, when light inflammable air and hepatic air were copioufly produced, and likewife fulphur was depofited in its crude ftate. When I ufed vitriolic or the nitrous acid, no fulphur was produced. I tried different nails, and likewife iron filings, with the fame refult. Thefe facts convinced me, that the fulphur was feparated from the iron ; but that all forts of iron contain fulphur is what I cannot pretend to know, as I have not tried fteel or varieties enough of malleable iron. However I have ftrong reafon to fufpect, that fulphur has more to do in the different properties of iron than we are aware of. That iron fhould contain fulphur, notwithstanding the different proceffes it muft neceffarily undergo before it acquires malleability, confidering the volatility of fulphur, points out the force of their attraction to one another ; and the feparation of this again by volatile fulphureous acid, fhews likewife the greater attraction of iron to fulphur and dephlogifticated air jointly. That volatile fulphureous acid fhould diffolve iron without the extrication of inflammable air or phlogifton, is a very ftrong inftance of the fallacy

of

of the phlogiftic doctrine *. If volatile vitriolic acid were a compound of phlogifton,
a certain bafis and dephlogifticated air, a
greater quantity of inflammable air fhould
have been difengaged during the folution
of iron in this acid than when the perfect
vitriolic acid is ufed. Let us even fuppofe
volatile fulphureous acid to be compofed of
the bafis of fulphur, phlogifton and dephlogifticated air, which is the opinion of all the
phlogiftians, though they differ with refpect to
the modification of thefe three principles; and,
likewife, iron to be compofed of a certain
bafis and phlogifton : I would afk the phlogiftians what becomes of the phlogifton of
the iron during its folution ? They cannot
fay it is difengaged in an aeri-form ftate, for
there is hardly any inflammable air produced.
Therefore, all they can fay is, that the phlogifton of the metal, and that of the volatile
vitriolic acid, are prefent in the folution ; but
this contradicts their own principle, viz. that
metals muft lofe their phlogifton, in order to

* A fmall quantity of inflammable air is produced,
but it is fo trifling, comparatively to what fhould be
produced from the quantity of iron diffolved, that it is
hardly worth noticing, and, in my opinion, proceeds
from a portion of perfect vitriolic acid, which is generally
infeparable from the volatile acid.

4   become

become foluble in acids. What principle is there in volatile fulphureous acid that can attract the phlogifton of the iron? The dephlogifticated air cannot unite to it, as being already united with phlogifton according to Mr. Kirwan. The bafis of fulphur can have no influence over it, being united to phlogifton and dephlogifticated air; or, if even the bafis of fulphur were to unite to the phlogifton of the metal, it muft have formed fulphur, which is in itfelf infoluble, and incapable of holding metals in folution. Befides, if the quantity of phlogifton they imagine be prefent in the folution, nitrous air ought to have been produced on the addition of nitrous acid, or inflammable air on the addition of the marine acid; neither of which had been procured, though they difplaced the volatile vitriolic acid, and united to the iron. A folution of nitrated iron thus prepared, and completely freed from volatile fulphureous acid, will yield a more perfect calx than vitriolated iron, when both are precipitated by pure fixed vegetable alkali. The nitre thus obtained will yield lefs dephlogifticated air, and more phlogifticated air, than the fame quantity of common nitre, but in what proportion I cannot fay. I am induced to fuppofe, that the difference of

E 3   purity

purity is in proportion to the quantity of dephlogifticated air united to the precipitate. I am forry I have not an opportunity at prefent to afcertain this, by a more accurate repetition of the experiment.

The folution of a metal in an acid without the production of inflammable air, and the decompofition of this again by nitrous acid without the production of nitrous air, is very well worthy of attention; more efpecially when we confider that nitrous acid is always partly decompofed during its union to metals in the common way. Surely thefe differences cannot arife from phlogifton; for if fuch a thing exifted in metals, it would be as prevalent in the folution, when we know it did not make its efcape, and likewife when it is evident that there can be nothing to envelope or protect it, as when the metal is introduced in its fimple ftate into diluted nitrous acid. When I treat of nitrous acid, I fhall have an opportunity of refuming the latter part of this fubject; and, as I have faid fufficient to anfwer my prefent purpofe, I will poftpone it until then.

The folution of iron in volatile vitriolic acid is quite clear, but when expofed to the air it acquires a brown colour in a very

little

little time; indeed, the furface of the liquor changes colour in a few minutes. I
expofed part of this folution to fixable air
confined by mercury, and the fame change
took place: fixable air and dephlogifticated
air mixed, affected this folution in a fhorter
time than either feparately. From the effects of fixable air as well on this folution
as on other preparations of iron, I am induced to fuppofe, that the brown colour of
ruft and of other calces of iron, is occafioned
chiefly by fixable air.

I precipitated fome iron from a common
folution of martial vitriol, and wafhed it
well. I put a part of this into perfect vitriolic acid, and another portion into the
volatile vitriolic acid; they feemed very
quiefcent, and no folution appeared to take
place. I clofed both up very tight in two
vials, and laid them by for two or three days,
when almoft all the iron was taken up.
I filtered both folutions, and into the vol.
vit. folution gradually dropped aerated volatile alkali, which threw down a bluifh precipitate. Aerated volatile alkali, dropped
into the other folution, difengaged a brown
precipitate, which was inftantly re-diffolved.
I continued dropping in the alkali until the
folution was faturated, when an orange-co-

E 4   loured

loured precipitate was obtained; very little
fixable air was produced, until the folution
was nearly faturated. I think we may attribute the re-diffolution of the precipitate to
fixable air : for the folution having a fuperabundance of vitriolic acid in it, the aerial
acid was more copioufly liberated than if it
had been a faturated folution; fo that the
difengaged calx was fo much the better fupplied with this folvent. Mild, fixed, vegetable alkali precipitated the iron from the
vol. fulp. acid of a darkifh blue colour; it
likewife precipitated the above folution of
perfect vitriolic acid of the fame colour.
Why was not the iron precipitated by the
volatile alkali from both folutions of the
fame colour? Or why did not the mild fixed
alkali precipitate as perfect a calx from the
latter folution as the volatile alkali did? Or
why did not the aerial acid diffolve the precipitate from the volatile acid, fo well as it did
that from the perfect acid? And laftly, why
was not inflammable air difengaged during
the folution of the iron in the above acids?
If the precipitate of iron from the vitriolic
acid by fixed alkali be dried or expofed to
air for fome time, the vitriolic acid will only
take up a fmall portion of it, for the moft
calcined part is left behind.

Hence

Hence we find, that a precipitate procured from a folution of iron in perfect vitriolic acid, diffolves as well in diluted vitriolic acid, as in the volatile vitriolic acid, without the production of inflammable air, though it is but $\frac{1}{2}$ calcined, or in other words, dephlogifticated. Why is not at leaft one-half the quantity of inflammable air, or phlogifton, difengaged here, that is feparated during the folution of fimple iron in vitriolic acid? I think this is not confiftently explicable in the phlogiftic doctrine; at the fame time that it is not only explicable in the antiphlogiftic theory, but likewife tends to prove the non-exiftence of phlogifton in iron, and to corroborate what has been already advanced relating to the folution of metals in vitriolic acid.

It has been already obferved, that fixed vegetable alkali precipitates iron from the vitriolic acid, and that perfect vitriolated tartar is obtained, though the iron is found to be partly calcined. Therefore it appeared, that the water furnifhed the dephlogifticated air, and that the iron contained only that portion which it received from the water. It has likewife been obferved, that this portion of dephlogifticated air, in addition to that contained in perfect

vitriolic

vitriolic acid, is the greateſt quantity that can be retained in the ſolution of iron, and that more dephlogiſticated air will decompoſe it. But it has been ſhewn, that volatile ſulphureous acid will diſſolve iron without the extrication of inflammable air, and that the ſolution contains but $\frac{1}{3}$ the portion of dephlogiſticated air contained in the ſolution of iron in perfect vitriolic acid. This ſhews, though a ſmall quantity of dephlogiſticated air will promote the union and ſolubility of iron and ſulphur, that more will do it better; but that a larger quantity will ſeparate them. Then, if this calx of iron contains only that portion of dephlogiſticated air taken from the water, and if this, in addition to the quantity contained in perfect vitriolic acid, be the *quantum ſufficit* for holding iron in ſolution ; no wonder that the union ſhould take place without the production of inflammable air, if this be diſengaged by the decompoſition of water; but if diſengaged from the iron, it is as remarkable we ſhould not obtain it. If a larger quantity of dephlogiſticated air were united to the above calx, it would then be, as already explained, inſoluble in perfect vitriolic acid, on the ſame principle that a ſolution
lution

lution of martial vitriol is decompofed when
expofed to air.

It may appear extraordinary that inflammable air is not produced during the
folution of iron in volatile vitriolic acid, at
the fame time that it is fo copioufly difengaged during its folution in perfect vitriolic acid. This, I confefs, puzzled me
for fome time before I could account for it.
I think it is demonftrable in the following
manner :

Let I be iron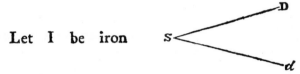

vitriolic acid: let us fuppofe I to attract
dephlogifticated air with the force of 7, and
S, from its divided attachment, to retain its
dephlogifticated air with the force of $5\frac{1}{18}$, as
ufual; and let us likewife fuppofe iron, from
the clofenefs of its texture, to prefent a
greater number of
ultimate particles
to a given furface
than the vitriolic
acid, particularly
than the dilute vi-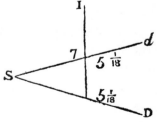
triolic acid from the interpofition of water.

Let

Let I and S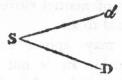

be brought within one another's influence
under thefe circumftances, and I will take
d D from S; or S, in confequence of its attraction for I, which is but very fmall, comparatively to the oppofite powers, will be
forced along with D *d*. This latter is not
likely to take place; for the force of 7,
exerted at once by a number of the martial
particles on D *d*, fuddenly fnatches them as
it were from S, which cannot move with
the fame pace towards I; becaufe, being in
contact with water, it exerts its whole force
on that compound. Therefore it is the
violence and fuddennefs of the pull from
the metal, and the velocity of the motion of
D *d* towards it, that leaves S fo circum-
ftanced as to be able to decompofe water in
the manner already defcribed.

The contrary takes place during the folution of iron in volatile fulphureous acid;
for though the iron attracts the dephlogifticated air of the volatile vitriolic acid
with the force of 7, it meets with the refiftance

fiſtance of 6$\frac{7}{4}$ 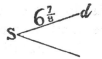 as before de-

ſcribed; ſo that that ſuperiority of force does not prevail here, as when perfect vitriolic acid is uſed. See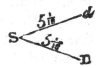

Indeed, if there were a greater inequality of force between S and I for d, S, from its attraction to d, and its tendency to I, would move with d towards I, and form the compound of S———d———I, already deſcribed. Let S attract d with the force of 6$\frac{7}{4}$: let I attract d with the force of 7, and let I attract S with the force of $\frac{1}{4}$ only; the attachment of S to d, and likewiſe its tendency to I, make up the force of 7. There-

fore the force of 7, S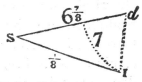

ſubſiſting between I and d, will influence S and d equally the ſame; ſo that S and d will move with equal pace to unite to I. Hence no decompoſition takes place, and of courſe no inflammable air is produced. Theſe two
important

important facts do not only throw mutual light upon one another, but likewife upon feveral abftrufe phenomena in chemiftry.

Sulphur, in its fimple ftate, will unite to moftly all the fubftances that vitriolic acid will. It unites to all the earths (the filiceous excepted), to the alkalies, to the metals (a few excepted), and likewife to the oils. The union of fulphur to the firft clafs of thefe does not throw much light on its nature, as we are as yet unacquainted with their conftituent principles.

The union of fulphur and volatile alkali admits of much more fpeculation than the former fubftances. It is now very well known, from the experiments of Mr. Berthollet and Doctor Auftin, that volatile alkali is compofed of phlogifticated air and light inflammable air. Sulphur will not chemically unite to inflammable air fo as to confolidate it; though, as I fhall hereafter be obliged to obferve, it enables fulphur to combine with fire, and acquire an elaftic ftate, whereby they are both held in folution, as fugar or Glauber falt is in water. Therefore, if fulphur be a compound of a certain bafis and phlogifton, this bafis muft be fully faturated with phlogifton. It is not certain that volatile alkali will unite to

any

any more light inflammable air than it is
known to contain in its ordinary ftate, fo
that we muft confider this likewife to be faturated with light inflammable air or phlogifton. Then, how can thefe fubftances
unite, when their bafes are already attached
and faturated with that to which they have
greater affinity, than they have to one
another? Should not the fame inertion prevail here, as when the perfect calx of iron is
mixed with the perfect vitriolic acid; or
when Glauber's falt is mixed with vitriolated
tartar; or when felenite and barofelenite; or
vitriol of zinc and vitriol of iron are mixed?
Do not like thefe, fubftances of the fame kind,
and which have no fenfible influence on one
another, interfere between volatile alkali and
fulphur? The fame may be obferved with
refpect to the union of fulphur to metals and
oils.

The effects of oils on vitriolic acid correfpond with the foregoing explanations.
A fmall quantity of oil, or any other vegetable or animal fubftance that attracts dephlogifticated air, or, in other words, that is
combuftible, will partly decompofe vitriolic
acid, and difcolour a large quantity. Vitriolic acid thus coloured, expofed to a
ftrong heat, will emit volatile vitriolic acid
in

in great abundance, and likewife fixable air, until it acquires its former tranfparency. Vitriolic acid, poured in fmall proportion on a large quantity of oil, will turn it to a darkifh brown colour. This expofed to heat will yield fixable air and volatile vitriolic acid, with a fmall quantity of phlogifticated and heavy inflammable air; and, if the charge be urged with a tolerable ftrong heat, a fmall quantity of fulphur may be produced. Hence we may infer, that the acid is only deprived of a portion of its dephlogifticated air. Animal and vegetable inflammable bodies have certainly ftronger affinity to dephlogifticated air than iron has, though they will not readily unite under any circumftance below the temperature of ignition. Oils, animal or vegetable, provided they be free from volatile alkali, will not mix or unite with water in a common temperature, but when diffufed with it by agitation will affume a globular figure, and inftantly feparate from it again on ftanding: here the repulfive force between oil and water is evident. If oil and water be boiled under the common preffure of the atmofphere, no decompofition will take place; but if water be gradually dropped into boiling hot oil, inflammable air will be produced,

duced, as has been firſt obſerved by Mr.
Lavoiſier. The joint action of air and
water can have no great effect on theſe,
and if any at all, it muſt be in a great
length of time. Suet and butter are not
decompoſed by water alone; for I can affirm, that I have been preſent when a ſmall
tub of butter had been taken from under
ground at leaſt three feet deep, and which,
from the ſituation of the ſoil and the decay
of the wood, muſt have lain there for upwards of fifty years. It was ſurrounded
with water, for it lay in a marſhy ſoil. It
had a diſagreeable taſte, and a ſpongy white
appearance, but did not ſeem much changed
in its chemical properties. From theſe,
and ſimilar facts too tedious to mention,
we ſee the difficulty of uniting oils, butter,
tallow, and charcoal to dephlogiſticated air
in a common temperature. In my opinion,
as I have heretofore conjectured, theſe are
protected from the action of air and water
by ſome repelling fluid that ſurrounds their
ultimate particles, independent of common
fire, and which they are deſtitute of while
enveloped in their reſpective kingdoms.
For all animal and vegetable organic bodies

which

which contain thefe, are readily decompofed by expofure to air and water, or to water alone.

Confidering thefe circumftances, it cannot be fuppofed that water fhould be decompofed, and inflammable air difengaged during the commixture of diluted vitriolic acid and oils. This reluctance oils have to unite to dephlogifticated air in a low temperature, in addition to their attraction for fulphur, oppofes that fudden decompofition of vitriolic acid, or rapid feparation of dephlogifticated air from the fulphur, by which, as in the inftance of the folution of iron in diluted vitriolic acid, it is enabled to decompofe the water.

When vitriolic acid, whether diluted or not, is mixed with oil, an ultimate particle of vitriolic acid influences with a certain force an ultimate particle of oil, while the latter attracts the vitriolic with the fame force. The oil will not take D *d* from S:

but from the joint at-   S $\Big\langle$ *d*   D

traction

traction of S———D———d to oil, they
will approach with equal pace, and combine. Thus this mixture more than mechanically, but not quite chemically united,
may be refolved into the different fluids
mentioned above. The particle of oil will
retain D or d, and form fixable air; at the
fame time that S will retain d or D with
its full force, and form volatile vitriolic
acid.

Volatile vitriolic acid is not fo readily
decompofed by oils as perfect vitriolic acid,
from the retention of its dephlogifticated
air with fo much the greater force. Therefore volatile vitriolic acid has not the property of charing oils as common vitriolic
acid has, but it mixes with them, and
forms a whitifh or a faponaceous-like fubftance.

What has been faid above, might be
very well illuftrated by minutely defcribing
the various phenomena attending the different ftages of that beautiful procefs of
making vitriolic ether.

Here the vitriolic acid retains the oleaginous and aqueous part of the fpirit of wine,
while the moft volatile part paffes over in

the

the ſtate of ether, the nature of which cannot be diſcuſſed here. Ether of my own
making, and which I carefully rectified
from deliquiated fixed vegetable alkali, expoſed to ſpontaneous evaporation, in the
temperature of 37 or 40°. of Fahrenheit's
thermometer, left a ſmall reſiduum of oil,
water, and vitriolic acid. The quantity of
vitriolic acid was ſo ſmall, that I could
only detect it by acetated barytes. However, it ſhews that vitriolic acid enters into
the conſtitution of vitriolic ether. A portion of the ſame ether left no reſiduum in
the temperature of 60°. A ſolution of
terra ponderoſa ſhewed no appearance of
vitriolic acid in this ether. It appears to
me, that ether is to light inflammable air,
what the groſſer oils are to the heavy
which is favourable to the explanation of
fermentation, &c.

Charcoal or oils will wholly decompoſe
vitriolic acid when combined with fixed
alkalies, and expoſed to heat. Two circumſtances favour this decompoſition :
1ſt, The attraction of the inflammable
matter for D d. 2dly, That of S for the
alkalies. Liver of ſulphur expoſed to the
atmoſphere,

atmofphere, or to dephlogifticated air in clofe veffels, will attract the latter, and form vitriolated tartar; though fulphur alone will have no effect on dephlogifticated air, nor will alkalies in their fimple ftate unite to it. On reflection, thefe circum-ftances appear very fingular; but if we confider that the fulphur is united to the alkali in its extreme divifion, and that its attraction to dephlogifticated air is ftronger than its attachment to the alkali, and like-wife that the attraction of alkalies for vi-triolic acid is greater than their attraction to fulphur, we may eafily account for all this. The fulphureous falt of Stahl expo-fed to air, will unite to the dephlogifticated part, and form a perfect vitriolic falt; though volatile vitriolic acid in its fimple ftate will not readily unite to dephlogifti-cated air. Thefe facts clearly demonftrate, why alkalies take vitriolic acid in its perfect ftate from iron, at the fame time that it is thrown down in a femi-calcined ftate; for, as I have before endeavoured to fhew, the iron takes D d from S, by its fuperior attraction to dephlogifticated air, at the fame time that S takes d from the water;

there-

therefore S———*d* holds I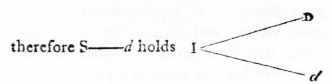

or the calx of iron in folution ; from which circumftance we might imagine, that S———*d*, or the volatile vitriolic acid, fhould unite to the alkali, and form the fulphureous falt of Stahl, and that the iron fhould be precipitated in a more calciform ftate, that is, united with D———*d*, or double the quantity of dephlogifticated air which the precipitate generally contains. But finding that S———*d*, or volatile vitriolic acid united to alkalies or earths, attracts dephlogifticated air with greater force than when in its fimple ftate, we can eafily explain why the contrary takes place.

Sulphur partly acquires an aeriform ftate, when difengaged from the different hepars by acids. Liver of fulphur in its dry ftate is quite inodorous ; but when moiftened with water, it emits a ftrong hepatic fmell, as Mr. Gengembre has obferved. From this effect of water on liver of fulphur it is evident, that it promotes the difunion and vola-

volatilization of a portion of the fulphur; but on what principle is not well underftood. If this fhould take place in confequence of a decompofition of water, vitriolic acid ought to be formed, and of courfe vitriolated tartar; but it has not been found, to my knowledge, that liver of fulphur, either earthy or alkaline, has ever been vitriolated by the decompofition of water alone, but always requires the accefs of air*. However, as the hepatic fmell, or emiffion of the gas, is moft predominant when only a fmall quantity of moifture is ufed, and on its firft application, it may be faid, that the dry hepatic compound has only then the power of decompofing water, and that the continuance of the fmell is occafioned by a portion of the gas remaining in the compound from the difficulty of its expulfion. Iron filings will unite to fulphur in a moderate degree of

* Since the above was written, Dr. Auftin informed me, that liver of fulphur will not afford an hepatic odour when wetted in clofe veffels, and confined in mercury. It feems he has made feveral experiments on liver of fulphur, which he has given to the Royal Society.

heat,

heat, and form a black brittle mass, which on the addition of an acid will yield hepatic air in the utmost purity, and in great abundance, though it will not produce an hepatic smell when moistened with water, as calcar. pond. or alkaline livers of sulphur will. This shews the greater attraction of alkalies and sulphur jointly to dephlogisticated air than that of iron and sulphur, and likewise tends to prove what has been already said on the precipitation of iron by alkalies.

Dr. Austin has passed the electric spark repeatedly in hepatic air, and by that means precipitated all the sulphur without changing its dimensions. The residuary air was incondensible by water, and when washed had no hepatic smell. On burning this with dephlogisticated air, it appeared to be light inflammable air. This shews the constituent principles of hepatic gas, better than any other experiment that has hitherto been made on the subject. That sulphur is suspended in its natural state in light inflammable air, may be inferred from the above experiment; but whether in its extreme division is difficult to determine; or whether

whether it be chemically united to the inflammable air, or combined independently
with its own atmofpheres of fire, and mechanically mixed with this, cannot be fatisfactorily proved. In my opinion it is
mere folution, fuch as takes place between
the neutral falts and water, or the alkalies
and water, or fugar and water, &c. Though
the facility whereby this is decompofed
favours the above hypothefis, yet there are
circumftances that are apparently againft it;
fuch as their united condenfation in water,
and their joint expulfion from it again.
Upon what principle this attraction exifts
between bodies, has not yet been explained,
or the difference between this and a chemical union ever defined. It appears to
me that folution, that power whereby water
diffolves aerial acid, alkaline air, vitriolic
acid air; and that power whereby light inflammable air diffolves fulphur and phofphorus; and likewife that power whereby
all the aeriform fluids diffolve water in their
elaftic ftate; and laftly, whereby water diffolves the neutral falts, &c. without changing their properties, is occafioned by a fort
of intermediate attraction, not differing from
chemical

chemical attraction but in its degree of force, and not at all different from that power whereby the heavenly bodies influence one another.

Dr. Auftin fufed fulphur in light inflammable air, in phlogifticated air, and in heavy inflammable air. The two former airs were not in the leaft altered; but the latter afforded one-third its original bulk of hepatic gas. It is remarkable, that the bulk of the air was not in the leaft altered in this procefs; and likewife that the refiduary air, when the hepatic air was feparated from it by water, fhould not appear in the leaft changed; for by inflaming it with a due proportion of dephlogifticated air, it yielded the ufual quantities of fixed and phlogifticated air. The fulphur acquired a coally appearance in this operation; which induces me to fuppofe that it muft have precipitated fomething from the air, the lofs of which enabled the inflammable air to take fulphur in exchange.

The fame philofopher paffed the electrie fpark repeatedly in heavy inflammable air, until it increafed nearly one-half in bulk; this he inflamed with dephlogifticated air

over

over mercury by the electric fpark. He
likewife inflamed the fame quantity of
heavy inflammable air, not treated .by the
electric fpark. By feveral repetitions of
the above experiments, and from an accurate comparifon of their refpective refi-
duums, he found that there was lefs fixable
air, and a larger quantity of phlogifticated
air in the former than in the latter; from
which he concluded that heavy inflammable air is phlogifticated and light inflammable air, and that fixable air is compofed of thefe two and dephlogifticated
air. He likewife concluded, and juftly,
from the increafe of bulk, and the fmall
quantity of the heavy inflammable air that
was decompofed, that if the entire were
decompofed it would increafe ten times its
bulk. The converfion of heavy inflammable air into hepatic air without increafe
of bulk, and without any change in the
refiduary air, does not favour the above
hypothefis: 1ft, Becaufe, as has appeared,
and as fhall be hereafter confirmed, light
inflammable air is held in hepatic gas at
its full extent. 2dly, Becaufe the decompofed air fhould increafe ten times in bulk.
3dly, Be-

3dly, Becaufe no increafe of phlogifticated air was found in the refiduary air.

However, the Doctor fuppofes that volatile alkali is formed, whereby a portion of the inflammable air and the entire of the phlogifticated air remain united. Volatile alkali contains not much more by meafure than four of inflammable to one of phlogifticated air; therefore the decompofed air fhould ftill increafe fix times its bulk. Befides, as this experiment was performed in dry mercury, the volatile alkali itfelf fhould remain in an claftic ftate.

As the Doctor intends to favour the public with thefe experiments, I fhall not prefume to fay much on the fubject. That heavy inflammable air contains light inflammable air, is certain from the formation of hepatic gas, as well as from its expanfion by the electric fpark; but I cannot avoid entertaining a doubt, whether the real matter of inflammable air with which dephlogifticated air forms fixable air, and which does not in the leaft differ from the ultimate particles of charcoal, be compofed of light inflammable air and phlogifticated air. Indeed, confidering that thefe are the

constituent

constituent principles of volatile alkali, it
appears rather improbable.

It seemed to me, for I was present, that
something was precipitated from the air by
the electric spark; for the lower part of
the glass tube appeared black, while the
sides seemed lined with a greyish substance.
It likewise appeared to me, after the air
acquired the expansion already mentioned, that a contraction took place by continuing the electric spark. This at least
I can say with truth, that one hundred
sparks at one time contracted it nearly
one measure in eight or nine; but how
much more it would diminish by continuing the operation, I cannot tell. I am
almost persuaded to think, that the matter
of charcoal in its extreme division, held in
solution in light inflammable air and water,
and combined with fire, constitutes the
heavy inflammable air, on the same principle that sulphur and light inflammable
air constitute hepatic gas; with this difference only, that the former gravitate more
towards each other, which causes a greater
condensation of the light inflammable air
in the heavy than in hepatic gas, and of
course

eourfe a greater difficulty of decompofing
it. Such likewife is the nature of phofphoric air, as has been obferved by Mr.
Gengembre, who I find, although I have
not feen his analyfis, has paid vaft attention
to this fubject. Fire, it is true, is the firft
folvent in nature ; next to this comes
water ; and next to this again light inflammable air, whether in its aerial or condenfed ftate, fuch as in ethers and fpirits.
To this property of light inflammable air,
I attribute partly the fpirituous fermentation, and chiefly the refult. From thefe,
and other fimilar circumftances, my doubts
arife refpecting the conftituent principles
of the heavy inflammable air, although
experience convinces me that it contains a
fmall quantity of phlogifticated air. Thus
far I have ventured to trefpafs upon the
patience of my reader, thinking that the
heavy inflammable air may tend to caft
light on the nature of hepatic gas, and
vice verfâ.

I mixed equal parts of hepatic air produced from iron filings and fulphur, and
dephlogifticated air obtained from nitre.
Seven meafures of the former were abforbed

forbed by water all to a small bubble, and the latter contained only one-tenth of phlogisticated air. Nine measures of this mixture were reduced by the electric spark to 2$\frac{1}{4}$; the nitrated solution of terra ponderosa condensed these to one-twelfth of a measure or less; and the solution did not appear in the least turbid, nor did any cloudiness take place on the addition of lime water. The residuum left un-absorbed was too small to be examined; but the portion condensed by the solution seemed by the smell to be volatile vitriolic acid. In order to be convinced of this, I inflamed another charge of the same airs, and transferred the residuum into a clean jar, which the sulphur deposited on the sides of the inflaming jar obliged me to do. To this I added an equal bulk of hepatic air, which instantly rendered it turbid, and reduced it to one-third, or a little more.

This assured me that the residuum was volatile sulphureous acid, and likewise that volatile sulphureous acid will not decompose nitrated terra ponderosa.

This experiment not only proves the constituent principles of hepatic gas, but absolutely

absolutely proves what I have advanced
respecting the proportion of the principles
of volatile vitriolic acid. It has been
shewn by Dr. Austin, that the solution
of sulphur in light inflammable air, neither contracts nor expands it; therefore
the above charge contained $4\frac{1}{2}$ measures of
light inflammable air, independent of the
suspended sulphur. These $4\frac{1}{2}$ ounce measures of light inflammable air, require at
least $2\frac{1}{4}$ of dephlogisticated air to condense
them. $2\frac{1}{4}$ measures more were expended
in the experiment, two of which must be
contained in the volatile vitriolic acid; and
as the most part of the phlogisticated air
disappeared, we may justly conclude, that
the remainder of the dephlogisticated air,
which is but one-fourth of a measure, was
expended in the formation of nitrous acid.
Hence we may conclude, that the two
measures of volatile vitriolic acid contained
two measures of dephlogisticated air; and
as the specific gravity of volatile vitriolic
acid, excluding the inflammable air, is the
mathematical main of the two fluids, we
must suppose that only the sulphur of two
measures

measures united to dephlogisticated air, and that the sulphur of 2¼ measures was precipitated. Hence likewise we may infer, that the molicules of volatile vitriolic acid are surrounded with as large atmospheres of fire as the particles of dephlogisticated air, or at least that they are as far asunder; and that the number of the ultimate particles of sulphur in hepatic gas, are to those of the inflammable air as nine to five.

SECTION IV.

Of Nitrous Acid.

NO ſubject in chemiſtry, until the de-
ciſive experiment of Mr. Cavendiſh,
favoured the phlogiſtic doctrine more than
the nitrous acid, from the variety of its
modifications.

The large quantity of dephlogiſticated
air contained in this acid, and condenſed
by ſo ſmall a portion of phlogiſticated air,
is very well worthy the attention of ſpecu-
lative men, at the ſame time that it enables
us to account for the eaſy decompoſition
(more eſpecially in part) of this acid; whereby it aſſumes the different appearances ob-
ſervable from the ſtate of dephlogiſticated
nitrous air, down to the moſt perfect ſtate
of colourleſs nitrous acid. It is not an
eaſy matter to aſcertain exactly the greateſt
quantity of dephlogiſticated air, that a
given quantity of nitrous acid may contain.
I always found nitre to vary in its product

of

of phlogisticated and dephlogisticated air, and likewise in their proportion to one another. The purest nitre will yield, about the middle of the proces, dephlogisticated air so pure as to contain but about one-thirteenth only of phlogisticated air. In the beginning, and nearly at the latter end of the proces, air will be produced about twice better than common air. I mixed the different products of a quantity of pure nitre, and found by exposure to liver of sulphur that one-sixth was left unabsorbed. This was the utmost degree of purity in which I obtained dephlogisticated air from nitre.

According to Mr. Lavoisier, 100 grains of nitrous acid contain $79\frac{1}{2}$ of dephlogisticated air, and $20\frac{1}{2}$ of phlogisticated air, which is not quite four to one. But his experiments contradict this; for whatever mode he adopted to decompose nitrous acid, it appeared that the proportion of dephlogisticated air was nearly as five, to one of phlogisticated air.

Mr. Cavendish has proved, that nitrous acid may be formed by taking the electric spark in a mixture of three parts of phlo-

gisticated

gifticated air, and seven of dephlogifticated air, which is but $\frac{1}{7}$ more of dephlogifticated air than nitrous air contains. This may apparently contradict Mr. Lavoifier's as well as my own eftimation of the proportion of the conftituent principles of nitrous acid when in its perfect ftate.

The red nitrous vapour contains three parts of nitrous air and one of dephlogifticated air, or one of phlogifticated and three of dephlogifticated air; but nitrous vapour may be formed with a lefs proportion of dephlogifticated air, and which, though it may not be fo condenfible as a more perfect nitrous vapour, yet will, when in contact with pure alkali, unite to it and form nitre, as was the cafe in the experiment of Mr. Cavendifh.

The common ftraw-coloured nitrous acid contains more dephlogifticated air than the red nitrous acid or vapour; the proportion appears to be four to one; but the colourlefs contains about five of dephlogifticated to one of phlogifticated air.

Having once a charge of nitre and vitriolic acid in a green glafs retort, I placed it in a fand-pot to diftil; but the pot being
                                        fmall,

fmall, the edge came too near the retort, about a quarter of an inch or more above the charge, which before the procefs commenced, and when it acquired more than the heat of boiling water, cracked it all round in that direction. Being thus fituated I was obliged to withdraw the fire, and, before the charge got cold, to ladle it into an earthen pan. I again introduced it into a frefh retort, and obtained from it nitrous acid nearly as colourlefs as water. As the vitriolic acid was not very perfect, I attributed the goodnefs of the nitrous acid to the purity of the nitre. Therefore I procured more of the fame nitre in order to lay in a ftock of nitrous acid; but to my furprife, though I ufed purer vitriolic acid than in the former procefs, my product of nitrous acid was of an high ftraw colour. Some months after, having an occafion for more nitrous acid, and recollecting the above circumftance, I mixed the vitriolic acid and nitre in due proportion, and expofed them in an earthen pan fet in fand to nearly the heat of boiling water for half an hour or more, continually expofing frefh furfaces to the air. When the charge

G 3   was

was quite cold I introduced it into a retort, and diftilled as colourlefs nitrous acid as the former. As the charge emitted no nitrous air during digeftion, it muft have attracted dephlogifticated air.

I would recommend this manner of treatment, to obtain nitrous acid in the utmoft degree of perfection.

Before I proceed any farther on this fubject, I think proper to mention the phlogiftians' opinion of this acid, particularly Mr. Kirwan's, who has adopted a new phlogiftic hypothefis refpecting the modification of the conftituent principles of the nitrous acid, and of all other acids.

This philofopher fuppofes, that 100 grains of nitrous acid in its pure colourlefs ftate, contain 38, .17 gr. of fixed air as its acidifying principle, 57, .06 of nitrous bafis, and 4, .77 of phlogifton united to the nitrous bafis; and that the nitrous bafis contains $\frac{1}{3}$ of its weight of phlogifticated air, and $\frac{2}{3}$ dephlogifticated air, both in a concrete ftate, and that it has an affinity both to fixed air and phlogifton. Mr. Kirwan moreover fuppofes, that nitrous bafis faturated with phlogifton, conftitutes nitrous air,

air, and that 100 gr. of this bafis take up
nearly 22 of phlogifton. By this he means,
that the principles of nitrous acid are fixed
air, dephlogifticated air, phlogifticated air,
and inflammable air, all in their concrete ftate.

According to this ftatement of nitrous
acid, 100 grains of it in its pure dry ftate,
provided the fixable air be decompofed,
fhould yield about 60, .25 of dephlogifticated air, 15, .75 of heavy inflammable
air, 19, .02 gr. of phlogifticated air, and
4, .77 gr. of light inflammable air*. But
if the fixable air fhould acquire an aeriform ftate, and fo pafs over in decompofing nitrous acid by heat, we fhould obtain the following proportion, viz. 38, .17
gr. of fixable air, 38, .04 of dephlogifticated, 19, .02 of phlogifticated air, and
4, .77 of light inflammable air, which in
its aeriform ftate fhould occupy nearly the
fpace of 200 cubic inches under the common preffure and temperature of the atmofphere; or if it fhould during the procefs be condenfed into water, 100 cubic

---

* The variation and increafe of weight which the prefence of water muft neceffarily produce in all aerial bodies are not here confidered.

G 4   inches

inches of dephlogisticated air must contribute to it : if this were the cafe, dephlogisticated air could never be obtained during the decompofition of nitrous acid.

I calcined 4 ounces of purified fixed vegetable alkali, to avoid any matter that may afford the inflammable principle of fixable air. On this I poured, diluted with diftilled water, ¼ more of the pure nitrous acid, obtained in the manner above defcribed, than was fufficient to faturate it. Having digefted it for half an hour in a matrafs, I charged it into a coated glafs retort, and expofed it to a gentle heat, until all the water and fuperabundant acid were expelled. I then gradually raifed the fire until the decompofition of the acid commenced. The firft meafure rendered lime water turbid, but the contraction was hardly meafurable.

Meafure   2 ditto.

            3 ditto.

            4 ditto.

            5 ditto.

            6 ditto.

            7 lefs turbid.

            8 ditto.

            9 ditto

Meaſure 10 hardly rendered lime water turbid.

16 no appearance of fixable air, and continued ſo until the charge diſſolved the retort. The quantity of fixable air obtained here could not amount to more than a cubic inch, and I make no doubt but this is an ample allowance for it, though 400 meaſures were obtained before the retort failed. As I made this experiment only with a view to aſcertain the preſence of fixable air, I attended to nothing elſe.

If fixable air be a neceſſary principle in nitrous acid, what became of it in the above proceſs ? If it had been decompoſed, we ſhould have obtained inflammable air, either light or heavy, neither of which was obtained. I frequently had an opportunity of examining the reſiduary alkali after the nitrous acid had been wholly expelled, and never could obtain from it either nitrous or fixable air, though there is generally an ebullition on the addition of an acid, occaſioned by the generation of heat. I aſk, what becomes of the 4, .77 grains of pure phlogiſton, or the matter of light inflammable air, contained, as Mr. Kirwan ſuppoſes,

pofes, in every hundred grains of pure dry
nitrous acid ? As has been obferved above,
no inflammable air had been produced;
and to fuppofe phlogifticated air to contain
light inflammable air, is an hypothefis
founded upon fuch weak grounds, that the
phlogiftians cannot produce one fingle inftance to prove it. Even Mr. Kirwan himfelf, who is fo ftrong an advocate for phlogifton, feems to doubt its prefence in phlogifticated air; for he fays, * " With refpect to phlogifticated air, it muft be owned
we have no direct proof that it contains
phlogifton, as no inflammable air has as
yet been extracted from it, nor is it the
general refult of phlogiftic proceffes; but
fince the nitrous acid formed of this air,
and dephlogifticated air, was found ftrongly
phlogifticated, and fince the phlogifticated
nitrous acid is conftituted fuch by its union
to nitrous air, it is evident that phlogifticated air muft contain phlogifton, if nitrous
air contains any." Befides, according to
Mr. Kirwan, the phlogifticated air in the
nitrous acid contains its own proper phlogifton, together with the 4, .77 gr. of pure

* Effay on Phlogifton, p. 40.

phlo-

phlogifton; fo that it cannot be faid they were expended in forming phlogifticated air. Therefore the only way left to account for them is, that they united to a portion of dephlogifticated air, and formed water. 4, .77 gr. of light inflammable air require about 34 grains, or 100 cubic inches of dephlogifticated air to condenfe them into water, and there are but 4 gr. more of dephlogifticated air left, according to Mr. Kirwan himfelf. If this were to take place, we fhould obtain the following products from every 100 gr. of pure dry nitrous acid, viz. phlogifticated air 19, .02 gr. fixed air 38, .17 gr. water refulting from the phlogifton, and dephlogifticated air 38, .77 gr. dephlogifticated air 4 gr. How far this proportion correfponds with the products of the different airs obtained from nitre, I leave my chemical reader to judge.

Mr. Cavendifh repeated his procefs for making nitrous acid on a tolerable large fcale laft fpring *. Dr. B———y, another gentleman, and myfelf, have had the pleafure of feeing it. The tube which confined the airs and foap-lees was accidentally

---

* Anno 1788.

1   raifed

raifed out of the mercury the day before, which gave me an opportunity not only of feeing but of tafting the nitre, which was in fmall cryftals on the furface of the mercury. It does not appear that Mr. Cavendifh ufed fixed air in the above procefs. But Mr. Kirwan attempts to obviate this by faying, that a fufficiency of fixable air may be fufpended in the fluids worked upon. This could not be the cafe; for as Mr. Cavendifh ufed foap-lees, he muft neceffarily pafs his airs in it, fo that no fixable air could be fufpended. It may be faid, that the foap-lees itfelf was not entirely free from fixable air. Even allowing this, it could have no fhare in the formation of the nitrous acid, as it muft be formed by the union of the dephlogifticated and phlogifticated air, before they can unite to the alkali.

I mixed three parts of light inflammable air, and two of dephlogifticated air, which ftood feparately over lime 24 hours. The dephlogifticated air contained $\frac{2}{10}$ of phlogifticated air. I inflamed 7 meafures, or about 2 cubic inches of this, which left a refiduum of $\frac{1}{5}$ of the charge, which mea-

4   fured

fured $\frac{1}{4}$ of an inch. I added another charge
to this refiduum, and after inflammation it
increafed to half an inch. I inflamed a third
charge, expecting a proportionable increafe
of refiduum; but here I was deceived; for
it contracted to $\frac{1}{4}$ of an inch, being only
the refiduum of one charge. I continued
the operation with nearly the like fuccefs,
until the refiduum got too large. I fired
12 charges in all, and the quantity of condenfed liquor was by eftimation about 4 gr.
The furface of the mercury and brafs conductors were much corroded. I let up a
quarter of an ounce of diftilled water, with
about 2 drops of cauftic fixed alkali, and
left the whole to ftand for a few hours. I
then filtered the liquor, and evaporated it
to drynefs. I collected the falt, which
weighed $1\frac{1}{2}$ gr. it feemed not to be faturated, for it attracted moifture ftrongly;
but ignited upon paper, it detonated like
nitre. Thus it appears that nitrous acid
had been formed in the above procefs,
though I am certain that neither the inflammable air, nor the dephlogifticated air,
contained an atom of fixable air. It cannot
be urged that the dephlogifticated and in-

flammable

flammable air by their union furnifhed fixable air; for I hope I have already fhewn
that they conftitute no fuch thing.

When I ufed very pure dephlogifticated
air, no fenfible portion of nitrous acid was
produced, unlefs the dephlogifticated air
predominated, and then there was very little
procured. Hence we may conclude, that
nitrous acid was formed in the above procefs, in confequence merely of the prefence
of phlogifticated air. When the above
proportions were reverfed, that is, when
the inflammable air predominated, though
the dephlogifticated air contained a large
quantity of phlogifticated air, little or no
nitrous acid was formed, which fhews the
fuperior attraction of light inflammable air
to dephlogifticated air. Thus we find,
provided the proportion be adjufted, that
two procefles may be carried on at once,
viz. the formation of nitrous acid and
water. I am confident, if we could get
entirely rid of the phlogifticated air, that
water may be produced in the above procefs in whatever proportion we mix our
airs, without a particle of nitrous acid.

Thefe

These facts must be sufficient to convince an unprejudiced person, that fixable air is not one of the constituent principles of nitrous acid, and that phlogisticated air is absolutely necessary to its constitution, and that the gravitating matter of light inflammable air, as some philosophers are pleased to suppose, is not one of the constituent parts of nitrous acid.

The formation of nitrous acid, without the presence of fixable air, or the materials to compose it, and the resolution of this again into its constituent principles, without the production of fixable air, must carry with them the utmost conviction. It may be said, that fixable air was produced during the decomposition of the above charge of nitre; but can it be supposed that 1, or even 8 cubic inches of fixable air, could render so highly acid as well as caustic, the quantity of nitrous acid that will saturate four ounces of fixed alkali? Besides, the fixable air obtained, was expelled at the commencement of the process; and before $\frac{1}{100}$ part of the acid could be decomposed, a true sign that it was rather an extra production proceeding from

from some impurity in the nitre, than one of the conftituent principles of the nitrous acid; for if fixable air were one of the conftituent parts of this acid, we fhould obtain it equally copious at every period of the procefs, particularly when its extrication depends upon the decompofition of the acid, and likewife when we know that the alkali, after the decompofition of the nitre, contains no fixable air. Indeed the alkali, from its attraction to fixable air, if the nitrous acid could furnifh this, fhould be obtained in a mild ftate; on the fame principle that the alkali of foliated tartar is, after its decompofition. For though foliated tartar requires a ftrong heat towards the end of the procefs to completely decompofe the acid, yet the alkali is always obtained in a mild ftate. Hence the reafon why we obtain lefs fixable air in the beginning, than towards the latter end of the procefs.

Confidering the univerfality of fixable air from putrefaction, combuftion, and refpiration, procefses which muft neceffarily be carried on wherever mankind exifts; and likewife confidering, that all animal

and

and vegetable fubftances contain more or
lefs of this in a combined ftate, and that
they are chiefly compofed of one of its
conftituent principles, and that nitrous acid
contains the other principle, it is not to
be wondered at, that we fhould obtain more
or lefs fixable air in all proceffes wherein
nitre is ufed. Indeed, it is impoffible for
the moft accurate experimentalift to guard
againft impregnations that may be productive of fixable air, 1ft, Becaufe the atmofphere is not only impregnated with aerial
acid already formed, but is likewife loaded
with moats that may adhere to our materials. 2dly, Our breath whilft we are
preparing our charge, and infenfible perfpi-
ration in addition to thefe, may all contribute to the generation of aerial acid.

I charged fome ounces of common falt-
petre, procured at the druggift's, into a
coated glafs retort. This I placed in a reverberating furnace; and when the air of
the veffels was expelled, I examined the
firft meafure, which rendered lime water
turbid; but the contraction was fcarcely
meafurable. The meafure I ufed contained

H about

about 8 cubic inches, and the proportion of fixable air was as follows:

Measures.		Fixable Air.
2	—— ——	$\frac{1}{30}$
4	—— ——	ditto.
6	—— ——	ditto.
7	—— ——	$\frac{1}{27}$
9	—— ——	$\frac{1}{20}$
12	—— ——	$\frac{1}{16}$
14	—— ——	$\frac{1}{16}$
18	—— ——	$\frac{1}{12}$
19	—— ——	ditto.
26	—— ——	$\frac{1}{23}$
30	—— ——	$\frac{1}{20}$

40 scarcely measurable.

50 by conjecture, scarcely sensible.

60 no appearance of fixable air, and continued so during the whole process. The greater quantity of fixable air procured here than in the former process, proves that its production must be occasioned by the impurity of the nitre.

All spongy bodies, or the most compact substances when reduced to powder, will, though they may not have any chemical attraction to it, condense a small quantity of fixable air by capillary attraction. Even

nitrous

nitrous acid will condenfe a fmall quantity
of fixable air, though it will not enter into
chemical union with it.

I deflagrated 2 ounces of pure nitre,
prepared as above defcribed, with about
7 dwts. of frefh made filings of zinc ; and
when the mafs cooled, diluted vitriolic acid
did not difengage a particle of fixable air
from it. The fame quantity of iron filings
and nitre, after deflagration, yielded a fmall
quantity of fixable air. If the fixable air
proceeded from a decompofition of the acid
in this laft experiment, why was not the
fame quantity of fixable air produced when
zinc filings were ufed ? Or, if the fixable
air was produced in confequence of an
union of the dephlogifticated air of the
nitrous acid and the phlogifton of the iron,
why did not a fimilar union take place when
zinc filings were ufed ? for, if the one contains phlogifton, the other muft. If the
difference fhould be attributed to the greater
quantity of phlogifton in iron than in zinc,
I would anfwer, that this could make no
difference, when there is a fufficiency in
both to decompofe the whole of the nitre.
Befides, as I have obferved before, light

inflam-

inflammable air and dephlogisticated air have never been known to form fixable air. I would likewife afk, what becomes of the phlogifton of the metal during deflagration? for, according to Mr. Kirwan, the dephlogifticated air of nitrous acid is already attached to phlogifton.

If nitrous acid were compofed of the principles Mr. Kirwan fuppofes; and likewife, if metals were compofed of a certain bafis and phlogifton, nitre would never be decompofed by metallic fubftances. The phlogifton of the metal being oppofed by the phlogifton of the nitrous acid, can have nothing to do in the decompofition; and as the union of all the ingredients nitre is compofed of, is diffolved when the dephlogifticated air is withdrawn from them, the metallic bafis alone muft overcome the following forces to unite to the dephlogifticated air, viz. 1ft, The force whereby the nitrous acid and the alkali attract each other. 2dly, The force whereby the phlogifticated air attracts dephlogifticated air. 3dly, The force whereby nitrous bafis attracts fixable air; and laftly, the attraction of their pure phlogifton to all thefe;

thefe; let us add to thefe forces, the attraction of the metallic bafis on the other
fide to its own phlogifton. Therefore, if
the metallic bafis fhould attract dephlogifticated air fo forcibly as to overcome all
thefe collectively, can it be fuppofed that it
would yield it again to phlogifton, or that
it would exchange it for phlogifton? Undoubtedly not; though an allowance be
made for the agency of fire in this circumftance.

If we confider nitrous acid to be compofed of what in my opinion it really
is, namely, dephlogifticated air and phlogifticated air, and metals to be compofed
of two principles, viz. earth and phlogifton,
we may account for the decompofition
of nitre upon a very rational principle;
viz. the joint attraction of phlogifton
and its metallic bafis for dephlogifticated
air. But we cannot account for the revivification of metallic calces again by inflammable air, upon this principle, confidering that the phlogifton or light inflammable air of the metal muft refift it, and
likewife that the attraction of the metallic

H 3   bafis

bafis itſelf to dephlogiſticated air adds to this reſiſtance.

It is true, it may be juſtly obſerved, that intenſe heat may weaken the union of the dephlogiſticated air, the metallic baſis, and its phlogiſton, and thereby enable uncombined phlogiſton, or light inflammable air, to unite to the former, or, what is the ſame in effect, to the metallic baſis, and diſengage its own phlogiſton and dephlogiſticated air in the ſtate of water.

If we admit this mode of reaſoning, it proves, that the metallic baſis has greater attraction to inflammable air or phlogiſton, than to dephlogiſticated air alone, or than to dephlogiſticated air and phlogiſton jointly.

This, conſidered abſtractedly, appears certainly very plauſible; but, if we take a more extenſive view of the ſubject, we ſhall find, that it will not correſpond with other connected facts. For if iron had ſtronger affinity to phlogiſton, or light inflammable air, than it has to water, or to dephlogiſticated air ſimply, light inflammable air could not be produced from iron filings and water in a boiling heat, whether it
comes

comes from the water or metal; or much lefs could this be produced by paffing fteam over the furface of red-hot or fufed iron, particularly over the latter, as in this ftate it feems to retain its phlogifton with greateft force, if affuming a metallic ftate be fuch. Do not all the calcinable metals in the dry way, mercury excepted, unite to dephlogifticated air in the ftrongeft degree of heat that our furnaces can produce? And will not inflammable air reduce thefe again to their metallic ftate in the fame degree of heat? Therefore dephlogifticated air cannot be retained in metallic calces by the double force of the metallic bafis and inflammable air, or its condenfed phlogifton. If, as I believe I have already obferved, the union of dephlogifticated air depended on the metallic phlogifton alone, inflammable air, by the affiftance of heat, would decompofe it. But, then, would this take dephlogifticated air from water? Indeed, I might as well have afked, if vitriolic acid would take fixed vegetable alkali from vitriolic acid? For furely phlogifton cannot take dephlogifticated air from phlogifton, more efpecially when it is already attached to the metallic bafis.

H 4

Thefe

These circumstances strictly considered, it appears to me, that in order to connectedly and confistently account for the decompofition of the different bodies into whose compofition dephlogifticated air enters by metallic fubstances, fulphur and phofphorus, phlogifton muft be left out.

If we confider metals as fimple bodies, and of courfe deftitute of the gravitating matter of light inflammable air; and likewife nitrous acid as a fubftance compofed of phlogifticated and dephlogifticated air only, we may be able to account for the decompofition of nitre and nitrous acid, by the different metals, &c.

It has been obferved, that metals have greater attraction to dephlogifticated air than fulphur, and fulphur than light inflammable air. Light inflammable air has greater attraction to dephlogifticated air than phlogifticated air has. Let us, in order to be the more explicit, fuppofe thefe different bodies to attract dephlogifticated air with the following forces:

Metals	— —	7,
Sulphur	— —	6,$\frac{7}{8}$
Light inflam.	—	6,$\frac{5}{8}$
Phlog. air	— —	3,

Let

Let us likewife fuppofe fixed alkali to attract nitrous acid with the force of 4, which in addition to 3 enables the nitre to retain its dephlogifticated air with the force of 7. Hence filings of iron or zinc, though they will decompofe the nitrous acid itfelf, will not decompofe nitre in powder, or in folution, in a common temperature. The conftituent principles of nitre attached with the above force, will recede from each other when expofed to heat by the interpofition of fire, whereby their union or mutual influence is weakened; and this diminution of the force of their attraction, is in a duplicate ratio to the fquares of their diftances. Metallic fubftances, having their ultimate particles likewife removed from each other when expofed to heat, by which their aggregate influence is diminifhed, attract dephlogifticated air with the greater force.

Thefe circumftances enable us to account for what takes place when we project nitre and zinc, or iron, or charcoal, and fulphur, into a red-hot crucible.

That famous philofopher, and accurate experimentalift, Mr. Lavoifier, having mixed

ed and reduced into a moſt ſubtile powder
708,6 grains of nitre, and 93,52 of charcoal, preſſed them into a copper tube, and
after ignition introduced the tube, with its
aperture turned down, under a jar of water,
where the whole of the charcoal was con-
ſumed, and the nitre decompoſed. The
products were as follow:

Materials. Gr.		Products.	Cub. Inches.	Weights.
Nitre	708,6	Fixed air	708,25	329,33
Charcoal	93,52	Phlogiſt. air	195,56	59,8
	———	Cauſtic alkali	-	406,5
	802,12			———
		Total of the products		795,63
		Loſs	-	6,49

Mr. Lavoiſier was juſtly led to conclude
from this experiment, that nitrous acid
was compoſed of dephlogiſticated and phlogiſticated air, and that the latter was in the
proportion of $\frac{1}{5}$ of the whole of the acid;
and likewiſe, that fixable air was compoſed
of the matter of charcoal and dephlogiſticated air.

The accuracy wherewith this experiment
was performed, and the inferences drawn
from it (particularly at a time when the
conſtituent principles of nitrous acid were
unknown),

4

unknown), fhew the excellency of this
great philofopher. There were 6,49 gr.
miffing, which muft certainly be water.
Indeed, confidering the quantity of water
in nitre, and likewife that the airs were
produced in water, the lofs of weight was
very inconfiderable. In my opinion, 100
gr. of pure nitre contain, of

Cauftic alkali	—	57 grains.
Dephlogifticated air	-	27
Phlogifticated air	—	,6
Water —	—	10

Total 100

From this ftatement I am induced to think,
that the 329,33 of fixable air produced in
the above procefs, contained the following
proportion of its conftituent principles, and
water :　　　　　　　　　　　Gr.

Dephlogifticated air	—	191,
Charcoal —	—	89,52
Water —	—	48,81

Total 329,33

59,8 of phlogifticated air contain, befides
its real gravitating matter, 18 grains of
water. The quantity of water held in folution

lution in both airs 66,81, in addition to 6,49, which was the lofs of weight, accounts for the water of the nitre and charcoal. The following is the proportion of the different ingredients contained in the whole charge:

		Gr.
Dephlogifticated air	—	191,
Charcoal	— —	89,52
Water	— —	73,30
Phlogifticated air	—	41,8
Caustic alkali	—	406,5

Total 802,12

In decompofing nitre *per fe*, when the proper apparatus was ufed for collecting the different products, I always obtained water flightly acidulated; but, as this is produced in the beginning of the procefs, I think, if the quantity of water contained in nitre were retained until the whole was decompofed, the different fluids would diffolve the entire of it, or rather more, if they could be properly fupplied with it. Therefore fixable air holds lefs water in folution, than the quantity of dephlogifticated air contained in it would in its fimple ftate.

ftate. There is no poffibility of afcertain-
ing the exact quantity of water 93,52 grains
of charcoal would hold in folution ; for,
during its converfion into an aerial ftate, a
portion of the water is generally decompofed, more efpecially if too much be ufed,
whereby we obtain fixable air and light,
and heavy inflammable air, in various proportion. Hence we cannot actually prove
the greateft weight 93,52 grains of charcoal would acquire, on its affuming an
aerial ftate. The pureft heavy inflammable
air is that which is obtained from foliated
tartar, and 5 parts of this require about 7
of dephlogifticated air to condenfe them
into fixable air; from which I infer, that
93,52 grains of charcoal, in order to arrive
at the above proportion, muft hold much
more water in folution in its elaftic ftate,
than 191 grains of the matter of dephlogifticated air, for there is very little difference
in the fpecific gravity of thefe two airs.

Mr. Kirwan fuppofes, that the whole
of the fixable air produced in the above
procefs, does not refult from the union
of charcoal and dephlogifticated air; but
that the nitre itfelf yields 91, 86 grains
of fixable air, as one of the conftituent

ent principles of the nitrous acid; and according to him, 708, 6 gr. of nitre contain but 92 gr. of dephlogisticated air, besides the portion combined in the fixable air. 11,43 gr. of pure phlogiston, or the matter of light inflammable air, besides phlogisticated air, are intimately united to the above portion of dephlogisticated air, which at least are sufficient to convert 430 cubic inches, or nearly 146 grains, or, to make an ample allowance for water, 80 grains of the pure solid gravitating matter of dephlogisticated air, into water.

Thus, according to Mr. Kirwan, the quantities of combustible matter and dephlogisticated air contained in the above charge, exclusive of what was already combined in the form of fixable air, were in the following proportion, viz.

Charcoal — —	93,52 gr.
The gravitating matter of light inflammable air - }	11,43 gr.
Dephlogisticated air —	92, gr.

Is this quantity of dephlogisticated air sufficient to saturate 11,43 gr. of light inflammable air, and consume 93,52 grains of charcoal? Undoubtedly not; and yet the

the whole of the charcoal was expended, and no inflammable air was produced. In my opinion, it needs no great fhare of fagacity to fee into the fallacy of this doctrine. The above portion of combuftible materials would require at leaft 261 gr. of the pure gravitating matter of dephlogifticated air, free from water, to confume or burn them; a quantity far exceeding the whole of the acid.

I fufed a quantity of nitre in a fmall earthen tubulated retort, whofe neck was elongated with a glafs tube which immerged in water, and introduced into it 10,33 gr. of red-hot charcoal, which was expofed to a ftrong heat for half an hour. It was a whole piece, and the weight was afcertained as foon as it was taken out of the fire. When it got in contact with the fufed nitre, a rapid deflagration enfued, attended with a copious extrication of fixable air. When I obtained about 40 cubic inches of air the deflagration ceafed, and the charcoal was about $\frac{2}{5}$ confumed. The fixable air was very pure, containing but 7 cubic inches of phlogifticated air. The difficulty of feparating the alkali from the refiduary charcoal

charcoal without wafte, and the impoffibility of confuming the entire of a quantity
of charcoal, as it muft be ufed whole in
this experiment, render it impracticable
to exactly afcertain the quantity of fixable
air a given quantity of charcoal would
yield; for, as foon as the nitre next the
charcoal is decompofed, the procefs ceafes.
In order to obviate this inconveniency as
much as poffible, I introduced a long and
flat piece of charcoal weighing 10 grains,
into a frefh charge of nitre; and as foon as
the deflagration commenced, I kept the
charge in continual agitation; which, with
the large furface the charcoal itfelf expofed,
enabled me to nearly confume the whole.
The quantity of charcoal left could not
exceed 2 grains. I obtained 80 cubic inches
of air, 67 of which were fixed air, and
the remainder phlogifticated air. Thefe
proportions induce me to fuppofe, that
either the charcoal Mr. Lavoifier ufed contained phlogifticated air, or that I ufed
purer nitre than he did; or, which is very
likely, that the nitre was only partially decompofed in the above experiment, whereby phlogifticated air had been retained.

As

As the charcoal ufed in this experiment contained neither water, phlogifticated, nor fixable air, being expofed to a ftrong heat for a confiderable time, (unlefs we admit that phlogifticated air is one of the confti-tuent principles of charcoal), 67 cubic inches of fixable air, or 31 gr. contain 8 gr. of charcoal, and the remaining 23 gr. are furnifhed by the dephlogifticated air and water.

That the real matter of charcoal enters into combination with dephlogifticated air, is hardly to be doubted, however fixable air is generated, whether by the combuf-tion of oils, fpirit of wine, refpiration, &c. or by uniting heavy inflammable air and dephlogifticated by the electric fpark. Sul-phur will decompofe nitre with various re-fults and phenomena, according to the pro-portion ufed; if two parts of nitre and one of fulphur be mixed, the nitre is de-compofed with detonation, and volatile vi-triolic acid, dephlogifticated air, and phlo-gifticated air, are produced; as Mr Berthollet has obferved. The fame philofopher found that one part of fulphur and four of nitre will not detonate, though the nitre is decom-

pofed

poſed, and nitrous air produced. He diſtilled 120 grains of nitre, and 30 gr. of
ſulphur, and obtained 108,8 cubic inches
of nitrous air, at the ſame time that the
whole of the nitre was decompoſed. This
experiment is explained in the following
manner, by Mr. Kirwan*.

According to this philoſopher, 120 gr.
of nitre, contain 55 of acid, comprehend-
ing the water which is inſeparable from it.
Of theſe ⅔ or 36,6 gr. are nitrous baſis,
which require 6,6 gr. of phlogiſton to
convert them into nitrous air; the remainder of the 55 gr. of acid is fixable
air: the following are his proportions, viz.

Nitrous baſis   36,6
Fixable air   18
                    ‾‾‾‾‾
                    54,6

There are 4-10ths of a gr. unaccounted
for. Mr. Kirwan having ſtated the principles of nitrous acid in the above proportion, ſuppoſes it to be decompoſed by a
double elective attraction, viz. the nitrous
baſis attracts the phlogiſton of the ſulphur,
which he computes to be 6,6 gr. at the

* Eſſay on Phlogiſton, p. 58-9.

ſame

fame time that the dephlogifticated bafis of the fulphur unites to its fixable air ; and as 18 gr. of fixable air, are too little to convert the dephlogifticated fulphur (as he is pleafed to call it) into fixed vitriolic acid, they convert it into vitriolic air, which unites to the alkaline bafis of the nitre. This is certainly a very ingenious mode of reafoning ; but, in my opinion, it is not difplayed in the caufe of truth.

Mr. Kirwan, in the laft ftatement of nitrous acid, left out the 2,73 gr. of pure phlogifton, which, according to himfelf, 55 grains of pure dry nitrous acid fhould contain, and which is united to the nitrous bafis*.

Therefore, counting this with the 6,6 gr. of phlogifton, which the bafis takes from the fulphur, the 36,6 gr. of nitrous bafis muft be united to 9,43 grains of phlogifton, which fhould increafe the weight of nitrous air proportionably ; fo that, inftead of 43,2, we fhould obtain 46,03 grains of nitrous air.

Thus we find, according to Mr Kirwan himfelf, that 100 gr. of nitrous bafis muft unite to 29,37 gr. of phlogifton,

* Effay on Phlogifton, p. 34.

I 2

though

though he says that 100 gr. of this, will take up but 22 of phlogiston. I think 2,73 grains of the matter of light inflammable air, in 55 gr. cannot be so very trifling as to be over looked in a compound of which dephlogisticated air constitutes the major part, more especially when we consider the quantity of dephlogisticated air which 2,73 of light inflammable air is capable of converting into water.

I think it is needless to say much more on the hypothesis of fixable air; it would be troubling my reader, and pointing out what, I flatter myself, he must be already convinced of. In my opinion, phlogiston must be entirely left out, in order to explain the different phenomena that attend the two last experiments. In the first of these experiments, Mr Berthollet used two parts of nitre, and one of sulphur: the nitre was decomposed, and the sulphur (to make use of the language of others) was dephlogisticated. Phlogisticated, and dephlogisticated air, were produced, but no nitrous air. When the same philosopher used four of nitre, to one of sulphur, vitriolic air, and nitrous air, were produced, and

the

the fulphur was likewife dephlogifticated ;
or (to make ufe of a more unexceptionable
expreffion) vitriolated.   In both experiments, it feems, the fulphur loft its phlogifton.

It appears extraordinary to me, if phlogifton fhould be one of the conftituent principles, both of the nitrous acid and fulphur,
that we did not the rather obtain nitrous
air, or, if not nitrous air, phlogifton, or
light inflammable air, when a greater quantity of fulphur was ufed, than a leffer. Mr.
Kirwan attempts to account for this by
faying, that the nitrous bafis itfelf is decompofed when it meets with too much phlogifton.

If the nitrous bafis were capable of uniting only to a limited quantity of phlogifton,
and that a greater portion was difengaged
in the procefs, the furplus fhould undoubtedly pafs over in the ftate of inflammable
air. Let us even, allow, for a fhort time, the
nitrous bafis to be decompofed, when we
ufe one of fulphur, and two of nitre ; and
let our quantities be 120 of nitre, and 60
of fulphur. According to Mr. Kirwan,
120 gr. of nitre contain 36,6 gr. of nitrous

I 3   bafis,

bafis, and 24,4 gr. of this is dephlogifticated air. 60 gr. of fulphur muft part
with 13,2 gr. of phlogifton, in order to
become volatile vitriolic acid; which in
addition to 2,73, make 15,93 gr. of phlogifton : therefore, the charge contained,
befides the quantity contained in the volatile vitriolic acid, and fixable air, which we
have nothing to do with at prefent, 15,93
gr. of phlogifton, and only 24,4 gr. of dephlogifticated air. It contained moreover,
18 gr. of phlogifticated air. The phlogifticated air is obtained in this procefs; but
the 15,93 gr. of phlogifton feem to be
totally loft, for no inflammable air is produced. The only rational mode of accounting for this loft phlogifton is, that
it united to the dephlogifticated air of the
nitrous bafis, and formed water. Is it poffible for 24,4 gr. of dephlogifticated air to
condenfe, or either to convert into water
or fixable air 15,93 gr. of the pure folid
matter of light inflammable air? Befides,
dephlogifticated air is obtained in this procefs; the quantity I cannot determine,
although I have repeated the experiment.
If we even leave out the fixable air fuppofed

to

to be contained in the nitrous acid, and admit its weight of dephlogifticated air, which, with the dephlogifticated air of the nitrous bafis, would amount to 42,4 gr. we fhould ftill find the quantity necef-fary to condenfe the phlogifton, fhort by 68 gr. at leaft. It cannot be faid that this is converted into fixable air, from facts already adduced ; befides, the fulphur is not more acidified here, than when ni-trous air is produced ; which could not be the cafe if fixable air were formed, and if this were the acidifying principle of the vitriolic acid. It is true, there is double the quantity of fulphur here, that is ufed when we obtain nitrous air ; but let it be confidered, that 48 gr. of the folid matter of fixable air fhould refult from the above quantity of phlogifton, or the matter of charcoal, which is the conftituent principle of fixable air.

These are my reafons for objecting, as well to Mr. Kirwan's doctrine, as to that of the phlogiftians at large. In my opi-nion, the decompofition of nitre by ful-phur may be accounted for more ration-ally in the following manner.

Although

Although I do not think fulphur contains phlogifton, or the folid matter of
light inflammable air, I by no means
fuppofe it to be a fimple body, but to be,
relatively to our knowledge of chemiftry, as
fimple as the earths, or the two fixed alkalies; all of which I make no doubt will
be analyzed at fome future period, when
the fcience of chemiftry will be more cultivated than at prefent, by men of genius,
fortune, and leifure.

Hence, I conceive the ultimate particles
of fulphur to unite in fpecie to thefe of
dephlogifticated air, as phlogifticated air
does during the formation of nitrous acid,
without lofing any thing but fire, which
is always difengaged when a chemical combination takes place.

Of the conftituent parts of the nitrous
acid I have given my opinion, as deduced
from facts. I have likewife fuppofed dephlogifticated air to be retained in nitre,
with the force of 7, and fulphur to attract
it with the force of $6\frac{7}{8}$. I do not mean to
intimate that thefe are their abfolute forces;
but, nearly the proportion they bear to one
another. Thus, fulphur will not decompofe

pofe nitre, until expofed to heat fufficient
to alter thefe forces. Nitre and fulphur
mixed and comminuted, and put on hot
iron, will not detonate, nor will the nitre
be decompofed, though the fulphur will
be burned out with a languid phofphore-
fcent-like flame. Gunpowder alfo will not
detonate, though the fulphur may be burned
out with the fame phenomenon, as may
be feen by putting a little on a hot cinder,
foon after it lofes ignition. But, when
nitre and fulphur are expofed to that degree of heat, which will fo relax the chemical tie of the conftituent principles of
nitre, as to caft the fcale in favour of the
fulphur, it will then rapidly unite to the
dephlogifticated air of the nitre, and prefent the phenomena of combuftion and detonation.

Thus, two parts of nitre and one of fulphur will detonate when expofed to fufficient heat, at the fame time that the nitrous acid is wholly decompofed. Sulphur
will not unite to more dephlogifticated air,
in the degree of heat neceffary to conduct
this procefs, than is fufficient to convert
it into volatile vitriolic acid; or if it even
did,

did, its attraction is not ſtrong enough to
take it from the nitre; as has been ſhewn in
the third ſection of this work. Therefore
we obtain, from the above proportion, volatile vitriolic acid, dephlogiſticated air, and
phlogiſticated air; there is likewiſe ſome
ſulphur ſublimed in the beginning of the
proceſs. When one part of ſulphur, and
four of nitre are uſed, the products are
different; for then, the quantity of ſulphur being very ſmall, it preſents but a
few ſurfaces when mixed with the nitre,
ſo that it can only take the portion of dephlogiſticated air from the nitre which is
over and above the quantity contained in
nitrous air; thus the nitrous air, being deprived of its dephlogiſticated air, is readily
expelled from the alkali. The reaſon no
deflagration takes place is, the particles
of ſulphur being but few, and interpoſed
by the nitre, the quantity of fire diſengaged
by the more intimate union of dephlogiſticated air to the ſulphur, is inſenſibly diſ-
ſipated; that is, it is not liberated in a
ſufficient degree of accumulation, to preſent the phenomena of light and combuſtion. The reverſe takes place when a

greater

greater quantity of fulphur is ufed: then the particles of fulphur being more numerous, and of courfe, clofer to one another, fire is difengaged in a more concentrated ftate; at the fame time that the whole, nearly, of the dephlogifticated air of the nitre is taken up. In order to deprive the nitre of the whole of its dephlogifticated air, it is neceffary to ufe more fulphur than can unite to the dephlogifticated air. 1ft, Becaufe an ultimate particle of fulphur can only take an ultimate particle of dephlogifticated air from the nitre, whereby it forms volatile vitriolic acid. 2d, As every ultimate molecule of nitre contains, moft commonly, four ultimate particles of dephlogifticated air, and one of phlogifticated air, which being enveloped thus in aggregates by alkali and water, are partly defended from the action of the fulphur.

Therefore, as the former cannot be fo ultimately divided as the latter; if only that quantity of fulphur be mixed with the nitre, which will expofe but furfaces enough to deprive the molecules of nitre of one half of their dephlogifticated air, nitrous air is produced; but if, on the contrary,

trary, a fufficiency be ufed to deprive the molecules of nitre of $\frac{3}{4}$ of their dephlogifti-cated air, we obtain phlogifticated, de-phlogifticated, and vitriolic air.

If four parts of nitre, two of fulphur, and three of charcoal, be mixed and well powdered, they will burn rapidly, and emit a volatile vitriolic, and an hepatic fmell. The entire of the fulphur is not here converted into volatile vitriolic acid. The charcoal having greater attraction to dephlogifticated air, unites to the moft part of it, while a portion of the ful-phur unites to the alkali of the nitre. Hence arifes the hepatic fmell during the inflam-mation of gunpowder.

Charcoal detonates with nitre in various proportions, but will not difengage nitrous air in any proportion whatever. If nitrous air were produced, in confequence of a cer-tain portion of phlogifton, as Mr Kirwan fuppofes, a lefs quantity of charcoal than is fufficient to decompofe a quantity of nitre, fhould difengage it, if charcoal contains phlogifton. I think this may be explained on the fame principle with the deflagration of fulphur and nitre. Charcoal and nitre
diftilled

diftilled in various proportion, will afford
phlogifticated and fixable air, but not a
particle of nitrous air is produced. I
would afk the phlogiftians, why nitrous air
is not procured here, when we obtain it
from fulphur and nitre under the fame
circumftances ?

Charcoal not only unites to a larger
quantity of dephlogifticated air, than fulphur does, in order to become volatile vitriolic acid, but likewife attracts the portion
neceffary to its converfion into aerial acid
with greater force. Thus charcoal mixed
with nitre in a very fmall proportion will
detonate, and fixable and phlogifticated air
is produced. Every fingle molecule of
charcoal (for we cannot reduce it into its
ultimate particles by attrition) is capable
of defpoiling a fingle molecule of nitre of
the whole of its dephlogifticated air ; and
this decompofition is fo rapid, that the
molecule of charcoal directs its whole attraction to the molecule of nitre, which
firft influences it ; otherwife we fhould expect that the charcoal would take a portion
of dephlogifticated air from different nitrous

trous - molecules at the fame time, and thereby difengage nitrous air.

Metals decompofe nitre, and prefent the fame phenomena which charcoal does, but with a different refult; for they produce little or no fixable air : and even the fmall quantity obtained from fome metals, particularly from iron, is fo liable to vary, that its prefence appears to be accidental. Nitrous air is not produced during the decompofition of nitre by iron filings. Mr Berthollet diftilled 472,5 gr. of nitre, with 236,23 of iron filings, and obtained 453,37 cubic inches of air, of nearly the fame ftandard with atmofpheric air*. In fhort, all the imperfect metals will detonate with nitre, without producing a particle of nitrous air. As this is explicable on the fame principle with charcoal and nitre, I fhall not trouble my reader with it; but only obferve, that if nitrous air were compofed of nitrous bafis and phlogifton, we could not but adjuft the proportion of the nitre and metal favourable to the production of it, provided the metals contained phlogifton.

* 2 pr. 217 mem. par. An 1782, p. 495; and 1783, p. 85.

The

The regulus of arfenic put on red-hot iron, will burn with a flame. This does not indicate its greater attraction than other metals to dephlogifticated air, but the weaker adhefion of its ultimate parts to one another. The white calx of arfenic, although it is capable of uniting to more air, will not prefent the fame phenomenon.

The regulus of arfenic will detonate rapidly with nitre. Equal parts of the white calx of arfenic and nitre, projected into a crucible hot enough to fufe them inftantly, will not detonate. Two of nitre and one of the calx will not detonate. Three parts of nitre and one of arfenic exhibit a few brilliant fparks here and there; as do likewife two of arfenic and one of nitre, provided the crucible be very hot : but it feems to me to proceed from a few reguline particles, accidentally interfperfed in the calx ; otherwife the deflagration muft have been more general. Nitrous air is produced from either of thefe proportions, but in a larger quantity when two of nitre and one of arfenic are ufed. Hence, we find that the regulus of arfenic *per fe* will unite to dephlogifticated air, and prefent the phenomenon of com-

combuſtion, and that the calx will not, and likewiſe that the regulus will detonate with nitre, and that the calx will not; and laſtly, that nitrous air is produced by the calx, and none by the regulus. Let us view theſe facts narrowly, and comparatively, and we ſhall find that they tend much to corroborate the foregoing explanation of deflagration, and the production of nitrous air.

That the regulus of arſenic combines with a certain portion of dephlogiſticated air, and that on this union depends its calciform ſtate, is unqueſtionable; and likewiſe that the calx of arſenic will unite to more air, is beyond a doubt, as ſhall preſently appear. Thus then, the regulus of arſenic, having greater attraction to dephlogiſticated air, and being likewiſe capable of uniting to a larger quantity than the calx, as being already nearly ſaturated with it, wholly decompoſes the nitre; and as a great number of the particles of dephlogiſticated air unite with ſuch rapidity and accumulation, in a given time, the phenomenon of combuſtion is produced.

When we take the calx, the reſult and

appear-

appearances are different from the former ; becaufe, being already combined with de-phlogifticated air, it can only unite to a fmall portion of it, and this it even attracts with lefs force than the quantity neceffary to its calcination. Thus, it can take only a portion of its dephlogifticated air from the nitre ; whereby, as has been already ex-plained, we obtain nitrous air, at the fame time that no deflagration takes place.

The phlogiftians would explain the above facts by faying, that the different pheno-mena proceeded from phlogifton. Does the calx of arfenic contain phlogifton un-combined *with* dephlogifticated air ? If it does, all the metallic calces contain phlogifton. Can any reafon be affigned for fuppofing the calx of arfenic to contain phlogifton, but its property of uniting to more dephlo-gifticated air ? Or, is the production of nitrous air a fure fign that the bodies that difengage it, lofe their phlogifton ? If fo, the following facts are quite repugnant to it. The white calx of arfenic expofed to heat, in a crucible, will decompofe nitrous acid, and difengage nitrous air very copi-oufly. Thus, if nitrous acid in fmall

K

quan-

tities be poured on it, from time to time,
when every preceding portion takes due
effect, the arſenic is acidified. In conducting this proceſs, the fire ſhould be gradually increaſed, in proportion as the arſenic draws near a ſaturation with dephlogiſticated air; for the violent ebullition that
takes place, particularly in the beginning,
ſwells the charge, and puffs it over. The
fumes ſhould likewiſe be guarded againſt.
Marine acid, mixed with the nitrous acid
in ſmall proportion, expedites this proceſs.
If the acid of arſenic, thus prepared, be expoſed to a ſtronger heat than is neceſſary to
its formation, it yields dephlogiſticated air,
and the arſenic is reduced to the ſtate of a
calx, and no fixable air is produced.

If the nitrous air were compoſed of nitrous baſis, and the vaſt quantity of phlogiſton which the phlogiſtians ſuppoſe, the
calx of arſenic muſt be deprived of a large
portion of phlogiſton in the above proceſs;
and if the preſence of this phlogiſton were
neceſſary to the reduction of the acid into
a calx again, how is it ſupplied? In my
opinion, this is inexplicable in the phlogiſtic
doctrine, unleſs we admit the hypotheſis
of

of fixable air; the fallacy of which, I flatter myfelf, my reader is already aware of. Mr. Kirwan would explain the above procefs by faying, that the fixable air of the nitrous acid unites to the calx, at the fame time that its phlogifton unites to the dephlogifticated bafis of the nitrous acid, and forms nitrous air; and that a ftronger heat decompofes the fixable air, whereby its phlogifton remains attached to the calx, at the fame time that its dephlogifticated air is expelled in an aerial ftate. As this mode of reafoning appears plaufible enough for equivocation, it may be adopted in this one circumftance. But what correfpondence does it bear to other connected facts? A concatenation of facts, which regularly correfpond with each other, will always bring truth to light; although a number of facts ever fo well underftood or arranged, are feldom without a few, which may feparately admit of a quibble, for thofe who wifh to confound truth with falfehood, either out of a fpirit of obftinacy, prejudice, or a defire of difplaying their ingenuity. Hence arife fo many theological controverfies, as well as difference of opinion in

philo-

philofophy. But happily for mankind, the moſt ingenious projects, which the moſt fertile imagination can produce to ſuppreſs truth, generally appear, ſooner or later, as ſo many evidences in her favour.

Having treated of the decompoſition of nitre, I am now to inquire into the nature of nitrous acid in its ſimple ſtate. In order to well underſtand the variety of changes which this acid is capable of undergoing by the mediation of different ſubſtances, it will be neceſſary, firſt, to be acquainted with the force by which its conſtituent principles are united.

In my opinion, the pureſt nitrous acid contains 5 of dephlogiſticated to 1 of phlogiſticated air. Nitrous air, according to Kirwan, contains 2 of dephlogiſticated to 1 of phlogiſticated air. According to Lavoiſier, 100 gr. of nitrous air contain 32 gr. of phlogiſticated air, and 68 of dephlogiſticated air. I am myſelf of the former philoſopher's opinion: I likewiſe am of opinion, that every primary particle of phlogiſticated air is united to two of dephlogiſticated air, and that theſe mo-

lecules

lecules are furrounded with one common atmofphere of fire.

To render this more explicable, let us fuppofe P to be an ultimate particle of phlogifticated air, which attracts dephlogifticated air with the force of 3 ; let *a* be a particle of dephlogifticated air, whofe attraction to P we will fuppofe to be 3 more, by which they unite with the force of 6 : the nature of this compound will be hereafter explained.

Let us confider this to be the utmoft force that can fubfift between dephlogifticated and phlogifticated air. 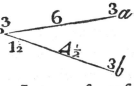 Let us fuppofe another particle of dephlogifticated air *b* to unite to P, they will not unite with the force of 6, but with the force of $4\frac{1}{2}$; that is, the whole power of P, which is but 3, will be equally divided and directed in two points towards *a* and *b*; fo that P and *a b* will unite with the forces annexed to them ; 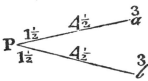 for the attraction of *a* and *b* to P meeting with no interruption, will

K 3

fuffer

suffer no diminution. This I confider to be the true ftate of nitrous air. Let us now fuppofe another particle of dephlogifticated air *c* to unite to P, it will combine only with the force of

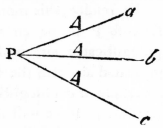

4, whereby *a b c* and P will gravitate toward one another. Such is the ftate of the red nitrous vapour, or the red nitrous acid.

Let us again fuppofe a fourth particle of dephlogifticated air *d* to combine with P, it will unite only with the force of $3\frac{3}{4}$. This I think is the ftate of the pale or ftraw-coloured nitrous acid.

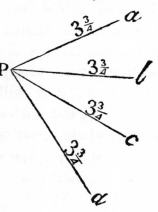

Laftly, let us fuppofe a fifth particle of dephlogifticated air *e*, to unite to P, it will combine with the force of $3\frac{3}{5}$, fo that *a b c d* and *e* will each grav tate towards P as their common

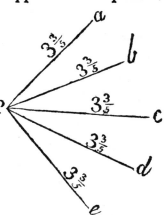

centre of gravity. This is the moft perfect ftate of colourlefs nitrous acid; and in my opinion no more dephlogifticated air can unite to the phlogifticated air, as having its whole force of attraction expended on the particles of dephlogifticated air, *a b c d e*. This illuftrates the nature of faturation. Thence we find that dephlogifticated air is retained with lefs force in the perfect or colourlefs nitrous acid, than in the ftraw-coloured, or in the red, or in nitrous air. This explains the eafy feparation of dephlogifticated air from perfect nitrous acid, when expofed to the fun, or even to an artificial light or heat, at the fame time that the

K 4   nitrous

nitrous acid is coloured *. If we expofe
nitrous acid in any other ftate to the fun,
we do not obtain a particle of dephlogifticated air, but moft frequently red nitrous
vapour.

If the red nitrous acid be expofed to the
air, it emits red nitrous vapour, and acquires a pale colour ; becaufe nitrous vapour cannot take dephlogifticated air from
the pale, as the pale retains it with as great
force as the red vapour attracts it. Nitrous
air will deprive either the ftraw-coloured
or colourlefs nitrous acid of a portion of
their dephlogifticated air. The former, as
Dr. Prieftley firft obferved, acquires an
orange colour, on combining with a portion of it ; but, on uniting to more nitrous
air, becomes green ; and laftly, when faturated with it, acquires a red colour, and
affumes the ftate of vapour. Nitrous air
will not deprive the red nitrous acid of any
portion of its dephlogifticated air, on the
fame principle that the red nitrous acid

* Dr. Prieftley found that dephlogifticated air was
produced from nitrous acid, by pafiing the electric fpark
in a fmall quantity of common air confined in it. Vol.
VII. p. 339.

will

will not decompofe the pale nitrous acid, or the pale, the colourlefs.

Hence we find that nitrous air, though it cannot take dephlogifticated air from the red nitrous acid, will take it from the pale; and likewife, although the red nitrous acid will not take dephlogifticated air from the pale, that it will take it from the colourlefs.

If the colourlefs nitrous acid be mixed with water, it will preferve its tranfparency; but the red nitrous acid treated in the fame manner, will acquire a blueifh green colour. Water in this cafe condenfes nitrous vapour fo much, from its attraction to it, that it has the fame effect as if a portion of it had been expelled.

Having premifed thus much on the different ftages of nitrous acid, I fhall now proceed to the decompofition of it again, and endeavour to explain it in as few words as perfpicuity will allow me.

If a metal be introduced into the red, pale, or colourlefs nitrous acid, it will be calcined, and nitrous air will be extricated; that is, it will deprive the nitrous air of that portion of dephlogifticated air necef-

fary

fary to its condenfation, or to the formation
of nitrous acid. The metal deprives the
particles of acid in contact with it, of the
whole of their dephlogifticated air. The
force of 7, with which we have fuppofed
metals to attract dephlogifticated air, being
fo much fuperior to 3⅔ if we make ufe of
the colourlefs, or to 3¼ if we ufe the pale,
together with the number of ultimate furfaces a metal muft prefent, deprives the
phlogifticated air (of the nitrous acid) of its
dephlogifticated air, with fuch quicknefs,
that it is at once left deftitute of both fire
and dephlogifticated air; but before it has
time to collect an atmofphere of fire, which
would prevent a fecond union, it exerts the
force of 3 on its neighbouring particle of
acid, which as yet did not reach the metallic influence, and thereby recovers that
portion of dephlogifticated air neceffary to
the formation of nitrous air. This again,
in paffing in the acid, if it be the pale or
colourlefs, will recover air fufficient to
form nitrous vapour, or red nitrous acid.
Thus it is, when firft a metal is introduced
into the pale or colourlefs nitrous acid,
though a folution takes place, that little or
no

no nitrous air is produced, until the acid
is coloured. As the metal, after it is calcined, requires red nitrous acid to hold it in
folution (for perfect nitrous acid will not
do, as fhall hereafter appear), the nitrous
acid, which the phlogifticated air deprives
of a portion of dephlogifticated air, unites
to it.

The foregoing explanation may appear,
at firft fight, more fpeculative than real.
But does not the decompofition of nitre
by metallic filings, whether thefe be deflagrated in a red-hot crucible, or diftilled
by a more gentle and gradual heat in a retort, tend to confirm it? Is not the acid
completely decompofed here, whatever proportion of the materials be ufed? In this
latter cafe, the metallic furface deprives the
nitrous molecules, in contact with it, of
the whole of their dephlogifticated air;
by which the phlogifticated air, as having
no fenfible attraction to the alkali, is difengaged in its fimple ftate, if uniting to
fire be fuch; for its attraction to dephlogifticated air is not ftrong enough to recover any portion of it from the joint force
of phlogifticated air and alkali.

I in-

I introduced fome iron filings, recently prepared, into a mixture of about 16 parts of water, and 1 of pale nitrous acid : when they ftood fome time, phlogifticated air was produced, but not a particle of nitrous air. It may be proper to acquaint my reader, that I gueffed the above proportion ; but as a variety of proportions will anfwer, the experiment cannot fail of fuccefs. Here the few particles of the nitrous acid which come in contact with the metal, are wholly deprived of their dephlogifticated air ; and as the phlogifticated air is at too great a diftance from the molicules of nitrous acid, and as its attraction is too weak to decompofe water, it inftantly collects atmofpheres of fire, which defend it, in its paffage through the folution, from the action of the dephlogifticated air of the fufpended acid.

When firft I made this experiment, I obtained inflammable air, which puzzled me very much ; but recollecting that I purchafed the acid at a common chemift's, I immediately fufpected what I afterwards found to be true ; for, on dropping the folution of filver in fome of this acid, an immediate

mediate cloudinefs fucceeded : therefore I was obliged to have recourfe to this method of purifying it.

In order to feparate the whole of the marine acid from the nitrous acid, without an impregnation of nitrated filver, I would recommend both time and patience. A fingle drop only of the folution of filver fhould be ufed at a time, and the cloudinefs of each drop fhould fubfide before another is added.

This experiment not only confirms the foregoing explanation of the decompofition of nitre and nitrous acid by metals, but likewife tends ftrongly to confute the phlogiftic theory. Here the metal is calcined, and there is neither inflammable nor nitrous air produced. Let us add to this an experiment already defcribed, viz. the folution of iron in volatile vitriolic acid, without the production of inflammable air ; and the decompofition of this again by nitrous acid, without the extrication of nitrous air or phlogifticated air, though the metal is calcined. Let the phlogiftians explain thefe two laft experiments on rational principles in their doctrine, and then I have done ;

unlefs

unlefs they fuppofe that phlogifticated air itfelf is a compound of phlogifton and fomething elfe; and they might as well fay, that the concrete matter of light inflammable air, or of dephlogifticated air, is a compound : befides, there is no phlogifticated air produced by decompofing a folution of iron in volatile vitriolic acid, by the nitrous acid. This experiment may be accounted for in the antiphlogiftic doctrine, in the following manner :

The volatile vitriolic acid, as has been already fhewn, diffolves the iron, by which it is reduced into its primary particles, and difperfed through the folution. Nitrous acid dropped into this, mixes likewife in the folution; and from the quantity of water which muft neceffarily be prefent in volatile vitriolic acid, and in nitrous acid, the ultimate molicules of both fubftances are removed from one another; whereby only a fingle primary particle of iron can meet only a fingle molicule of nitrous acid, which can fupply it with both dephlogifticated air of calcination and acid of folution; and thus no nitrous air is produced.

The

The multiplicity of ultimate furfaces, which are as if it were concentrated, or crowded into fo fmall a compafs in metals, from the nature of their texture, is the chief caufe of the decompofition of nitrous acid during their folution in it; particularly when the pale or colourlefs nitrous acid is ufed.

Mr. Lavoifier, to whom we are chiefly indebted for reducing this ufeful fcience into a rational fyftem, and expelling that gloom which had overwhelmed it for all ages paft, took 945 gr. of nitrous acid, whofe fpecific gravity was 1,316, and to this he added 1104 gr. of mercury *. The whole of the mercury was diffolved, and he obtained 273,234 cubic inches of nitrous air. He afterward expofed the mercurial falt to a red heat, and obtained from it 287,742 cubic inches of dephlogifticated air, at the fame time that the mercury was revived.

Mr. Lavoifier juftly drew the following conclufions from the above experiment: 1ft, That the weight of the airs produced

* Mem. Par. 1776, p. 670.

gave

gave the weight of the real acid contained in 945 grains of fpirit of nitre, whofe fpecific gravity was 1,316. 2d, That nitrous air was a conftituent principle in nitrous acid; and that its production merely depended upon a portion of dephlogifticated air being withdrawn from it, as it formed nitrous acid again on the reftoration of its dephlogifticated air. Laftly, That the mercury lofes nothing; but that its calcination depended folely upon its union to dephlogifticated air, as it had been revived by the mere expulfion of it again.

Mr. Kirwan objects to thefe conclufions *, 1ft, Becaufe the whole of the acid could not be decompofed, as a portion muft have neceffarily paffed over during the diftillation of the mercurial folution. 2dly, Becaufe it had not been proved by Mr. Lavoifier, that the nitrous air was not produced at the expence of one of the conftituent principles of the mercury. 3dly, As the fame quantity of nitrous acid had not been produced by the re-union of both airs, and as there had been an excefs of one of them.

* Effay on Phlogifton, p. 63.

I do

I do not fee the force of the firſt of theſe ob-
jeſtions ; for what does it avail whether the
acid was in part, or wholly decompoſed ?
The only inference that can be drawn from
it, is, that the ſpirit of nitre uſed contained
more real acid than Mr. Lavoiſier or Mr.
Kirwan himſelf ſuppoſed ; or, that the airs
contained more water than they imagined,
or ſomething elſe which did not exiſt in
the ſpirit of nitre, and which of courſe the
metal muſt impart. But Mr. Kirwan
allows, that the airs do not acquire any
additional weight from the mercury ; for
he ſays *, "The weight of the acid aſtually
combined with the mercury during the ſolution, muſt agree with that of the airs obtained ; for, though the phlogiſton of the
nitrous air was taken from the metal, and
therefore foreign to the acid, yet, as the metal was at laſt revived, it muſt have taken
from the acid as much phlogiſton as it gave
to it."

Mr. Kirwan's ſecond objeſtion is certainly the only loop-hole left for the phlogiſtic theory, and for that reaſon requires

* Eſſay on Phlogiſton, page 67.

L   the

the ſtricteſt ſcrutiny. He ſuppoſes, as I
have already obſerved, and as I ſhall mention here in a few words, that the mercury
gives up its phlogiſton to the nitrous baſis,
by which it is converted into nitrous air, at
the ſame time that the fixable air of the nitrous acid unites to the metallic baſis and
forms a calx. He likewiſe diſpoſes of another portion of phlogiſton, by ſaying, that
it decompoſes part of the nitrous baſis, and
forms fixable air by uniting to its dephlogiſticated air. The remainder of the phlogiſton, as he ſuppoſes, combines both with
19 grains of phlogiſticated acid that come
over uncombined, and with the compound
of acid and calx. After thus diſtributing
the quantity of phlogiſton contained in the
metal (and indeed he might have contrived
to diſpoſe of as much again in the ſame
manner), he ſuppoſes that the fixable air
is decompoſed during the revival of the
mercury; and that its phlogiſton unites to
the metallic baſis, at the ſame time that its
dephlogiſticated air is expelled in its ſimple
aerial ſtate. But, as the quantity of phlogiſton in the fixable air is not equal to the
quantity the mercury gives out in order
to

to become calcined, and of courfe infufficient to revive the metallic bafis, he con-
trives to have this deficiency fupplied by
that portion combined with the acid and
calx. This is Mr. Kirwan's opinion, and I
muft confefs I do not fee how he can juftify
it. Therefore, convinced that his method of
fupporting this hypothefis carries with it
no fort of conviction, to avoid prolixity, I
fhall not enter into a detail of it, but refer
my reader to the author's own words *.

Mr. Kirwan's calculating the quantity of
phlogifton contained in the ingredients ufed
in the above experiment, does not in the
leaft tend to prove the prefence of the
fmalleft quantity of phlogifton, or the matter of light inflammable air. It is a very
eafy matter to make numbers agree with
what never exifted but in imagination.

The hypothefis of fixable air being de-
monftrably erroneous, the phlogiftic doctrine appears very defective in the above experiment. The phlogiftians muft actually
acknowledge, that either the metal or the
nitrous air contains no phlogifton.

* Effay on Phlogifton, pages 67-8-9.

L 2

If

If nitrous air were compofed of nitrous bafis, faturated with phlogifton, how comes it to pafs that metals are calcined in it?

Dr. Prieftley fufed fome iron in nitrous air; it calcined and increafed in weight, and nothing but phlogifticated air remained *. Mr. Kirwan explains this experiment by faying, that the dephlogifticated air of the nitrous air unites to both the phlogifton of the metal and to that contained in the nitrous air itfelf, and forms water, which unites to the metallic bafis. Here he fuppofes a calx to be formed by the union of water to the metal, and in other circumftances by the union of fixable air. Is this confiftent? 122 gr. of nitrous air, according to Mr. Kirwan, contain 22 gr. of phlogifton, 66,36 gr. of dephlogifticated air; or, to make a good allowance for it, let us fay 68 gr. and the remainder is phlogifticated air. By this, the proportion the dephlogifticated bears to the inflammable air, is nearly as 3 to 1.

According to Mr. Lavoifier, the proportion of dephlogifticated air in water, is to the inflammable air as 7 to 1; and indeed,

* vi. Pr. 304.

agreeable

agreeable to all experience, it is at leaft 6
to 1.

Therefore, laying afide the phlogifton of
the metal, after the condenfation of the
dephlogifticated air into water, we fhould
have a large refiduum of inflammable air in
the above experiment. Befides, if metals
be faturated with phlogifton in their perfect
ftate, they muft either part with it on uniting to water, or elfe, by the joint attraction
of it, and the metallic bafis, unite with dephlogifticated air fimply, and leave the whole
of the phlogifton of the nitrous air behind.

The fame excellent philofopher reduced
nitrous air, by taking the electric fpark in it
to $\frac{1}{3}$ of its bulk; nitrous acid was produced,
and the refiduum was phlogifticated air. At
another time he reduced nitrous air to $\frac{1}{4}$ of
its original bulk by the electric fpark,
and the refiduum contained $\frac{1}{4}$ of nitrous
air *. He likewife, in one experiment,
reduced one and a half meafure to 0,4 of a
meafure, by electric explofions taken in a
veffel of mercury, with water on the furface of it. The water was acid to the tafte,
and his iron conductor was partly diffolved.

* Vol. vi. p. 312.

L 3   Mr.

Mr. Kirwan explains thefe experiments, by fuppofing, that the dephlogifticated air unites to the phlogifton of the nitrous air, and forms water ; and that the nitrous acid produced was originally formed and fufpended in the air. From what I have already faid, it appears, if nitrous air contained phlogifton, we fhould have a refiduum of inflammable air in thefe experiments, as not containing dephlogifticated air enough (according to Mr. Kirwan's own calculations), at leaft by $\frac{1}{2}$, to convert the whole of the phlogifton into water. July 1787 I repeated the above experiment (with a view different to the prefent) ; and, after paffing the nitrous air in cauftic volatile alkali, reduced it by repeatedly taking the electric fpark in it to about $\frac{1}{4}$ of its bulk, nitrous acid was produced, and the refiduum was pure phlogifticated air. Having narrowly attended to this experiment, I was at that time induced to fuppofe, but am now fully convinced, that nitrous acid is formed here in confequence of a decompofition of part of the nitrous air, whereby the remainder is furnifhed with dephlogifticated air, and fo forms nitrous acid, at the fame time that gifticated

the phlogifticated air of that portion of dephlogifticated air that forms the new compound, remains fingle and alone. Whenever Dr. Prieftley diminifhed nitrous air by
fufing iron in it, no acid (as he obferves)
was formed. He likewife found, that minium could not be reduced by the heat
of his burning lens in nitrous air *.
If the quantity of phlogifton, which Mr.
Kirwan fuppofes, exifted in nitrous air,
metallic calces fhould be revived in it;
but, on the contrary, metals are calcined
in it. This muft be very unfavourable to
Mr. Kirwan's doctrine; for the fuppofition
that nitrous air retains, as one of its conftituent principles, the phlogifton of the metal, is the whole fupport of his theory; as,
by this, he is enabled to fay, that the fixable air is decompofed by giving up its
phlogifton to the metal, whereby we obtain
dephlogifticated air in its fimple aerial ftate.
But if the metal fhould not lofe its phlogifton, fixable air cannot by any means be
fuppofed to be decompofed; and of courfe,
if it were one of the conftituent parts of

* Vol. VI. p. 11.

L 4

nitrous

nitrous acid, it fhould be obtained from the calx in its natural ftate. Indeed, if we compare the quantity of fire difengaged, during the union of dephlogifticated air and light inflammable air, or the heavy inflammable air, or even the folid matter of charcoal, fulphur, and phofphorus, to that developed during the rapid combination of nitrous air and dephlogifticated air, we fhall not hefitate a moment to fay, that it unites in this latter to a fubftance quite different from either of the former fubftances, and that the compound is of a different nature. Dr. Prieftley found, that nitrous air, confined above a year in contact with iron ftanding in water, was reduced, and that the refiduum was phlogifticated air *. I have expofed nitrous air to iron filings and water for three months; it was diminifhed nearly $\frac{2}{3}$, and extinguifhed a candle.

It is very well known, that iron expofed to water alone will produce inflammable air; then if nitrous air were compofed of light inflammable air, dephlogifticated air and phlogifticated air, we fhould obtain

* Vol. ii. p. 177.

pure

pure phlogifton, or light inflammable air, in
the above experiment.

Is it not contrary to all laws, fo far as experience has enabled us to judge, to fuppofe that iron, if it were faturated with
phlogifton, fhould give it out in contact with
water, which is compofed of dephlogifticated air and light inflammable air, at the
fame time that, expofed under the fame circumftances to an aerial compound of light
inflammable air, dephlogifticated and phlogifticated air, it fhould abforb an additional
quantity of phlogifton? This likewife appears the more extraordinary, when we find
that iron, and other metals, unite in the dry
way to a fufficiency of dephlogifticated air to
faturate them; which fhews, if they attract
it in confequence of phlogifton, that they
contain phlogifton enough of their own,
without the affiftance of foreign phlogifton.
Hence I fhould fuppofe, that iron could
not influence the phlogifton of nitrous air;
or if it fhould attract it and dephlogifticated
air jointly, that it muft part with its own
phlogifton.

This circumftance alone of metals withdrawing dephlogifticated air from nitrous

air,

air, and leaving only phlogisticated air behind, proves that either the metal or the
nitrous air contains no phlogiston ; and indeed, in addition to other adduced facts, it
convinces me, that neither contains a particle of the matter of light inflammable air.

It is now very well known, that hepatic
air is composed of light inflammable air
and sulphur. If equal parts of hepatic air
and nitrous air be mixed, they will contract
to more than ¾ of their bulk ; sulphur will
be precipitated, and the residuum is dephlogisticated nitrous air ; which, as shall
hereafter appear, contains no such thing as
phlogiston. Is it reasonable to suppose,
that hepatic gas should take light inflammable air, or phlogiston, from the nitrous
air, when it is already saturated with what
they call phlogiston ? Dr. Priestley likewise
reduced nitrous air to more than one half,
by exposing Homberg's pyrophorus to it,
which had taken fire in it, and the residuum
was dephlogisticated nitrous air, and no
acid was produced. These facts tend strongly to prove, that nitrous air does not contain the matter of light inflammable air.

Mr.

Mr. Kirwan's third and laſt objeċtion does not appear to me to be of ſuch moment as the former. It is true, as this philoſopher obſerves, there had been an exceſs of dephlogiſticated air produced : I mean by exceſs, a greater quantity than the nitrous air obtained could condenſe in the ordinary way of mixing them.

The quantity of nitrous air obtained was 273,234 cubic inches, or 101,09 gr. and the dephlogiſticated air amounted to 287,743 cubic inches, or 97,83 gr. The above quantity of pure nitrous air contains 91,78 cubic inches of phlogiſticated air, and 182,156 cubic inches of dephlogiſticated air, which, in addition to the quantity expelled from the calx, make 469,898 cubic inches of dephlogiſticated air; which, ſubtraċting 14,512 cubic inches from them, make five of dephlogiſticated air to one of phlogiſticated air, being the exaċt proportion of perfeċt nitrous acid.

By theſe calculations I find, if Mr. Lavoiſier uſed perfeċt nitrous acid, that the exceſs of dephlogiſticated air is not ſo great as Mr. Kirwan imagines. Before we attempt to judge of the exceſs of dephlogiſticated

gifticated air, in the above experiment, the quantity of phlogifticated air mixed with both the airs fhould have been firft afcertained, by which we might eftimate the quantity of nitrous air this would form.

Mr. Kirwan feems to make no allowance for this, though he acknowledges that phlogifticated air is difengaged, which partly mixes with the nitrous air, and partly unites to the fixable air combined with the calx; which, he fays, is partly decompofed during the decompofition of the fixable air by the revivification of the mercury *. I do not underftand what he means by the decompofition of phlogifticated air, for it has not, to our knowledge, been as yet decompofed. Mr. Kirwan likewife mentions, that during the decompofition of nitre *(per fe)* a portion of the phlogifticated air is decompofed and burned, without any farther information on the fubject. If he can decompofe this, he certainly will do more than I at prefent fufpect.

Taking the foregoing circumftances into confideration, by what I can infer from Mr.

* Effay on Phlogifton, p. 69.

Lavoifier's

Lavoisier's experiment, together with my own obfervations on the fame fubject, I think both the combined and uncombined phlogifticated air muft be to the dephlogif-ticated as one to four, which is the portion of the pale nitrous acid. Can this be called an excefs? Nitrous air is allowed to contain one of phlogifticated to two of dephlogif-ticated air: pure nitrous air will readily unite with half its bulk of dephlogifticated air, and form the orange coloured nitrous acid. Every 54 gr. of this acid contain, including the water which the airs hold in folution, 41,6ɔ5 gr. of dephlogifticated air, and 12,335 gr. of phlogifticated air. There-fore it contains 5 grains in 24 more than the red nitrous vapour does. Thefe pro-portions differ widely from thofe of the perfect nitrous acid, which fhews, though nitrous air will not readily unite to more air in the ordinary way than the proportion mentioned above, that it will in time con-denfe a larger quantity. Analogous to this is the formation of vitriolic acid; for ful-phur will not combine during its combuf-tion with much more dephlogifticated air than is fufficient to convert it into volatile vitriolic acid, but in time, by help of water,

heat,

heat, and expofure to air, it abforbs a fufficient quantity to form perfect vitriolic acid.

Red nitrous acid expofed to dephlogifticated air, will gradually abforb it, and in time, if fupplied with a fufficient quantity of it, will become colourlefs. I repeated this experiment to my fatisfaction in the year 1786. I do not claim the originality of it; it is to Dr. Prieftley we are indebted, as well for this, as for his many other valuable experiments. The fame philofopher found, that fuming fpirit of nitre, which is not the moft perfect, phlogifticates, as he is pleafed to call it, common air*. He likewife obferves, that the colourlefs nitrous vapour will not affect dephlogifticated air, or vitiate common air †. I expofed dephlogifticated air to the perfect nitrous acid for three weeks, and it was not in the leaft changed. I found, that the red nitrous vapour will diminifh common air, but not fo readily as the red nitrous acid. Though the perfect nitrous vapour will not diminifh dephlogifticated air, yet it has the reverfe effect, for it will readily contract nitrous air. This fhews that it is fully

* Vol. II. p. 165.   † Vol. II. p. 165.

faturated

faturated with dephlogifticated air, and is in the ftate already defcribed. Dr. Prieftley found, that melted nitre abforbs dephlogifticated air *. A folution of nitre, which had been melted, likewife abforbed dephlogifticated air. I have fhewn, that nitre and vitriolic acid, heated together, abforb dephlogifticated air, whereby we obtain the moft perfect nitrous acid. Hence it is evident we are not rafhly to conclude, that, becaufe dephlogifticated and nitrous air will only unite in certain proportion, the compound will not take in more dephlogifticated air under more favourable circumftances. Thefe are my reafons for differing from Mr. Kirwan, in his objections to Mr. Lavoifier's conclufions refpecting the decompofition of nitrous acid by mercury.

As moftly all animal and vegetable fubftances, which have an affinity to pure air, decompofe nitrous acid on the fame principle with the metals, I fhall pafs them over in filence, except the two following. Charcoal does not decompofe nitrous acid, even by help of digeftion ; the acid may

* Vol. II. p. 165.

be

be expelled from it in whitiſh fumes. It is extraordinary, if nitrous air be produced in conſequence of phlogiſton, that it is not obtained in the above proceſs; for the baſis of nitrous air will take phlogiſton from the metals, and the metals will take it from charcoal; which proves, that metals, if they do contain phlogiſton, hold it with greater force than charcoal. In ſhort, almoſt the whole of charcoal is phlogiſton, if ſuch we may call a ſubſtance which will wholly unite to dephlogiſticated air, or, in other words, burn.

It is true it may be ſaid, that the attraction of the metallic baſis to the fixable air of the nitrous acid, enables the nitrous baſis, by virtue of a double affinity, to combine with its phlogiſton during the ſolution; and that there is nothing in charcoal to attract the fixable air. In anſwer to this, I would obſerve, that the production of nitrous air by oils and ſpirits of wine and turpentine, contradicts ſuch an hypotheſis; for they contain nothing to attract fixable air, and they even produce uncombined fixable air, which ſtrongly proves, if nitrous air contains phlogiſton, that it can expel fixable

able air from its bafis, in confequence of its
fuperior affinity to it.

I have already fhewn the difficulty of
uniting charcoal to dephlogifticated air,
notwithftanding their ftrong affinity to each
other; and that this proceeds from the
aggregate attraction of charcoal. I have
likewife obferved the neceffity of applying
heat fufficient to overcome this attraction,
in order to combine charcoal with dephlogifticated air; and I think this is the moft
reafonable mode of accounting for the
above experiment.

The carbonaceous matter is held in chemical folution, in oils and fpirit of wine,
by light inflammable air, water, and a fmall
quantity of fixable air; therefore two fubftances contribute to the decompofition of
nitrous acid in oils and fpirit of wine,
by which we obtain fixable air, phlogifticated
air, and nitrous air, at the fame time that
water is likewife formed.

Mr. Prouft found, that ftrong nitrous
acid will fet fire to charcoal, if it be rendered very dry *. He likewife remarked,
that charcoal expofed a few hours to the

* Tourn. de Medicine, 1778.

M   air,

air, after calcination, was unfit for the experiment. Charcoal, as Mr. Prouft well observes, attracts moisture very forcibly. Therefore the firft effect of the charcoal on the nitrous acid, is to withdraw a portion of its water from it, by which it is rendered highly concentrated, at the same time that the condensation of the water heats the charcoal in a small degree, but sufficiently to volatilize a nitrous vapour; which as soon as it reaches that portion of dry charcoal next the humid part, is condensed by it, and generates heat enough to promote the decomposition of the nitrous acid. Hence we find, why the experiment will not succeed if the acid be poured on the surface of the charcoal.

The effect of nitrous acid on blood is very fingular; and though it has not much to do with what we are upon at present, yet, hoping that any fact relating to so interesting a subject may be acceptable to my reader, I shall give as brief an account of it as I can.

Two parts of blood procured fresh at the butcher's, one of ftrong nitrous acid, and about ⅓ of the whole of water, were di-

gefted

gefted in the heat nearly of boiling water (fresh portions of water being occasionally added), until the whole of the acid was expelled, when it acquired nearly the colour, and exactly the tafte, of bile. When mixed with a large quantity of water, it acquired a fine yellow colour; and, on standing, depofited a fubftance of a brighter yellow, though the fupernatant liquor ftill retained a yellow colour, and bitter tafte, but not fo intenfely as when the precipitate was fufpended in it.

The different ftages of this procefs were well worthy of obfervation. No nitrous air was produced, and the acid was expelled in the ftate of a white vapour. I tafted the liquor at different periods of the procefs, and was highly pleafed at the gradual progrefs of the bitternefs in proportion as the acidity vanifhed. About the middle of the procefs the folution firft tafted acid, but was quickly fucceeded by a bitter fenfation. It appears to me that the nitrous acid took dephlogifticated air from the blood; for though I ufed the red nitrous acid, it was expelled in a perfect ftate. At this time I had not leifure to make any farther in-

quiries

quiries into this fubject, being bufy in affift-
ing at a public courfe of chemiftry, at Oxford ; nor have I had fince an opportunity
of enjoying the pleafure I then promifed
myfelf in fo interefting an inveftigation.

I think a feries of experiments made on
this fubject, could not fail of being productive of fome benefit to mankind. For
how can chemiftry be better applied than
in thofe inveftigations, which may tend to
throw light on the different diforders incident to man?

Dr. Prieftley has difcovered a fpecies of
nitrous air which fupports combuftion, de-
ftroys animal life, and is condenfible in water.
This he has called dephlogifticated nitrous
air. I confider dephlogifticated nitrous air
to be the laft ftage of nitrous acid, and to
be lefs underftood than the four preceding.
I expofed four equal quantities of nitrous air
in different tubes, to a nearly equal proportion of iron and water. In three weeks the
air was diminifhed $\frac{1}{6}$, and the refiduum
extinguifhed a candle, and reduced common
air. In three weeks more it was reduced
about $\frac{1}{4}$, and the refiduum fuffered a candle to burn in it faintly. When it ftood a
fort-

fortnight longer, the diminution was nearly $\frac{1}{4}$ of its bulk, and a candle burned in the residuum with an enlarged flame. I let the other tube stand until the air contracted to more than $\frac{1}{3}$ of its original bulk; the residuum was phlogisticated air, and had the smell of volatile alkali. From the progress of these experiments, I did not hesitate to conclude, but that which is called dephlogisticated nitrous air, is common nitrous air, deprived only of a portion of its dephlogisticated air. Dr. Priestley found that nitrous air, which stood in contact with iron and water for four months, extinguished a candle *. He likewise found that a candle burned with an enlarged flame in nitrous air which had been in contact with iron, over mercury, about six months. The same philosopher found that nitrous air exposed to liver of sulphur for a day was diminished $\frac{1}{4}$ of its bulk; a candle burned in the remainder with an enlarged flame, and it was not in the least diminished by nitrous air †. I have frequently observed that nitrous air, when reduced to

* Vol. II. p. 177.   † Vol. II. p. 178.

of

$\frac{2}{3}$ of its bulk, always admitted a candle to
burn in it with an enlarged flame; but that
in proportion as it got below this ftandard,
it fupported flame fo much the worfe, until
it was reduced nearly to $\frac{1}{3}$, when it extinguifhed a candle.

Thefe facts leave no room to doubt, but
that dephlogifticated nitrous air contains
lefs dephlogifticated air than the common
nitrous air.

Dr. Prieftley found that clean fmall
needles expofed to nitrous air, confined in
dry mercury, did not in the leaft diminifh
it, though they had ftood fix or eight
months in the fame ftate. But when he
introduced a few drops of water, the air
was diminifhed in a few days, and conti-
nued fo to do until $\frac{1}{3}$ difappeared, and the
refiduum was dephlogifticated nitrous air *.
He likewife found that a quantity of nitrous
air which had been expofed nine months to
iron filings, over mercury, was diminifhed
$\frac{1}{2}$, and a candle burned in the remainder,
better than in common air, though a moufe
died in it. Thefe two experiments fhew

* Vol. VI. p. 316.

that

that moifture promotes the decompofition
of nitrous air. For, 1ft, when the materials
were perfectly dry, no fenfible change took
place in the nitrous air. 2dly, When water was added, the abforption took place
very foon. 3dly, When lefs moifture was
ufed, the decompofition went on very flow.
Hence it appears that the water is decompofed, and that its dephlogifticated air
unites to the metal, at the fame time that
the dephlogifticated air of the nitrous air
combines with the inflammable air, at the
very inftant of its liberation, and rege-
nerates water. I have already rather conjectured on what principle this laft union
takes place.

It is very well known that iron, when
expofed to a very dry atmofphere, does not
ruft; and likewife that iron confined in
water will yield inflammable air, though it
will produce no inflammable air when ad-
vantageoufly expofed both to water and dephlogifticated air. Thus iron filings and
fulphur wetted with water, and expofed
to dephlogifticated air, will yield little
or no inflammable air, until the whole
of the dephlogifticated part is nearly ab-

M 4   forbed,

forbed, and then inflammable air is produced in abundance. Dr. Prieſtley re-
ſolved dephlogiſticated nitrous air into
its conſtituent principles, viz. phlogiſticated and dephlogiſticated airs, by heating bits of dry crucibles in it *. He likewiſe rendered this air wholly immiſcible
with water, by paſſing the electric ſpark in
it, and it was of the ſtandard of 1,45. I
repeated this experiment with a view to the
preſence of fixable air, and inflammable
air, but I could not detect a particle of
either. It is evident from the correſpond-
ence of theſe facts, that nitrous air and
the dephlogiſticated nitrous air are compoſed only of two principles, namely, phlogiſticated and dephlogiſticated air, and that
they only differ in the proportion of theſe ;
and likewiſe that neither contains a particle
of light inflammable air, or fixable air.

It is the opinion moſt generally received
from the formation of volatile alkali,
during the diminution of nitrous air, by
iron and water, that the property of dephlogiſticated nitrous air proceeds from a
condenſation of a portion of its phlogiſti-

* Vol. VI. p. 332.

cated

cated air. I was inclined to this myfelf; but when I confidered the greater number of furfaces which the dephlogifticated air muft expofe to the iron, than the phlogifticated, being in the proportion of two to one; together with the greater affinity of dephlogifticated air to inflammable air than the phlogifticated, I began to be in fufpenfe. It is true, a portion of phlogifticated air is condenfed, but the quantity is trifling in comparifon to that of the dephlogifticated air; for generally $\frac{1}{3}$ of the bulk of a quantity of nitrous air is left unabforbed, which is nearly the whole of its phlogifticated air. There is no volatile alkali formed during the combuftion of Homberg's pyrophorus in nitrous air, for it contains nothing to condenfe phlogifticated air, and yet the refiduary air after the combuftion is dephlogifticated nitrous air. The fame may be obferved with refpect to the contraction of nitrous air, by liver of fulphur: it can neither withdraw phlogifticated air nor light inflammable air from it, and yet there is a refiduum of dephlogifticated nitrous air obtained, when the air is diminifhed $\frac{1}{3}$. The

progrefs

progrefs of this laſt experiment may atteſt the truth of what I fay.

Indeed the method of procuring dephlo-giſticated nitrous air, by the folution of metals in nitrous acid, favours the foregoing notions; for we can never obtain dephlo-giſticated nitrous air from nitrous acid, until it is nearly faturated with a metal; and then by introducing more of the fame metal, or a different metal, we obtain de-phlogiſticated nitrous air.

In order to underſtand this, we muſt firſt confider, that the nitrous acid which holds the metallic calx in folution, is in the ſtate of red nitrous acid; or rather more imperfect. Therefore, though the metal deprives the acid of folution in con-tact with it, of the whole of its dephlo-giſticated air, yet the particles of phlogiſti-cated air recover a portion of it again from their neighbouring particles of acid, on principles which I have already en-deavoured to explain.

To render this the more perfpicuous, let us fuppofe the acid of folution to be

P a

I

P *a b c.* Let *a b c*
be its portion of
dephlogifticated air,
combined with the
annexed forces ; if
a metal be introdu-

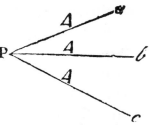

ced into fuch folution, it will deprive P of
a b c; then P being in contact with another
particle of acid of folution, will inftantly
deprive it of either *a* or *b* or *c*. I fhould fuppofe, from what has already been faid on
this fubject, that it would be fuperfluous
to explain here, why P cannot unite to
a b or *b c*.   I have fhewn above, that the
conftituent principles of the new compound
P—6—*a*, or dephlogifticated nitrous air,
are united with the force of 6.

It may at firft fight appear, that a metal
introduced into the red nitrous acid in its
fimple ftate, fhould on this principle produce dephlogifticated nitrous air.   But be
it confidered, that though a particle of
phlogifticated air can only take one particle of dephlogifticated air from a fingle
molecule of acid ; yet that another molecule
in its vicinity will fupply it with another
particle of dephlogifticated air, by which
perfect

perfect nitrous air is formed. This cannot take place in the metallic solution; for when once P is supplied with *a*, its power of attracting more dephlogisticated air is so diminished as to be equipoised, even by the weak attachment of the acid of solution to its suspended metal.

Having thus endeavoured to explain the nature of perfect and imperfect nitrous airs, for such I shall for the future take the liberty of calling them; we can readily account to a degree of certainty, why these do not affect each other when mixed. Let *p*—6—*a* be imperfect nitrous air, and P—*a* —*b* perfect nitrous air;

$$P \overset{4\frac{1}{2}}{\underset{4\frac{1}{2}}{\diagdown}} \begin{matrix} a \\ b \end{matrix}$$

if these be mixed, P—*a* cannot take *a* or *b* from P, for P retains them both with as great force as P—*a* can attract either. Why this species of air is more soluble in water than the perfect nitrous air, is what I cannot account for, unless it be from the smallness of its atmospheres of fire, which admit the molecule of air to come within the gravitating influence of the water. It is rather remarkable, that

the

the imperfect nitrous air fhould favour combuftion, when the perfect nitrous air,
though it contains more dephlogifticated
air, has the reverfe effect. It is likewife
very fingular, that the perfect will unite to
more dephlogifticated air in a common
temperature, and that the imperfect will
not, though it has greater attraction to
dephlogifticated air than the former.

That the red nitrous vapour, which contains much more dephlogifticated air, with
lefs force than the two former, fhould not
favour combuftion, is ftill more fingular.
Again, why Homberg's pyrophorus, as has
been obferved by Dr. Prieftley, will burn
in perfect nitrous air, and not in the imperfect, is difficult to be accounted for;
unlefs it proceeds from a better fupply of
moifture by the one, than by the other.

As thefe facts cannot be fatisfactorily
accounted for, I think it better to fufpend
my opinion, than to attempt plaufible explanations, which are generally more productive of evil than good, and only ferve
as fo many allurements to decoy us out of
the right path.

If we confider that neither light nor

.3   heavy

heavy inflammable air, nor dephlogisticated air, will unite to phlogisticated
air, notwithstanding their attraction to
it, without the aid of fire, either the
electric or a common spark ; and compare
this to the easy union of dephlogisticated
air and nitrous air, though the latter attracts dephlogisticated air with less force
than the three former; we cannot help
attributing it to something that surrounds
their gravitating particles, and this we
must suppose to be partly fire, as it is difengaged during their condensation. But
why fire should not exert this power when
nitrous air and dephlogisticated air are
brought in contact, is very extraordinary ;
more especially when we know, as I have
already demonstrated, that their atmospheres of fire must be nearly thrice deeper
than those of phlogisticated air ; and likewise when we have every reason to suppose
that nitrous air contains nearly the quantity
of fire which the dephlogisticated and phlogisticated airs contained in their simple state
It is true, fire is not developed during the
union of these last two fluids, which may
favour their combination. But how do
their

their extensive atmospheres so blend as to bring their gravitating particles within each other's influence ?

The condensation of dephlogisticated air, by perfect nitrous air, without the seclusion of fire, is certainly a very striking fact *.

That nitrous acid contains nearly as much fire as its constituent principles contained before their union, can hardly be doubted; and that it parts with very little of this by its union to an alkali, is also as true as it is singular. Here then nitre contains, in a solid state, fire sufficient to give elasticity to at least 100 times its bulk of dephlogisticated air.

Hence arise the deflagration of nitre and charcoal in close vessels, and the quantity of fire disengaged, though fixable air is produced at the same time.

These facts convince us, that fire unites chemically to bodies, and of course must gravitate towards them. Can we therefore doubt but that fire is a substance, and not a quality, as some philosophers are pleased to suppose ?

* There is heat generated, but not more than should be expected from the re-action of the new formed acid upon the suspended water.

Although

Although the conftituent principles of nitrous acid are known, and though they have been united by art, yet we do not well know how nature performs this operation.

Some philofophers, but Mr. Thouvenel in particular, have found that putrefaction favours the production of nitrous acid. All animal fubftances, during their decay, give out a vaft quantity of phlogifticated air; therefore, if dephlogifticated air be prefent, it will unite to the phlogifticated air in its nafcent ftate, and before it unites with fire. However, I have had an opportunity of obferving, that nitrous acid may be copioufly generated, where no putrid proceffes are carried on. The chemical elaboratory at Oxford is near fix feet lower than the furface of the earth. The walls are conftructed with common lime ftone, and arched over with the fame; the floor is alfo paved with ftone. It is a large room, and very lofty. There are feparate rooms for the chemical preparations, fo that nothing is kept in the elaboratory, but the neceffary implements for conducting experiments. There is an area adjoining it on a level with the floor, which, though not very large, is

fufficient

fufficient to admit a free circulation of air.
The afhes and fweepings of the elaboratory
are depofited in it. There is a good fink in
the centre of this area, fo that no ftagnated
water can lodge there. The p——y, which
is feldom frequented, is over ground, and
unconnected with the elaboratory. Notwithftanding all this, the walls of the room
afford frefh crops of nitre every three or
four months.

Dr. Wall, who paid particular attention
to this circumftance, and who told me it
contained fixed vegetable alkali, requefted I
would analyze it, and let him know what
proportion of it a quantity would yield. Accordingly I did, and found that two ounces
of it contained fix drachms of nitrated fixed
vegetable alkali, and three of calcareous
nitre. The nitre firft appears in fmall
whitifh filaments, as fine as cob-web, which,
when they get a little larger, drop off, fo
that they never acquire growth fufficient to
diftinguifh their figure to a naked eye. On
finding that they contained fixed vegetable
alkali, I concluded that it proceeded from
minute vegetation; but in this I was mif-
taken; for I found that they were foluble in

N   water,

water, and that they detonated with charcoal at every ftage of their growth. Having
fwept this faline efflorefcence from the wall,
I dug deep into it, but could not obtain
nitre from it. When a part had been
white-wafhed, it yielded nitre, but not fo
abundantly as a neighbouring fpot which had
not been treated in the fame manner. Hence
it is evident, that nitrous acid may be formed without the affiftance of putrefcent proceffes, in a ftill damp air, where there is a
fubftance to attract it when half formed,
whereby it is in time brought to perfection.
The above facts moreover prove, that fixed
vegetable alkali is a compound. Thus we
find that chemiftry is ftill in its infancy, and
that there is a great deal to be done in order to bring it to perfection.

SEC-

SECTION V.

Of the Marine Acid.

THE bafis of marine acid has not as yet been difcovered; but that dephlogifticated air is one of the conftituent principles of this acid is very evident, if it enters into the conftitution of the nitrous or vitriolic acid.

Charcoal, fulphur, *light* inflammable air, or phofphorus, cannot take its dephlogifticated air from the marine bafis, whether the acid be combined, or in its fimple ftate.

Lead will take the acid from the fixed alkalies without decompofing it, as will likewife iron when expofed to a damp air for a confiderable time, as the eelebrated Scheel has obferved. I mixed common falt and manganefe in various proportions, and expofed them in a reverberating furnace in a well clofed crucible for three hours, to heat nearly fufficient to melt caft iron. I treated manganefe, falt, and charcoal, in

the

the same manner, but with no effect. I mixed clay, salt, and charcoal, and salt and clay alone, with very little success. I treated calcined bones, salt, and charcoal, and calcined bones and salt, and likewise lime and salt, in like manner, without effecting any apparent change in the salt.

I have been informed by a Mr. Robertson, an apothecary in Bishopsgate-street, who has made several attempts to decompose common salt, that he partially alkalized it, by exposing it and clay to a fierce heat ; but, soon after it got into contact with air, that it became neutral again. It is certain, that salt loses a portion of its dephlogisticated air very readily, as may be seen by its property of accelerating combustion when thrown on the fire. If common salt and litharge be fused, it is in part decomposed ; the acid suffers no decomposition, but unites to the lead ; whereby it acquires, when the saline matter is washed away, a yellow colour. It is evident from these facts, that the basis of marine acid is a combustible body, and quite different from light inflammable air, charcoal, or any known inflammable substance ; and that it attracts de-

phlogisticated

phlogifticated air with greater force than any fubftance hitherto difcovered. Though charcoal will decompofe all other acids (except a few), when united to bodies which will fix them until they acquire a fufficient degree of heat, yet it has no effect on marine acid. In my opinion, metals decompofe marine acid during their folution in it, though iron will condenfe marine air without decompofing it.

Mr. Kirwan is of opinion, that the marine acid confifts of a particular bafis united to phlogifton, and a certain proportion of fixable air ; and that when the marine bafis is deprived of its pholgifton, its affinity to fixed air becomes much ftronger, whereby it unites to a large portion of it *. Though I have attentively perufed Mr. Kirwan's Fifth Section on Phlogifton, wherein he treats of marine acid, I muft confefs I could not make out on what grounds he founded this hypothefis. However, before I prefume to offer my opinion decifively upon it, I fhall minutely inquire into it. Therefore, let us firft fuppofe iron to be

* Effay on Phlogifton, p. 74.

compofed

compofed of a certain bafis, and phlogifton,
intimately combined. Let us alfo fuppofe
marine acid to confift of a peculiar bafis,
and phlogifton, intimately united to fixable
air, and that this bafis attracts fixable air
with greater force than it does phlogifton. This granted, when thefe are
brought in contact, what is likely to
take place, according to well known chemical laws ? for, in matters of ambiguity,
we are juftified in reafoning from analogy,
more efpecially when it is an eftablifhed
fact, that the decompofition and compofition
of all bodies, whether they prevail by
virtue of a fingle or double affinity, are
regulated by the fame power, though va-
rioufly modified. The acid moft undoubtedly cannot be decompofed, as the attraction
of its bafis to fixable air on the one fide,
together with the attraction of the metallic
bafis for its own phlogifton on the other
fide, are fufficient to prevent it; for, as
the inflammable matter or phlogifton of
the metal is expelled in its aëriform ftate,
a double affinity does not prevail in the
operation, laying afide the agency of fire,
which

which does not much interfere with the
prefent fubject.

Hence it appears that the acid, without
fuffering a decompofition, unites to the
metallic bafis, and expels its phlogifton;
which is Mr. Kirwan's opinion. In this
cafe, pure fixed alkali, or lime, fhould precipitate the metallic bafis in its purity, and
thereby enable us to obtain that fubftance,
which occafions fuch a conteft amongft
philofophers.

I faturated half an ounce of marine acid
with clean iron nails, firft having afcertained
the quantity of pure fixed alkali neceffary
to faturate fo much acid in its fimple ftate,
and found that the folution required the
fame quantity of alkali to precipitate the
whole of the iron; nor did I find any difference in both falts, when evaporated to
drynefs. Therefore the acid was not in
the leaft decompofed, though the metal
was calcined, and its phlogifton difengaged.
Whence did it receive its dephlogifticated
air; or, according to Mr. Kirwan, its fixable air? The phlogiftians have but one
mode of anfwering this, which is, that the
metallic bafis unites to water. If metallic

N 4   fubftances

fubftances were calcined, as Mr. Kirwan himfelf obferves, and as I had an occafion to mention in treating of vitriolic acid, in confequence of water alone, it fhould not remain fo inert when metals are introduced into it, in a common temperature, when iron is calcined by marine acid in the fame temperature very rapidly.

If metallic calces, precipitated by pure alkali from the different acids, owed their additional weight and colour to an union with water; a given weight of iron, calcined in the different acids, fhould be precipitated by the fame pure fixed alkali of the fame weight and colour. I obferved that the precipitates of 20 gr. of iron from the vitriolic, the marine, and the nitrous acid, dried and treated exactly in the fame manner, varied in their weights; that from the nitrous being the heavieft, and the marine precipitate next to it again: they likewife differed in colour, which fhews their different degrees of calcination. To make this experiment accurately, the precipitates fhould be well wafhed with hot diftilled water, and by no means expofed to the

the air while they are drying; for they change colour in a few minutes by abforbing both fixable and dephlogifticated air from the atmofphere. The precipitate of iron attracts fixable air in fmall proportions, with as great avidity as the alkalies, and I fufpect with as great force as pure lime; but this fixable air may be expelled again from it by a ftrong heat, without being decompofed. Hence I am induced to fuppofe, that fixable air is never decompofed during the reduction of mercury by heat. Why are the precipitates from the different acids of unequal degrees of calcination, if water be the calcining fubftance, if the acids do not impart fomething to them, more efpecially when they are equally well fupplied with water? That the acids take an active part in the folution of metals, cannot be denied; for it is very well known that water will not diffolve them, and that it will not even in any length of time ruft gold, filver, platina, or mercury; though they are foluble in different acids. Then I afk, How the marine acid acts, when iron is introduced into it? Whether the acid or water divides it into its ultimate particles,

and

and expels its phlogiston ; or whether
they do this jointly ; or whether the acid,
by its folvent power, only diffolves what
the water calcines and deprives of phlogifton, by which it may enable the water
to attack frefh furfaces ?

This laft is certainly the moft plaufible
phlogiftic hypothefis in favour of the doctrine of water ; although it may with equal
plaufibility be faid, that the marine acid
alone unites to the metallic bafis, diffolves
it, and expels its phlogifton ; and when the
acid is withdrawn from it by lime or alkalies being in its extreme divifion, that it
inftantly rufhes into union with water, and
forms a calx. Allowing the phlogiftians
all this, which is the moft that can be urged in their favour ; there is one circumftance which, I think, if ftrictly inquired
into, will be found fufficient to overthrow
it ; namely, the precipitation of metals by
each other in their metallic ftate.

In order to know the full force of what
I am going to obferve, it will be neceffary,
firft, to confider, that if calcination depends
upon the union of water, and the expulfion of phlogifton, the metallic bafis muft
have

have greater attraction to water than it has to phlogifton; as evidently appears from the calcination of metals by fteam. Therefore, on this principle, a metal could never precipitate another metal in its metallic ftate, from a very dilute folution of marine acid, or of any other acid. For if water, agreeably to the firft phlogiftic hypothefis, fhould calcine the metal, while the marine acid diffolved it, how could iron, though it unites to the acid, precipitate copper in its metallic ftate? Confidering that it is furrounded with uncombined water, is it likely that it would influence the water attached to the metallic bafis in any degree?

Then all that can be faid with the fmalleft appearance of plaufibility is, that the difengaged phlogifton of the precipitating metal expels its water, and unites to the bafis. This I think needs no contradiction. The fecond and laft hypothefis that I confidered moft favourable to the phlogiftic doctrine, is that of the water uniting to the metallic bafis, the inftant the alkali deprives it of its acid of folution. In this cafe, all the phenomena may be accounted for thus, viz. that the precipitating

I   metal

metal takes the acid from the precipitated, at the same time that it imparts phlogiston to it, whereby it is reduced. This most undoubtedly, losing sight of all analogical reasoning, seems very plausible, and may appear, to superficial inquirers into this subject, very satisfactory. I must own I should be thoroughly convinced of the truth of it myself, were it not for the following considerations: 1st, The easy expulsion of inflammable air from metals by water; which shews, if this comes from the metals, the greater affinity of their bases to water than to phlogiston. 2dly, The ultimate division of the precipitated metal, which favours calcination. 3dly, The presence of such an abundance of water, which they consider to be the calcining substance.

Thus far I have impartially inquired, on the phlogistic principle, into the nature of marine acid by its effects, as we cannot obtain its constituent parts separately; and though I am not much pleased with it, yet I leave my reader to judge for himself.

Let us now trace the same subject so far in the antiphlogistic doctrine, and without prejudice compare them to each other.

But

But before we proceed on this, I would have my reader not to lose fight of the following facts, which have already been particularised: 1ft, The feparation of the marine acid from the metallic folution in its perfect ftate. 2dly, The precipitation of the metal in a calciform ftate. 3dly, The active part acids take in the calcination of metals. 4thly, The inconfiftency of fuppof-ing that the calces of metals are compofed of water and a metallic bafis. 5thly, The feparation of inflammable air, during the folution of metals. And laftly, the pre-cipitation of one metal by another in its metallic ftate.

It appears to me, and indeed I have no other rational mode of accounting for it, that the acid is firft decompofed, and that its bafis inftantly decompofes the water, and liberates inflammable air; although I think the marine bafis has greater attraction for dephlogifticated air than the metals have. It likewife feems to me, that marine acid is compofed of two principles only, viz. an unknown inflammable bafis, and dephlogif-ticated air, intimately combined. It may appear rather ftrange at firft fight, that me-

tals

tals should deprive this basis of its dephlogisticated air, notwithstanding their weaker
attraction to it. However, I think this may
be very well accounted for on the following
principles : Let B be the basis of marine
acid, D dephlogisticated air ; and let these
attract each other with the force of 8 ; and
let this be the utmost sum of their joint forces.
Let B be possessed of one half of this force,
and D of the other half. In this state, metals which I have supposed to attract dephlogisticated air with only the force of 7,
could not deprive B
of D. Let B, in order
to form common ma-
rine acid, be united to

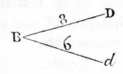

another particle of dephlogisticated air *d.*
They will only unite with the force of 6 ;
that is, the whole force of B will be divided
between D and *d,* on principles which I
have already explained, in treating of the
vitriolic and nitrous a-
cid. Therefore B will
retain its dephlogistica-
ted air with only the

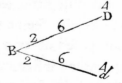

force of 6 ; for B can only gravitate with
the force of 2 towards D, although D gravitates

vitates with the force of 4 towards B, and fo with *d* and B. If iron, whofe attraction for dephlogifticated air is 7, were brought in contact with the above compound in the prefence of water, whofe conftituent principles are united with the force of $6\frac{5}{8}$, would it not deprive B of both D and *d*, and would not B inftantly re-act on the water, and take from it half the quantity of dephlogifticated air which it before gave up to the metal, and then unite to the calx? Dry marine acid air will unite to iron, without producing inflammable air; which fhews that it muft come from the water. It is true, it may be faid, that the union of marine air to iron, without any feparation of its principles, is unfavourable to the hypothefis of the decompofition of marine acid, when in contact with water. But be it confidered, although the force of 7 overcomes the attraction of B to dephlogifticated air, that the force of $\frac{1}{1000}$ is fufficient to move it with its dephlogifticated air towards the iron, when there is nothing elfe to influence it; and we may fuppofe that the iron itfelf muft attract it with greater force than this. When water is prefent,

the

the cafe is different : for, when the iron influences the dephlogifticated air of the marine bafis with fo fuperior a force as $3\frac{1}{7}$ to 2 ; B, or the marine bafis, being in contact with water, which retains its dephlogifticated air with the force of $6\frac{5}{8}$, or, laying afide reciprocal attraction, with only the force of $3\frac{5}{16}$, yields its own dephlogifticated air to the iron, and directs the whole force of its attraction, which is 4, towards the dephlogifticated air of the water ; by which it is decompofed, and inflammable is produced. The marine bafis being thus furnifhed with half the quantity of dephlogifticaed air which is neceffary to the formation of common marine acid, unites to the calx, and diffolves it. To render this the more intelligible, let I—d be a molecule of water,

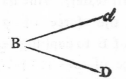

a molecule of marine acid, and I a furface of iron ; let us fuppofe thefe to be influenced with the different forces expreffed by the numbers annexed to them ; is it not reafonable to fuppofe, as foon as I, or iron, fhould influence d D, that B would re-act

on

on *d*, or the dephlogiftica- ted air of the water, and dif- engage I, or inflammable air.

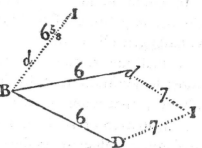

I make no doubt but a good mathema- tician (for I acknowledge my own defi- ciency) would demonftrate this to a degree of certainty. However, although I am convinced of the truth of it myfelf, I would have my philofophical reader to ftrictly in- quire into it before he either approves or difapproves of it.

The reft of the antiphlogiftians differ from me with refpect to the manner in which water is decompofed; for they fup- pofe (if I miftake not) that the marine or vitriolic acid firft unites to the metal, and that the compound decompofes the water, from the joint attraction of its conftituent principles to dephlogifticated air. If this were true, water, when brought in contact with iron united to marine air, would yield inflammable air, which is not the cafe; or iron would yield inflammable air with greater rapidity in volatile vitriolic acid, than in perfect vitriolic acid; or marine

O   acid

acid would produce inflammable air during the decompofition of a folution of iron in volatile vitriolic acid.

I fhall not trouble my reader with any more demonftrations on this fubject, but only obferve, that when metals are calcined by the mediation of acids and water, there is lefs inflammable air produced, by one half, as Dr. Prieftley obferves, than when they are calcined by fteam *. This is not only explicable on the foregoing principles, but alfo tends ftrongly to corroborate them ; and, if narrowly infpected, will be found very unfavourable to the phlogiftic theory. If the calcination of metals depended folely upon their union to dephlogifticated air, it muft be fupplied by water, when fteam is brought in contact with them ; and as every particle of light inflammable air is united but to a fingle ultimate particle of dephlogifticated air, inflammable air muft be difengaged in proportion to the quantity of dephlogifticated air which unites to the metal ; or, in other words, according to the degree of calcination it acquires.

* Vol. VI. p. 102.

But

But this is not the cafe when metals are calcined in the marine or in the vitriolic acid; for though the bafes of thefe acids impart two or more portions of dephlogif- ticated air to the metal, they can recover but one half of it from the water, as has been fully demonftrated. Therefore, when acids are ufed, only one half of the quan- tity of inflammable air fhould be produced, that is extricated when fteam is the cal- cining menftruum; which could not be the cafe, if light inflammable air were one of the conftituent princi ples of the metal.

It is true, it may be faid, that the metallic precipitate from the above acids corre- fponds in its degree of calcination with the quantity of inflammable air or phlogifton difengaged, and for that reafon retained phlogifton in folution. But I have already fhewn, in treating of the vitriolic acid, that the precipitant, whether it be an alkali or an earth, enables the bafis of the acid, in quitting the metal, to take from it, its full portion of dephlogifticated air, by which the precipitate contains but the portion taken from the water. When the nitrous acid is ufed, which contains more dephlogifticated

air

air lefs intimately combined than the marine or vitriolic acid does, the precipitate is found united with more dephlogifticated air ; and the nitre obtained by precipitating a neutral folution of nitrated iron by fixed alkali, is far from being fo perfect as what may be produced by combining thefe previous to the above treatment. When iron is introduced into a neutral folution of marine copper, the latter is precipitated in its metallic ftate, and no inflammable air is produced. This fact, feparately confidered, appears very favourable to the phlogiftic theory. Iron attracts dephlogifticated air with greater force than copper does, although iron alone will not reduce the mere calx of copper diffufed in water; but, aided by the bafis of marine acid, it will wholly deprive it of its dephlogifticated air. The marine acid, having greater affinity to iron than to copper, quits the latter to unite to the former; and, affifted by the iron itfelf, it forces with it the dephlogifticated air feparated from the water. Thus, by their joint forces, they accomplifh what the iron alone could not; and as this quantity of dephlogifticated air is fufficient for the fo-

lution

lution of the iron, no decompofition of water takes place, and of courfe no inflammable air is produced. In fhort, the dephlogifticated air of the marine acid itfelf, together with the fmall portion feparated from the water during the folution of the copper (for but little inflammable air is produced), move jointly to unite to the iron, and affect it as dephlogifticated marine acid would, which is known to diffolve metals without generating inflammable air.

Having, as fairly as lay in my power, inquired into the nature of marine acid on the antiphlogiftic and the different phlogiftic principles, fo far as it is affected by metals, I fhall now proceed to its other principal properties.

When common marine acid is diftilled over red lead or manganefe, it undergoes a very great change, as the celebrated Scheel has difcovered, in tafte, fmell, volatility, &c. : diftilled or mixed with nitrous acid, it acquires partly the fame properties. I doubt whether arterial blood would not effect the fame change in it. Marine acid thus treated is faid to lofe phlogifton, or the matter of light inflammable air: hence

O 3   it

it has got the name of dephlogisticated marine acid.

Some phlogistians attribute this change
in marine acid to a lofs of its phlogiston,
and an union to dephlogisticated air; others,
to an union of dephlogisticated air to its
phlogiston : but Mr. Kirwan imagines, that
it exchanges its phlogiston for fixable air,
in order to become what is called dephlogisticated marine acid. Thus the phlogiftians themfelves differ in opinion ; a clear
proof of the inconfiftency of their doctrine.

The antiphlogiftians, on the contrary,
are of opinion, that the bafis of marine
acid, from its great attraction to dephlogifticated air, is capable of uniting to a greater
portion of it than it is found combined
with in its ordinary ftate, provided it be
prefented to it under favourable circumftances.

* Mr. Kirwan affirms, that he has obtained
dephlogisticated marine acid from chalk.
Chalk has no fenfible attraction to inflammable air; therefore the marine bafis muft

* Effay on Phlogifton, page 80.

attract

attract fixable air with greater force than it
does phlogifton, for a double affinity does
not prevail here. According to Mr. Kirwan, common marine acid muft part with
phlogifton in order to unite to fixable air;
for he fuppofes, that the marine bafis cannot retain both when in the ftate of dephlogifticated marine acid: then I afk, whether
Mr. Kirwan obtained inflammable air in
this experiment, or what became of the
phlogifton of the marine acid? However,
Mr. Kirwan has been more fuccefsful than
I have been; for I attempted in vain to prepare dephlogifticated marine acid by means
of chalk: in fhort, it had the contrary effect, for it decompofed dephlogifticated marine acid obtained from manganefe.

I faturated a quantity of pure volatile alkali with dephlogifticated marine acid carefully prepared; phlogifticated air was produced, but not a particle of fixable air, and
the refulting falt was found to be common
fal ammoniac. Volatile alkali is compofed
of light inflammable air and phlogifticated
air; therefore it muft be partly decompofed,
by which phlogifticated air is obtained; and
the inflammable air muft unite to fomething

O 4 elfe,

elfe, which attracts it more forcibly than the phlogifticated air. I afk, to what? Not to the marine bafis, for it appears to have already parted with phlogifton to unite to fixable air; therefore it muft have greater attraction to it than it has to phlogifton.

Befides, the attraction of the phlogifticated air to light inflammable air, renders fuch an union very improbable. Or, allowing that the gravitating matter of the light inflammable air united to the marine bafis, it muft then let go its fixable air in order to become common marine acid; for it cannot hold both, according to Mr. Kirwan himfelf. Then I afk, what becomes of its fixable air? for I diftilled the falt to drynefs, and could not obtain it. It cannot be faid, that it has been decompofed by the inflammable air of the alkali; for it would be inconfiftent to fuppofe, that phlogifton fhould influence dephlogifticated air already faturated with phlogifton, and united to another fubftance.

Equal parts of dephlogifticated marine air and light inflammable air mixed over water. will form, according to Mr. Kirwan *, a denfe white cloud; more than one

* Effay on Phlogifton, page 80.

half

half is abforbed, and is found to be common marine acid, and the refiduary air is pure inflammable air. Mr. Kirwan confiders this experiment as very favourable to his hypothefis, and fufficient to fubvert that of the antiphlogiftians. In my opinion, if it be narrowly inquired into, it will be found more unfavourable to the former than to the latter doctrine. Therefore, allowing dephlogifticated marine air to be convertible into common marine acid by the mere admixture of light inflammable air: how does the inflammable air act in this cafe? Does it unite to the bafis of marine acid? If fo, fixable air (if it were one of the conftituent principles of the dephlogifticated marine acid) fhould be difengaged; but Mr. Kirwan himfelf has fhewn, that not a particle of fixable air is produced. Then all that can be faid in favour of the doctrine of fixable air is, that it is decompofed. I fhould like to know how fuch a decompofition can take place; for, in order to this, the marine acid bafis muft exert a certain force on the phlogifton of the fixable air on the one fide, while the light inflammable air pulls at its dephlogifticated air on the other, and

3   fo,

so, by their contrary powers, force the conftituent principles of fixable air afunder. Is this conformable to the laws of nature, so far as they govern chemical attraction? May not we as well say, that a rope which fufpends a weight should firft break in the ftrongeft part? Is it not more reafonable to fuppofe, that the marine bafis would the rather unite to the difengaged phlogifton, than ftruggle for that which is already intimately combined? Even allowing fuch a decompofition, fixable air should be regenerated; for, according to Mr. Kirwan himfelf, water has never been formed but in a red heat *.

The black calx of manganefe, free from calcareous earth and iron, will not yield a particle of fixable air by expofure to heat. The acids, even thofe that will diffolve it, do not expel a particle of fixable air from it. I fufed manganefe and borax into a vitrefcent mafs, and yet no fixable air was produced, and little or no dephlogifticated air; but this I do not wonder at, as dephlogifticated air enters into the conftitution of

* Effay on Phlogifton, p. 26.

glafs.

glafs. If fal ammoniac and manganefe be diftilled, the fal ammoniac is decompofed, and the volatile alkali is obtained in a cauf- tic ftate ; and the acid is dephlogifticated, as Mr. Kirwan obferves. Hence he infers, that the fixable air of the manganefe unites to the marine acid ; but he fhould firft prove that the manganefe contains fixable air. I have diftilled cauftic volatile alkali and manganefe, and yet the alkali was ftill cauftic. Cauftic fixed alkali boiled over manganefe received no fixed air from it. Lime and manganefe treated in the fame manner did not fhew the fmalleft veftige of fixable air ; and the manganefe thus treated, afforded the ufual quantity of de- phlogifticated air. Thefe circumftances induce me to believe that manganefe, when free from calcareous earth, does not contain fixable air in any confiderable pro- portion ; and that dephlogifticated marine acid does not contain a particle of fixable air, as one of its conftituent principles. In my opinion, the phlogiftians muft have re- courfe to fome other mode of accounting for the formation of dephlogifticated ma- rine acid, befides that of fixable air ; and

what

what can this be ? They cannot attribute it
to the mere feparation of phlogifton from
the marine acid ; for it is evident that dephlogifticated air unites to it, during its
diftillation with manganefe, when we can
expel it from the acid again by uniting it to
fixed alkali, and when the falt is found to
be the fame as if the alkali had been combined with common marine acid. Befides,
the manganefe, after the diftillation of marine acid, will yield no dephlogifticated air,
although previous to this procefs it affords
it in abundance. Hence it appears, that
the phlogiftians muft allow the prefence of
dephlogifticated air in the dephlogifticated
marine acid ; and to fupport the doctrine
of phlogifton, they can only fay, that the
manganefe unites to it at the famo time that
it imparts dephlogifticated air to the marine
acid. If the marine acid parts with phlogifton to unite to dephlogifticated air, how
does it recover this again on uniting to fixed
vegetable alkali, when its dephlogifticated
air is expelled ? for it is converted into
common marine acid, and, according to the
phlogiftians, the prefence of phlogifton is
indifpenfably neceffary to this ftate. Let
us

us now inquire into the nature of dephlogifticated marine acid, and aqua regia, in
the antiphlogistic doctrine.

I have already defcribed the nature of
marine acid with refpect to the attraction
of its bafis for dephlogifticated air, and the
intimacy of their union when in the ftate
of common marine acid. No wonder then
that it fhould unite to more dephlogifticated
air, when it meets with it condenfed and
united with lefs force than its bafis attracts
it. A moderate degree of heat will expel
dephlogifticated air from red lead and manganefe ; but the fierceft heat we can produce will not expel the whole of their dephlogifticated air from them. Hence we
may infer, that the marine bafis may with
very little refiftance deprive thefe of a portion of their air, and thereby affume the
character of dephlogifticated marine acid.
The calces of iron, tin, copper, antimony,
&c. will not part with dephlogifticated air
in the moft intenfe heat; which fhews
that they retain it with greater force than
the former calces, and of courfe will not
give it up to the marine bafis fo readily.

I have endeavoured to fhew, that dephlogifticated air is retained with lefs force in

the

the nitrous acid than in the vitriolic acid ;
and in the vitriolic, than in the marine acid.
I would now obferve that, though the marine bafis, when united to its natural portion
of dephlogifticated air, cannot take this
from the vitriolic acid, it will deprive the
nitrous acid of a portion of its dephlogifticated air, as holding it with fo inferior a
force.

Thus, when marine acid is mixed with
the nitrous acid, nitrous air is fometimes
produced, according to the proportion ufed.
If thefe two acids be mixed in the proportions of two of the nitrous to three of the
marine, provided the acids be ftrong and
complete, and the mixture be kept in a
cool place, nitrous air will firft be difengaged, attended with heat ; but on ftanding
for fome time, and when it gets cool,
the nitrous air ceafes coming over, and
fmall bubbles of air are generated in different parts of the mixture, which are
abforbed almoft as foon as they get birth.
Thefe fometimes make their firft appearance
at the bottom of the liquor, and are carried
upwards in flender ftreams, gradually di-
minifhing in their progrefs, until they can

be

be no longer traced, and attended with a hif-
fing noife, occafioned by the abforption.
I endeavoured in vain to obtain fome of
this air. This beautiful appearance does
not always take place. A fimilar phenomenon may be obferved in preparing nitrous
ether in Dr. Black's method.

Thus we find that the marine acid will
take dephlogifticated air from the nitrous,
with as much facility as from the calx of
manganefe, and that it affects this acid
as the metals do, by withdrawing dephlogifticated air from it, and not, as the phlogiftians imagine, by imparting phlogifton
to it; for I flatter myfelf I have already
fhewn that nitrous air contains no fuch
thing.

It is very well known that fixable air will
not affect nitrous air in the leaft, and that
they cannot be combined by any means
whatever. It is likewife very obvious, that
nitrous air will not form nitrous acid without the prefence of dephlogifticated air.
Yet Mr. Pellitier formed nitrous and common marine acid, by mixing dephlogifticated marine air and nitrous air, 26 Roz.
393. This is not only a convincing proof

of

of the entry of dephlogifticated air, in its
fimple ftate, into the conftitution of dephlogifticated marine acid, but likewife points
out the weaknefs of the phlogiftic theory.
For, if nitrous air were difengaged during
the action of the marine on the nitrous
acid, in confequence of the marine imparting phlogifton to it, and withdrawing from
it either dephlogifticated air or fixable air;
is it likely that they would decompofe each
other again, efpecially when they are in an
aërial ftate, and guarded by fire ? Indeed,
the phlogiftians may urge a fimilar objection againft the antiphlogiftic doctrine,
by faying that, if the marine acid deprived
the nitrous air of its dephlogifticated air, in
order to become dephlogifticated marine
acid, nitrous air could not deprive it of
this again. All this is very fair, and would
be difficult to get over, were it not for
our minute inquiry into the nature and internal ftructure of the acids ; and likewife
the force with which their conftituent principles unite, and the manner in which this
force muft be influenced, according to the
proportion of dephlogifticated air united
to their bafes.

I have

I have already fuppofed, that the imperfect or dephlogifticated nitrous air is united to its dephlogifticated air with the force of 6; the perfect or common nitrous air with the force of $4\frac{1}{2}$; the red nitrous vapour, or perfect red nitrous acid, with the force of 4; the pale with the force of $3\frac{3}{4}$; and the colourlefs or perfect nitrous acid with the force of $3\frac{3}{5}$. But I would obferve that thefe are often mixed, fo that it is a difficult matter to obtain them feparately, particularly the red and pale, for the colourlefs cannot exift in contact with the red. I have likewife fuppofed that the marine bafis, though it attracts dephlogifticated air with the force of 8, is only attached in its common ftate to its dephlogifticated air with the force of 6 ; and that it has a tendency to unite to more dephlogifticated air when it meets with it combined with a force inferior to its own attraction to it.

From this ftatement of the force of union of the conftituent principles of common marine acid, and its tendency to unite to more dephlogifticated air, we may fuppofe that its bafis attracts the quantity neceffary

P

to its dephlogifticated ftate with the force
of 4.

Thus ftating the comparative attraction
of both acids to dephlogifticated air, rather
than their abfolute forces, which I think
are impoffible to be afcertained, we fhall
be the better able to account for the following facts.   Mr. Pellitier has obferved,
if the nitrous acid be added in fmall proportion to the marine acid, that it is wholly
decompofed, and that its phlogifticated air is
difengaged, notwithftanding phlogifticated
air attracts the quantity of dephlogifticated
air neceffary to the formation of perfect
nitrous air, with greater force than the
marine acid.

This I think is only explicable on the following principles : When a fmall portion of
nitrous acid is diffufed in a large quantity of
marine, the latter expofes furfaces enough
to at once feparate the whole of its dephlogifticated air from the phlogifticated.   For
the force of 4 is fufficient to overcome, if
the perfect nitrous acid be ufed, the force of
$3\frac{3}{7}$, or if the pale $3\frac{3}{4}$; but if the red nitrous
acid be ufed in its purity, it will not be
decompofed, for it retains its dephlogifti-

4   cated

cated air with as great force as the marine
acid attracts it ; therefore they will partially unite without a decompofition.

I have already obferved the nature of the
above decompofition of nitrous acid, in
treating of the effects of metals on it when
highly diluted.

When a larger quantity of nitrous acid
is mixed with the marine acid, nitrous air
is produced ; for, as a molecule of the marine can only deprive a fingle molecule of
nitrous acid at moft but of two ultimate
particles of dephlogifticated air, there are
not a fufficient number of the former in
contact with the latter to effect a total decompofition; and as it cannot take place
but by a number of uniform pulls from
different quarters at once, while the nitrous molecule is perfect, the nitrous air,
retaining its fmall portion of dephlogifticated air with greater force than when united
to a larger quantity, paffes off unmolefted
in its aerial ftate in the marine acid.

Thus it is that nitrous air is difengaged
by the marine acid, though the nitrous air
will take its dephlogifticated air from dephlogifticated marine air.

P 2　　　　　I think

I think the dephlogifticated marine air retains its dephlogifticated air with nearly as
great force as the nitrous air attracts it; for
when the airs are perfectly dry, and mixed over
mercury, no decompofition feems to take
place until water is introduced. Hence I infer, that water affifts in the decompofition
from its attraction to marine acid. If a fmall
quantity of marine acid be mixed with a
large portion of perfect nitrous acid, no
nitrous air is produced, and no change appears in the acid. If more be added, the
acid changes colour; but if a larger quantity be added, nitrous air is produced, but
no phlogifticated air. This confirms the
above demonftration of the totaldecom-
pofition of nitrous acid; for we find a correfpondence in reverfing the proportion of
the acids.

If marine ammoniac be mixed with the
nitrous acid in the temperature of 70° or
80°, a violent action takes place, and a
large quantity of nitrous air is extricated,
mixed with a fmall portion of dephlogifticated marine air and phlogifticated air. Here
the marine ammoniac is decompofed; for
the nitrous acid, from its fuperior attraction

to

volatile alkali, takes it from the marine acid.
The marine acid in its turn takes dephlogifticated air from the remainder of the
nitrous acid, and forms aqua regia, or -de-
phlogifticated marine acid; a portion of
this dephlogifticated marine acid re-acts
on the newly formed nitrous ammoniac,
withdraws from it its inflammable air, and
converts it into water, by fupplying it with
dephlogifticated air, at the fame time that
its phlogifticated air is difengaged. This
accounts for the greater production of nitrous air when we ufe marine ammoniac,
than when the quantity of marine acid
which it contains is ufed. If the regulus
of antimony in fine powder be expofed to
the airs difengaged during the action of nitrous acid on marine ammoniac, it is inftantly calcined, and fparks of fire are emitted. This beautiful appearance will not
take place, if the regulus be expofed to the
dephlogifticated marine air alone ; fo that
it requires the prefence of nitrous air. This
is very unfavourable to the phlogiftic doctrine ; for, if the nitrous air be already faturated with phlogifton, how can it
contribute to the rapid calcination of the

antimony ?

antimony? Or, if it fhould take place in confequence of the attraction of the marine acid to phlogifton, the metal muft retain it with lefs force than the nitrous air. But if this fhould depend on the attraction of the metallic bafis for fixable air, at the fame time that the dephlogifticated bafis attracts its phlogifton, and fo by a double affinity promote the calcination or decompofition, it fhould take place in pure dephlogifticated marine air. It cannot be attributed to water; for fteam in its rareft ftate cannot produce it, nor will fteam and nitrous air afford this phenomenon.

It appears to me, that it can only take place at the very inftant that the dephlogifticated marine air unites to red nitrous vapour, which is formed by an union of atmofpheric air to the nitrous air, extricated with the dephlogifticated marine air; for both acids attached and deftitute of water, which would imperceptibly carry off the fire difengaged by the rapid union of dephlogifticated air to the metal, favour calcination more when thus partially condenfed, than either would feparately in an

aerial

aerial ftate, being then too intimately united to fire.

The marine acid will condenfe red nitrous vapour in confequence of its dephlogifticated air; and provided the proportion
be adjufted, little or no nitrous air will be
produced. In like manner, red nitrous vapour, or red nitrous acid, from its attraction
to dephlogifticated air, will unite to dephlogifticated marine acid, and not a particle of nitrous air will be produced : here
the attraction of both acids to dephlogiftilo-
cated air is nearly equal; therefore they
unite without a feparation of either of their
principles. Hence arifes the difference between what is called aqua regia, and dephlogifticated marine acid; for when marine
acid is even combined with a fufficiency of
dephlogifticated air to form dephlogifticated
marine acid, it will influence the nitrous
vapour fo as to render it impoffible to feparate them, from their nearly equal degree of
volatility. Although the heat generated by
the admixture of the marine and perfect nitrous acid, fhews the more intimate union
of the dephlogifticated air of the nitrous
acid to the marine ; yet the volatility of the

compound

compound, or the little force with which its molecules gravitate towards each other, accounts for the specific gravity of aqua regia.

Dr. Prieftley diminifhed common air by paffing the electric fpark in it, in contact with marine acid; and though he continued the operation fome time after the contraction took place, the refiduum neither increafed nor diminifhed*. Dephlogifticated marine acid expofed to the folar light will yield dephlogifticated air, 29 Roz. 82. Thefe two facts, not to adduce any more, are fufficient to confirm the antiphlogiftic doctrine. When Dr. Prieftley took the electric fpark in common air, in contact with dephlogifticated marine acid, it was diminifhed to one half; but I fufpect, as fome of the phlogifticated air difappeared, that nitrous acid had been formed.

Thus finding that this change in marine acid depends upon its union to dephlogifticated air fimply, we can eafily account for the calcination of metals in this acid, without the extrication of inflammable air; for though the metal takes this de-

* Vol. VI. p. 340.

phlogifticated

phlogifticated air from the marine acid, it cannot recover it again from the water; therefore it re-acts on the metallic calx, and diffolves it. From the attraction of common marine acid to dephlogifticated air, it will diffolve the calces even of thofe metals which it has no power over when in their metallic ftate, without producing inflammable air. We can explain on the fame principle, why dephlogifticated marine acid will not diffolve metallic calces; for the marine bafis and the metals being faturated with dephlogifticated air, cannot influence each other until either lofes a portion of its air, by which this neutrality or equilibrium is deftroyed. The effect of perfect or pale nitrous acid on manganefe and other metallic calces confirms this; for, as the immortal Scheel has long fince obferved, this acid muft be deprived of a portion of its dephlogifticated air, before it can diffolve them; and this is done by the addition of any fubftance which attracts dephlogifticated air, fuch as fugar, fpirit of wine, &c.

The converfion of fulphur into vitriolic acid by dephlogifticated marine acid, is ra-

ther

ther againft the phlogiftic theory, when we confider that this again, when combined with clay, and expofed to heat, will yield dephlogifticated air. This I mention, becaufe Mr. Kirwan urges it againft the antiphlogiftians. Bergman fays, that fulphur is not vitriolated in dephlogifticated marine acid; but, not having repeated the experiment, I muft reft in fufpenfe. Several other facts might be adduced in favour of the antiphlogiftic doctrine, but in my opinion it is unneceffary to fay any more. Indeed I think every fingle fact in chemiftry is in its favour, even thofe that have been urged in oppofition to it. Therefore it appeared unneceffary to felect from the general ftock of facts, which induced me to adopt fuch truths as firft occurred to me in my demonftrations.

SECTION

SECTION VI.

Of the Calcination of Metals Via Sicca.

ALL the metals, except gold, platina, and filver, are calcined by the joint action of air and fire. That is to fay, they are deprived of their metallic brilliancy, affume an earthy appearance, and acquire an additional weight.

Philofophers vary in opinion refpecting the nature of the calcination of metals. The antiphlogiftians fuppofe that metals are fimple bodies, which unite to dephlogifticated air, and form calces; and that the mere expulfion of it is fufficient to reduce them again to their metallic fplendour; and likewife when charcoal is ufed to reduce the refractory calces, that it imparts nothing to the metal; but that, by its fuperior attraction to dephlogifticated air, it feparates this from it, by which it is revived.

The phlogiftians, on the contrary, are of opinion, that metals are compofed of two

principles,

principles, viz. metallic bases, and phlogiston (or light inflammable air), in a solid state. Although all the phlogistians allow that dephlogisticated air unites to some of the metals during calcination, yet they do not agree with respect to the nature of the union. Some phlogistians suppose that the dephlogisticated air unites to the phlogiston of the metal, and forms water, which combines with the metallic basis, and constitutes the calx. Others are of opinion, that fixable air is sometimes formed. Dr. Priestley thinks that metals, during their calcination in dephlogisticated air, unite to the water suspended in it, at the same time that the gravitating matter, or acidifying principle of the dephlogisticated air, unites to its phlogiston, and forms an acid.

These are the latest received opinions in the phlogistic doctrine respecting the calcination of metals. That metals give out nothing, but take in dephlogisticated air during calcination, appears from Dr. Priestley's and Mr. Lavoisier's experiments; but that this absorption depends on inflammable air (or phlogiston) has not been proved, and, in my

7

my opinion, there have been very little grounds for fuch an hypothefis.

Allowing metals to be what the phlogiftians fuppofe, is it likely that phlogifton, which muft be the fame wherever it is, or however combined, fhould at one time form fixable air, and at another time water; or, according to Dr. Prieftley, nitrous acid? The former doctrine is certainly an excellent improvement on the phlogiftic theory; for, without it, this could not ftand its ground much longer. But although this hypothefis of fixable air may at firft feem plaufible in calcination in the dry way, yet that advantage is totally loft when acids are ufed. Fixable air is formed during the calcination of mercury *per fe*, according to Mr. Kirwan; fo that mercurius calcinatus is a compound of a metallic bafis and fixable air, as are likewife all the mercurial calces. The phlogiftians may perfift in this hypothefis, for, in my opinion, it appears very favourable to them. 1ft, Becaufe it is very well known that fixable air is compofed of dephlogifticated air and heavy inflammable air, and therefore can be fuppofed to impart phlogifton during its decompofition.

compofition. 2dly, Becaufe a vaft quantity of nitrous air is produced during the calcination of mercury in the nitrous acid, which they fuppofe to be the phlogifton of the metal and nitrous bafis intimately combined. 3dly, Becaufe this laft fuppofition of nitrous air could not be admitted but on the doctrine of fixable air, as the nitrated calx is reduced without addition ; which, according to the phlogiftians, would be impoffible, as the nitrous air carried off its own phlogifton, unlefs it was united with fomething which could impart phlogifton to it. Hence we find that, laying afide the prefence of fixable air, phlogifton muft be fubverted. As the phlogifton of the mercury is carried off in the nitrous air, according to the phlogiftians, and of courfe no phlogifton left to form fixable air, which is neceffary to the calciform ftate of the mercury, Mr. Kirwan has been pleafed to fay, that fixa' air is one of the conftituent principles of nitrous acid itfelf, and that it unites to the mercurial bafis ready formed. I have already given my reafons for refufing my affent to this ; and it has appeared that phlogifton, or light inflammable air, does not

enter

enter into the conftitution of nitrous air; therefore it is evident, that the doctrine of fixable air is as delufive as any other phlogiftic doctrine. Mercury, as that great philofopher Mr. Lavoifier has firft obferved, unites to a certain portion of dephlogifticated air during its calcination *per fe*, and the additional weight of the calx correfponds with the weight of the air abforbed. By the mere application of heat the air is expelled again, and the mercury is revived. Laying afide all prejudices, this moft undoubtedly is a ftrong argument in favour of the antiphlogiftic doctrine, and is to me, together with the facts already adduced, a convincing proof of the truth of it. Mr. Kirwan would explain this procefs in the following manner, viz. That the phlogifton of the metal unites to the dephlogifticated air, and forms fixable air, which, re-uniting to the metallic bafis, conftitutes the calx; but when a greater degree of heat is applied than was neceffary to the calcination, that this fixable air is decompofed, by which its dephlogifticated air is difengaged, at the fame time that its phlogifton re-unites to the metallic bafis. Even lofing fight of what

what has been already adduced on the fubject, it appears to me, that this mode of
reafoning, if ftrictly fcrutinized, will be
found to carry with it felf-contradiction.
For, in the firft place, it fhews that phlogifton, or the matter of light inflammable
air, has greater affinity to dephlogifticated air than it has to the metallic bafis.
In the fecond place, during the revivification,
this evidently appears not to be the cafe.
If mercurius calcinatus were compofed of
three principles, viz. a metallic bafis, phlogifton, and dephlogifticated air; and if the
two latter were intimately combined from
their fuperior attraction in the ftate of fixable air, and attached to the metallic bafis,
is it likely that any degree of heat, but particularly that fufficient to revive mercury,
would feparate the conftituent principles of
the fixable air; more efpecially when they
attract each other with greater force than
the metallic bafis does either? This ftill
appears the more improbable, when we
confider the volatility of fixable air and of
its conftituent principles. Is it not the
property of fire to promote the elective attraction of bodies, or elfe to refolve compounds

pounds into their conftituent principles?
And is not this eftablifhed law wholly per-
verted, if we fuppofe mercury to contain
phlogifton (or the gravitating matter of
light inflammable air)?

Indeed, there are fome circumftances in
which bodies will decompofe others of fuperior attraction, when expofed to heat; as,
for inftance, phofphoric acid will decompofe
vitriolated tartar; but this proceeds from
the extreme fixity of the alkali and phofphoric acid, and the volatility of vitriolic
acid; a circumftance which does not interfere in the reduction or calcination of
mercury.

If mercury were a fimple body, whofe
ultimate particles attract dephlogifticated
air, but which, from their own influence
on each other, cannot unite to it until this
is counteracted by heat, we could account
for the calcination of mercury, and the decompofition of the calx again when expofed
to a ftronger heat, on the fame principle
that copper and zinc, or gold and mercury,
or tin and mercury, unite in a low heat, and
feparate again in a higher degree.

If the calces of mercury contained fixable air, they would yield it during their re-

Q   duction

duction in light inflammable air; which is not the cafe, as appears from Dr. Prieftley's experiments. This philofopher heated red precipitate of mercury in contact with light inflammable air, in clofe veffels, until eight ounce meafures were abforbed, and no fixable air was produced, but a fmall portion of water*.

Mr. Kirwan would fay, that the fixable air is here decompofed, or rather condenfed into water; which hypothefis is founded upon no experiment whatever. For I am perfuaded that no chemift can convert all the principles of fixable air into water, or into any other fluid.

If fixable air was decompofed during the reduction of mercurial calces, the fame fhould take place during the revivification of white lead in light inflammable air, which, we know, contains fixable air in great abundance; but this does not appear to be the cafe. If fixed air be convertible into water by intenfe heat, as Mr. Kirwan fuppofes, fixed vegetable alkali, or barites, fhould not yield it after they have been expofed to a ftrong heat for fome time; or the

* Vol. VI. p. 129.

electric

electric fpark would condenfe it into water, which Dr. Prieftley has fhewn does not happen; though, as he has obferved, a partial decompofition had taken place. I frequently mixed an afcertained quantity of fixable air with a charge of light inflammable and dephlogifticated air; and though I inflamed them by paffing a ftrong electric fpark in them, I found no fenfible change in the fixable air. From thefe and many other fimilar circumftances I am led to believe, if the calces of mercury contained fixable air, that we fhould obtain it when we fupply the metallic bafis with pure phlogifton.

It is furprifing to me, if metals be compofed of fo volatile a fubftance as light inflammable air and fixed bafes, that we cannot feparate them in the moft intenfe heat. Surely all the metallic bafes are not the fame. Therefore we fhould fuppofe that there might be one or more amongft them all, that would be fo little tenacious of their phlogifton as to yield, if not the whole, a portion of it when urged with a fierce heat. Yet the phlogiftians themfelves could never obtain from metals what they fo earneftly contend for, without the

Q 2   prefence

presence of water. Indeed, Dr. Priestley acknowledges that metals will not give a particle of air without water. As to a metallic basis, they have not yet been able to produce it. Therefore it is obvious, that the contention or difference between the phlogistians and antiphlogistians is this: the former are led away by imagination, and the latter confine themselves to the evidence of their senses. I charged four drachms of iron filings, which I carefully prepared, into a small glass retort; and though I applied heat sufficient to melt the glass, I obtained little more than one cubic inch of inflammable air; and this was produced in the beginning of the process; so that it must have proceeded from moisture. I exposed lead, tin, zinc, bismuth, cobalt, copper, and regulus of antimony, to heat sufficient to melt cast iron, in a well closed deep crucible; and although I sublimed and dissipated all of them (copper excepted), I could not effect the smallest change in their constitution; for what sublimed and adhered to the upper part of the crucibles, possessed its natural brilliancy and specific gravity. Mr. Kirwan supposes that

fixable

fixable air is only formed during calcination in a low heat, but that water is formed in a higher degree. If it were fo, red lead would not yield dephlogifticated air; for the phlogiftians will not allow the decompofition of water. Mr. Kirwan attempts to obviate this by faying, that red lead is prepared in a low degree of heat, but that litharge, which requires a higher, will afford none. However, I converted litharge into red lead in a degree of heat not much fhort of that which will convert red lead into litharge; and it gave dephlogifticated air in fmall quantities; and by the addition of oil of vitriol I obtained dephlogifticated air from it in abundance, but not a particle of fixable air. Part of the fame red lead, expofed to the atmofphere for a few weeks, yielded fixable air both with and without vitriolic acid; which induces me to think that fixable air is not a neceffary ingredient in red lead, but that it abforbs it after it is formed.

The truth is, minium contains more dephlogifticated air than litharge does; and, in its tranfition from the former to the latter, it parts with it, as Dr. Prieftley has fhewn.

Q 3   And

And as litharge contains lefs of dephlogifticated air than minium, it is the more tenacious of it, and will not give it up until fomething elfe is prefented to it which has greater
affinity to the air than the lead has.   Dr.
Higgins has fhewn, that 7581,5 gr. of litharge, when completely reduced, will yield
6835,2 gr. of pure lead, and that 7680 gr.
of red lead will yield but the fame quantity ;
whence he juftly inferred, that 6835,2 gr. of
lead require, in order to become minium,
98,5 gr. more of air than is neceffary to its
converfion into litharge.   To confirm this,
he converted the above quantity of minium
into litharge, and obtained during the procefs 98,5 gr. of air, 24 of which he found
to be fixable air,   and 74,5 dephlogifticated
mixed with phlogifticated air *.   This does
not correfpond with Mr. Kirwan's account
of a fimilar procefs ; for he found that minium, during its tranfition to litharge, abforbed air†.

The expulfion of fixable air from minium and other metallic calces, which Mr.
Kirwan feems to lay great ftrefs upon, does

* Exp. and Obf. on Acet. Acid, &c. p. 210.
† Effay on Phlogifton, p. 111.

not in my opinion favour his hypothefis in the leaft; for, if the dephlogifticated air abforbed, formed fixable air by an union to the phlogifton of the metal, confidering that fome metals are revived again without the addition of foreign phlogifton; it fhould feem that metals never fuffer any part of their natural portion of phlogifton to be carried off: and, indeed, if metals contain what they call phlogifton, it muft be fo; for I found that red precipitate, or turbith mineral, recently prepared, afforded no fixable air, although Dr. Prieftley difcovered a trifling portion of it in dephlogifticated air obtained from mercurius calcinatus. But much depends upon the time they are kept; for they abforb fixable air from the atmofphere, like all other fpongy or porous fubftances. Hence I think, that the fixable air obtained as well during the calcination of metals, as afterwards from their calces, depends upon fome impregnation in the materials, and does not in the leaft tend to prove the exiftence of phlogifton in metals. Iron quickly calcined by fire, or in the nitrous acid, will not yield a particle of fixable air, though ruft of iron will afford it in

Q 4   abundance.

abundance. Mr. Kirwan may object to the
former procefs, by faying, that water is
formed during the calcination; but this
cannot be faid when the calx is prepared by
nitrous acid. Therefore, if the calcination in
the nitrous acid depended upon an union to
fixable air, why fhould not this afford fixable air as well as the ruft of iron, when
both appear equally well calcined ?

Dr. Prieftley calcined iron fhavings over
mercury in dephlogifticated air, by means
of a burning lens, and found fome fixed air
in the refiduum, but it was not more than
the 13th of a meafure, after the abforption of
7 ounce meafures of dephlogifticated air.
The fame philofopher reduced a quantity of
the calx of iron, carefully prepared, by
means of fpirit of nitre in light inflammable air; but it does not appear that he obtained fixable air*. He likewife reduced
17 gr. of lead in alkaline air : the refiduum
was phlogifticated air, and it did not contain a particle of fixable air. Dr. Prieftley
reduced 150 ounce meafures of light inflammable air to 10 ounce meafures, by re-

* Vol. VI. p. 16.

ducing

ducing in it the calx of lead over mercury, and the refiduum contained no fixable air *.

If the fixable air generated during the calcination of the iron, in the above experiment, proceeded from its phlogifton and dephlogifticated air, why was not fixable air formed during the reduction of the calces, whereas they were expofed only to the fame degree of heat?

In my opinion, metals contain fomething not at all neceffary to their conftitution, which forms fixable air with dephlogifticated air. The phlogiftians muft all allow, if metals contain phlogifton or inflammable air, that it is of the explofive kind; for no other is obtained during their calcination in the humid way, whatever menftruum is ufed. Then why does not this form fixable air with the dephlogifticated air during the revival of the calx of mercury in it, if a fubftance of the fame fort be united to it in the ftate of fixable air in the calx? The phlogiftians will fay, that the heat neceffary to the reduction is too great for the formation of fixable air. But then, if fo, why will inflammable air from foliated tartar, or from charcoal, which

* Vol. VI. p. 9.

are known not to contain a particle of ready formed fixable air, generate this under the same circumstance ? Or why will it form fixable air in the most intense degree of heat ? I ask, if there ever has been an instance of the formation of fixable air by an union of light inflammable air and dephlogisticated air ? It appears to me a matter of impossibility. Therefore, how can we suppose that the fixable air produced when we use iron filings and red precipitate, results from an union of both these airs ?

Dr. Priestley obtained 40 ounce measures of fixable air from one ounce of red precipitate and two ounces of iron filings *. From 300 grains of iron newly filed, and 240 of red precipitate, Mr. Kirwan obtained no air ; but, on the contrary, there was an absorption. When he used precipitate *per se*, instead of red precipitate, and varied the proportion, and sprinkled the ingredients with water, he got 4,5 cubic inches of fixable air, and 36 of a mixture of dephlogisticated and inflammable air. Mr. De la Metherie obtained no air from equal

* Vol. VI. p. 27.

parts

parts of red precipitate and iron filings;
and from two ounces of red precipitate,
and one drachm of iron filings, he obtained
a very fmall quantity of fixable air*. Equal
parts of lead and red precipitate gave no air
at all to Mr. Kirwan, though the lead was
nearly calcined. 240 gr. of bifmuth, and
the fame quantity of red precipitate, diftilled with a low heat, afforded Mr. Kirwan
two ounces of fixable air. The fame mixture, urged with a ftrong heat, gave but
one cubic inch of fixable air, and the bifmuth was calcined. Equal parts of red
precipitate and zinc did not produce any
air; nor did 200 gr. of copper, and 240 of
red precipitate, though the mercury was revived †.

One ounce of red precipitate, and one
ounce and a half of iron filings newly made,
diftilled in a fmall coated glafs retort, afforded but fix ounce meafures of fixable air,
and about one ounce meafure of phlogifticated air, though the mercury was nearly
revived, and the iron a good deal calcined.
I fufpect that the iron was impure, for the
air had the fmell of volatile vitriolic acid

* 27. Roz. 146.
† Effay on Phlogifton, p. 114, 115.

4   towards

towards the end of the procefs; and as I was obliged to receive the airs in water, a fmall portion might have been abforbed. However, thefe experiments differ widely from Dr. Priestley's, and clearly prove, that fixable air is not a necessary production in them; but that it depends upon chance, and the prefence of fome foreign fubftance which we are not aware of.

Dr. Priestley partially calcined lead in mercury by repeated agitation, with free accefs of air; and after feparating the fluid mercury from a black powder thus obtained, it afforded fome fixable air. From fix ounces of this black powder he obtained four and a half ounce meafures of air, one and a half of which was fixable air *. 10 ounces of the fame powder gave 23 ounce meafures of air; 8 or 9 ounces of which were fixable air. 4 ounces of this black powder, and 2 ounces of iron filings, gave only 4 ounce meafures of fixable air †. 20 ounces of this, and one of iron filings, afforded but 4 or 5 ounce meafures of fixed air ‡. 2 ounces of this black powder, moiftened and dried again, gave very little fixed air §. Al-

* Vol. VI. page 258.　　† Ib. p. 261.
‡ Ib. p. 262.　　§ Ib. p. 265.

though

though 4 ounces, treated in the fame manner, afforded 120 ounce meafures of air, 12
meafures of which were fixed air.

Thus we find how thefe experiments
vary in their refults ; which fhews that the
fixable air proceeds partly from fome impurities in the materials, but chiefly from
abforption of fixable air from the atmofphere. I diftilled fome mercury with iron
filings, in order to obtain it pure, and introduced fix ounces of it, and fome lead
filings, into a five ounce phial with a ground
ftopple, and tied a bladder half full of
dephlogifticated air, which I previoufly
wafhed in lime liquor, to the neck of it.
The bladder being flaccid, I could take out
the glafs ftopple at pleafure, and let in dephlogifticated air when I thought neceffary. Having by repeated concuffions produced fome of this black powder, though
the air in the bladder did not feem much
diminifhed, I difcontinued the procefs, fear-
ing that the wet bladder might be a fource
of fixable air. When I feparated the running mercury from it, it weighed near half
an ounce, which I quickly introduced into
a fmall coated glafs retort, and obtained

I   from

from it one ounce meafure of air, which, although it rendered lime-water a little turbid, was not fenfibly diminifhed, and a candle burned in it fomewhat better than in common air.

Having enumerated thofe experiments which the phlogiftians adduce as the chief fupport of their doctrine, I think, they do not in the leaft help to prove the exiftence of phlogifton in metals. Let us review them all, and carefully compare their different products of fixable air, and we fhall be convinced that it cannot refult from any neceffary principle in metals; for, if fo, the products fhould be invariably the fame under the fame circumftances.

Befides, I think, the reduction of one metal by another, in the dry way, rather proves that they contain no fuch thing as the matter of light inflammable air, or phlogifton. For, let us fuppofe the dephlogifticated air to be united to the phlogifton of the metal, in the ftate either of fixable air or water, and thefe to be attached to the metallic bafis with any force; is it likely that the phlogifton of another metal, which is intimately ined with its own bafis, fhould difturb

this

this union in the leaſt? The phlogiſtians may ſay, that the baſis of the reviving metal (we will take, for inſtance, copper) attracts the fixable air or water of the calx at the ſame time that the baſis of the calx attracts its phlogiſton; and ſo, by a double affinity, effect a decompoſition. But I would obſerve, if ſuch a decompoſition ſhould take place, in conſequence of the influence of their different metallic baſes, that it muſt be impoſſible for us to obtain either water or fixable air, as a product reſulting from any of the conſtituent principles of the metal, in the degree of heat neceſſary to reduce red precipitate. Becauſe, if the iron, or copper, or zinc, or biſmuth, all of which will reduce a mercurial calx, ſhould exchange their phlogiſton for the fixable air or water of the calx, they muſt undoubtedly retain this with at leaſt as much force as they do their phlogiſton; and it is well known that no heat will expel this from them.

SECTION

SECTION VII.

Of the Calcination of Metals by Steam, and the Decompofition of Water.

MR. Lavoifier has fhewn us, that fteam, when brought in contact with red hot iron, calcines it, at the fame time that inflammable air is abundantly produced; from which he inferred, that the water is decompofed. He likewife found that the water is decompofed by iron without the affiftance of heat; for he obtained inflammable air by confining iron filings and water over mercury. Dr. Prieftley, who has made a vaft number of very accurate experiments on the fame fubject, has found that 294 gr. added to the weight of a quantity of iron, made it to yield 1000 ounce meafures of inflammable air, which he eftimates would weigh 60 gr. and which is nearly 5 to 1*. But this eftimation, ac-

* Vol. VI. p. 121.

cording

cording to Lavoifier and Kirwan, is too
high. Dr. Prieftley likewife found, that
the addition of 12 ounce meafures of dephlogifticated air added 6 gr. to the weight
of the iron which had been fufed in it.
Therefore, the dephlogifticated air abforbed, carries with it into the calx the quantity of water it holds in folution. Whether a quantity of dephlogifticated air, when
as much water as poffible is abftracted from
it, would calcine the fame weight of iron,
or any other metal, that it would in its ordinary ftate, is very well worth afcertain-
ing. As this cannot be done without the
affiftance of a lens, it is not in my power,
at prefent, to make the experiment. The
fame philofopher obferves, that, making an
allowance for the fmall quantity of dephlogifticated air expended in the formation of
fixable air during calcination, which did
not exceed the 13th of an ounce meafure in
7 ounce meafures of dephlogifticated air, the
quantity of water produced by the reduction of the iron in light inflammable air,
nearly correfponded with the weight of
both airs. He moreover obferves, that the
lofs of weight in the iron, after its reduc-

R   tion,

tion, was equal to that of such a quantity of dephlogisticated air as would have been one half of the bulk of the inflammable air that disappeared in the process *. A mixture of 1 part of dephlogisticated air and 2 of light inflammable air, provided the airs be pure, will, by passing the electric spark in it, form water, as Mr. Cavendish has shewn ; which proportion very well agrees with the above estimation of Dr. Priestley. All these facts strongly concur in favour of the decomposition of water. I charged half an ounce of charcoal into a small tubulated retort ; the orifice was very small, and well fitted with a stopple, though, from its conical figure, it was readily taken out at pleasure. Having then exposed the charcoal to a strong heat until nothing came over but pure inflammable air, and this very slowly, I took out the stopple, and poured in nearly half a thimble full of water, and instantly closed it again ; when 3 or 4 ounce measures of air gushed from the retort with violence, and then ceased giving out any more until fresh water was

* Vol. VI. p. 121.

introduced.

introduced. Thus I obtained 10 or 12 cubic inches of air, of which one-fifth was fixable air, and the remainder inflammable, intermediate, I thought, between the light and heavy.

It is very well known that charcoal is wholly convertible into inflammable air, and that this inflammable air cannot, by any means whatever, form fixable air without the prefence of dephlogifticated air *. Therefore water muft have been decompofed in the above experiment, by which the matter of charcoal was fupplied with dephlogifticated air. Dr. Prieftley converted the whole of a quantity of charcoal into inflammable air, without the flighteft appearance of fixable air †.

---

* It may be fuppofed that the atmofpheric air, by preff-ing into the retort, contributed to the formation of the fixable air; but if fo, fixable air would have been produced by merely taking out the ftopple, which was not the cafe: befides, atmofpheric air could not rufh in during the fhort time the ftopple had been out, confider-ing that the charcoal yielded inflammable air, and that the preffure of the water up the neck of the retort muft more than counterbalance the external preffure of the atmofphere.

† Vol. VI. p. 245.

Mr.

Mr. Lavoifier, having carefully calcined a quantity of charcoal, in order to expel any water or fixable air it might contain, introduced 248,62 gr. troy of it into an iron tube lined with copper, and having paffed through it 1122 gr. of water, in the ftate of fteam, obtained 6644 cubic inches of air, whofe weight he eftimated at 550 gr. one-fourth of the bulk of which he found, by introducing cauftic alkali, to be fixed air; and there remained 5 grains of afhes in the tube. As the weight of the airs produced was more than double that of the charcoal, he inferred that the water muft have been decompofed; its oxygenous principle uniting to a portion of the charcoal, and forming fixable air, while the remainder acquired an aerial ftate, and mixed with the inflammable air of the water. That water had been decompofed in this experiment is evident; elfe, whence came the fixable air? for, from Mr. Lavoifier's previous treatment of the charcoal, it could not contain any.

Mr. Kirwan does not allow the decompofition of water in the above experiment. He fuppofes that the fixable air came from

the

the charcoal, being one of its conftituent principles, and that the inflammable air is its other conftituent principle, and that the additional weight proceeded from the folution of water in both airs.

Mr. Kirwan's firft fuppofition is abfolutely contradicted by Dr. Prieftley's experiments[*], where he has fhewn that charcoal does not contain an atom of fixable air. Therefore, to fay any more on the fubject would be fuperfluous. That water is held in folution in all airs, is what we do not difpute, but not in that quantity which the phlogiftians imagine. A fmall quantity of moifture is undoubtedly neceffary to the converfion of charcoal into pure inflammable air: if a little more be ufed, fixable air is produced in very fmall quantities; but if a larger portion of water be ufed, the quantity of fixable air is ftill greater. The extremes Dr. Prieftley obferved in the proportion of fixed to the inflammable air has been from one-twelfth to one-fifth of the whole. Why the fmall quantity of water neceffary to the aerial ftate of charcoal fhould not be decompofed, is difficult to be ac-

[*] Vol. VI. p. 345.

counted

counted for, especially when a larger quantity is readily decompofed. I expofed fome wort to dephlogifticated air until it began to ferment, yet the air was not in the leaft diminifhed, though the liquor acquired an acid tafte. The fame change took place in the liquor when I prevented all communications with dephlogifticated air.

Thefe facts narrowly inquired into, will remove all doubts refpecting the decompofition of water. If it were not decompofed, we could not account for feveral facts relating as well to the calcination, as the reduction of metals. Let us even fuppofe the inflammable air to come from the metal in confequence of a fuperior attraction of its bafis to water; is it likely that this would diflodge the water again in any degree of heat, efpecially when the inflammable air is combined with fire? It may be faid, that intenfe heat diffolves the union of the water and the metallic bafis. But fhould not, as already obferved, the fame caufe prevent the union of the inflammable air to the metallic bafis, if it even were as fixed as water, and uncombined with fire, unlefs we fuppofe phlogifton to have greater

attraction

attraction to the metallic bafis than water has? Then, water could never expel inflammable air from the metal.

To account for the calcination of metals by fteam, &c. and for the reduction of thefe again to their metallic fplendour in inflammable air, we muft, in my opinion, have recourfe to a mode of reafoning quite different from the preceding; and confider metals to be fimple bodies, whofe ultimate particles attract dephlogifticated air with greater force than light inflammable air. The phlogiftians may fay, that light inflammable air in this cafe could not decompofe metallic calces; but this is foreign to that which I urged laft againft them. For, metals being fixed bodies, and dephlogifticated air having ftrong attraction to fire; when calces are expofed to heat, the force of union between them is much weakened, as is evident by the reduction of gold, filver, and mercury by heat alone, having lefs attraction to dephlogifticated air than the other metals.

To render this more intelligible, let us fuppofe dephlogifticated air to be attached to the metal in a common tem-

R 4   perature,

perature, with the force of 7, and the attraction of light inflammable air to dephlogisticated air to be any degree below this,
we will say the force of 6. Let us now
suppose this compound or calx to be exposed
to intense heat, though not strong enough
to decompose it, yet sufficient to reduce its
force of union to its dephlogisticated air to
5$\frac{1}{7}$. If inflammable air were brought in
contact with the calx in this state, is it not
reasonable to suppose that it would deprive
it of its dephlogisticated air? But then I
ask the phlogistians, whether the inflammable air could unite to the metal under these
circumstances?

I think this alone, strictly considered,
would go a great way towards overthrowing
the phlogistic theory.

SECTION

SECTION VIII.

Of the Reduction of Metallic Calces by means of Charcoal, and the Formation of Fixed Air.

DR. Prieftley has obferved, that fixable air muft have been actually formed during the union of heavy inflammable air and dephlogifticated air, as he often found that the fixable air produced, exceeded the weight of the inflammable air.

Dr. Higgins has fhewn (and I think I am authorized to particularize it, for I had an active fhare in all the experiments fet down in his laft publication), that 3,15 gr. of the pureft dephlogifticated air, and 1,1 gr. of inflammable air from foliated tartar, afford, when inflamed by the electric fpark, 2,85 gr. of fixable air.   As the weight of the fixable air fell fhort of that of the two airs employed, by 1,4 gr. and as there had been a quantity of moifture precipitated, Dr. Higgins fuppofes that a part of the dephlogifticated

phlogifticated air unites to phlogifton, **and** forms water, while the remainder, **which** he eftimates to be two thirds of the whole, unites to the acid matter of acetous acid, as he is pleafed to call it, and forms the fixable air. When he ufed inflammable air from charcoal, the refult was the fame. Thefe experiments clearly fhew, that fixable air is compofed of the matter of charcoal and dephlogifticated air. I have my doub's refpecting the water produced in the above experiment : in my opinion, the moft part of it is precipitated from both airs on their contracting an union, as the compound cannot hold in folution as much water as its conftituent principles in their fimple aerial ftate ; although heavy inflambable air from foliated tartar contains light inflammable air, as appears from Dr. Auftin's experiments. But this I confider to be as foreign to the gravitating matter of charcoal, as the matter of fulphur is to the inflammable air, which holds it in folution in the ftate of hepatic gas. For both will burn, or, in other words, will unite to dephlogifticated air, and form feparate compounds. I think, neglecting to difcrimi-

nate

nate between the light and heavy inflammable airs, has been the chief caufe of all the errors and confufion that at prefent prevail in the fcience of chemiftry.

Dr. Higgins introduced fome pieces of well burned charcoal into a deep crucible, and covered them over an inch deep with powdered charcoal. Having luted on a cover, he expofed them for two hours to heat fufficient to melt filver; he then placed the crucible in fuch a manner, that the powder might remain red hot for fome time after the pieces next the bottom had cooled. This he had done in order, as the charcoal muft imbibe fomething on cooling, both to fupply it with inflammable air, and to prevent a communication with the external air, which the charcoal would have otherwife imbibed.

One hundred and twenty grains of this charcoal quickly powdered were well mixed with 7680 gr. of litharge, which had been previoufly fufed to feparate any uncalcined lead which it may contain. This mixture was charged into a coated retort juft large enough to contain it, fo that the common air muft have been nearly fecluded. Being then

then placed in a reverberating furnace, and heat duly applied, it yielded by eſtimation, after cooling to the mean temperature of the atmoſphere, 384 gr. of fixable air, at the rate of ,57 gr. to a cubic inch, 8,704 of phlogiſticated air, and 0,911 gr. of dephlogiſticated air, beſides 49 gr. of water. On breaking the retort, 3888 gr. of revived lead were found, beſides ſome vitrified litharge ; but not an atom of charcoal was left, nor was there a particle of inflammable air produced*. Now let my reader conſider the weight that 3888 gr. of lead acquire by its converſion to litharge, and the quantity of inflammable air that 120 gr. of charcoal will afford (which, according to Dr. Prieſtley, is about 360 ounce meaſures), and he will find, making an allowance for the phlogiſticated air, that theſe nearly correſpond with the proportion of heavy inflammable air and dephogiſticated air neceſſary to the formation of fixable air by the electric ſpark. Hence we may conclude, that not a particle of charcoal entered into the conſtitution of the

* Exp. and Obſ. on Acet. Acid, Sect. XIX. p. 274-276.

4   revived

revived lead, but muſt have been wholly converted into fixable air. Mr. Kirwan cannot ſay, that this quantity of fixable air exiſted ready formed in the charcoal, when it is more than two thirds the weight of the charcoal; nor can he attribute this weight to water. Then I aſk the phlogiſtians, whence came the dephlogiſticated air which formed this fixable air? If they can anſwer this without contradicting themſelves, it is more than I at preſent foreſee. For, in the firſt place, if they ſhould ſay that the metallic calx affords fixable air, or that its fixable air is decompoſed, by which the charcoal is furniſhed with dephlogiſticated air, they contradict their own aſſertion; for they do not allow the refractory calces to contain any ſuch thing, but, on the contrary, they ſuppoſe theſe to be combined with water. In the ſecond place, if they ſhould ſay that the dephlogiſticated air is ſupplied by the water of the calx, it is contradictory to their own principles; for they do not allow the decompoſition of water.

SECTION

SECTION IX.

Of the Solubility of Metals.

METALS in their simple state are insoluble in water; but when combined with acids they are soluble. Iron and sulphur fused form an insoluble mass; iron and dephlogisticated air form likewise an insoluble compound; but iron, dephlogisticated air, and sulphur will form a very soluble compound. Phlogisticated air in its simple state has no sensible affinity to metals; yet, when combined with dephlogisticated air, it will unite to them and render them soluble. The affinity of the marine basis to metals is not known; but that they have greater attraction to the dephlogisticated air attached to it than they have to the basis itself, has been already demonstrated. That the attraction of the marine basis to metals is increased by their previous

union

union to dephlogifticated air, may be inferred from its property of diffolving the calces of thofe metals which will not yield to it in their fimple ftate. That common marine acid has an attraction to dephlogifticated air, is very well known; and it has been above obferved, that, when fully faturated with this, it will not affect metallic calces, though it will diffolve thofe metals which the common marine acid will not touch. Oils will not diffolve metals in their fimple ftate, provided the oils be pure, except iron and copper, which are deftructible wherever they meet moifture and fixable air, both of which are generally prefent in oils. But the oils will unite to the calces, and conftitute foluble faponaceous compounds. As oils have an attraction to dephlogifticated air, though they cannot unite to it in a common temperature, nor take it from the metals but by the affiftance of a ftrong heat; it may fo far influence them as to promote their union to metallic calces. It is clear from thefe facts, although dephlogifticated air alone will not render metals foluble in water, that it is through its mediation,

3

tion, or influence, that a third body will unite, and form a foluble compound. But which of the three fubftances has this folvent power moft inherent in it, is what we cannot pretend to explain ; nor is it neceffary towards the eftablifhment of the antiphlogiftic theory to know this. It is fufficient for us to prove, that dephlogifticated air is indifpenfably neceffary for the folution of metals in every menftruum, except a few which I fhall prefently obferve. The foregoing principles will account for Mr. Kirwan's firft four queries, Section 10. I muft confefs I do not fee the force of thofe eleven queries of his, nor can I find how they oppofe the antiphlogiftic theory in the leaft.

The moft rational of his queries are explicable in this doctrine ; and of thefe the moft difficult to be accounted for is the folubility of fome calces in the nitrous acid, while others are infoluble in it. But we may attribute this in a great meafure to their property of uniting to more dephlogifticated air when in folution, than they can retain in their dry, pure, calciform ftate. Thus the calces of lead are foluble in all the acids

acids. The calces of gold, mercury, and silver are likewise soluble in the nitrous acid on the same principle. The calces of iron, tin, bismuth, cobalt, zinc, antimony, &c. when perfectly calcined, contain more dephlogisticated air, together with the quantity which enters into the constitution of perfect nitrous acid, than is necessary for solution; therefore either must lose a portion of their air before they can unite. I do not dispute but the bases of the different acids have, independent of their dephlogisticated air, different degrees of attraction to the different metals. I have shewn this to be the case in treating of the vitriolic and marine acid.

Mr. Kirwan's 10th query is not easily accounted for: before we can attempt this, we must be acquainted with the constituent principles of fixed alkali. I doubt whether he can give even a plausible explanation of it himself, in his own doctrine. The dissolution of copper in volatile alkali, likewise, cannot be accounted for in any theory until we know more of chemistry. I at one time supposed that it proceeded from the absorption of dephlogisticated air from the

S   atmosphere;

atmofphere; but I found this not to be the cafe by experiment. Indeed Mr. Kirwan might as well have afked why liver of fulphur, or mercury, diffolves gold. Mr. Kirwan's laft and 11th query has been amply accounted for in defcribing the effect of metals on vitriolic acid.

SECTION

SECTION X.

Of the Precipitation of Metals by each other.

THAT some metals attract dephlogisticated air with greater force than
others, is now an established fact. Gold,
platina, and silver will not unite with it
in the strongest heat of our furnaces. Mercury, likewise, will not unite to dephlogisticated air until heated several hundred
degrees above that which is necessary for
its fusion only. The rest of the metals
will absorb dephlogisticated air by mere
fusion, but some with greater rapidity than
others; as for instance, zinc, bismuth, and
arsenic will present the phenomenon of
combustion, when sufficiently heated in
atmospheric air. Again we find, that those
metals which combine with dephlogisticated
air with most difficulty, will yield it with
the greatest facility. Mercury, gold, silver,

and

and platina are reftored to their metallic brilliancy by mere heat; while all the other calces require the addition of fomething which has greater affinity to dephlogifti-cated air than their refpective metals, before they can be reduced to their fimple ftate.

The fame order takes place in the preci-pitation of metals by each other in their metallic ftate. Gold is precipitated in its femi-metallic ftate by filver, and filver by mercury, and mercury by copper; and all three yield to the reft of the metals. The fame law holds good with refpect to moft of the refractory metals. They precipitate each other according to their different affi-nities to dephlogifticated air; although there are a few exceptions; but thefe, I fancy, proceed chiefly from the attachment of the acid bafis to the different metals. Thus iron will not precipitate lead from marine acid; and regulus of arfenic precipitates mercury with difficulty from the vitriolic acid. Marine acid will take filver from the nitrous; and as we cannot attribute this to dephlogifticated air alone (both acids having this in their conftitution), it is evident, that

the

the acid bafes are differently influenced by the different metals. Indeed, if they had not different forces of attraction as well to the metals as to the alkalies and earths, we could not very well account for the expulfion of one acid by another from thefe different fubftances, more efpecially when the acids are in their perfect ftate; although we may attribute this very frequently to the agency of fire. Hence we may conclude, though the acid bafis difturbs the affinity of the oxygenous principle to metals in a few inftances, that we are not from thence to pronounce the invalidity of the antiphlogiftic theory.

I have already fhewn, in treating of marine acid, that the bafis of this acid contributes much to the reduction of the precipitated metal, otherwife the precipitating metal could never deprive it of the whole of its dephlogifticated air; and the fame may be faid of the other acid bafes.

In a neutral mixture of vitriolated copper, the calx is held in folution by volatile vitriolic acid, which is lefs intimately attached to the copper than its dephlogifticated air.

S 3   Iron

Iron will precipitate the copper from this
folution in its fimple metallic ftate.

In order to illuftrate this decompofition,
I think it neceffary to have recourfe to the
following method:

Let C be copper, D dephlogifticated air,
which (let us fuppofe) attract each other
with the force of $2\frac{2}{7}$, (to avoid perplexity,
reciprocal attraction is not confidered) and
let this be the calx of copper. Let V,
or volatile vitriolic acid, be attached to this
compound with the force of 3, and let us
fuppofe 2 of this force to proceed from the
dephlogifticated air attached to the copper,
and the remainder, which is but 1, to be
in confequence of the influence of the copper itfelf on the fulphur and dephlogifticated air of the volatile vitriolic acid; therefore let G be
the centre of
gravity of V.
Let us fup-
pofe this to be

the ftate of a neutral folution of copper in the
vitriolic acid. Here the copper attracts V
and D with only the force of $3\frac{2}{3}$, and C
and D attract V with the force of 3. Let
us

us again fuppofe I to be iron, which attracts
V, or volatile vitriolic acid, with the force of
3, it cannot take it from C and D, which
hold it with the force of 3 ; but it fo counteracts the attachment of D and V to C,
that it is reduced to $\frac{2}{3}$. Let us now fuppofe
I, from its attraction to dephlogifticated
air, to influence D with the force of 1 : in
this cafe C will be deprived of D and V,
for the force of $3\frac{2}{3}$ muft readily obey the
power of 4. This, in my opinion, is what
takes place in all metallic precipitations.
If the precipitant cannot take up the whole of
the dephlogifticated air of the precipitated,
it is thrown down in a femi-reduced ftate.
Thus lead and filver will precipitate gold of
a dirty purple colour, while copper and
iron throw it down in its brilliant metallic
ftate. If the iron united firft to the volatile
vitriolic acid, the refulting compound would
not deprive the calx of its dephlogifticated
air. For the calx of copper, diffufed in a
folution of iron in volatile vitriolic acid
(although no inflammable air had been difengaged), was not in the leaft reduced.
Hence we may infer, that the whole force
of the iron, in order to throw down the

copper

copper in its pure ftate, muft be exerted at once towards V and D; by which, with the affiftance of V, V and D move jointly to unite to I, or iron.

If tin be introduced into a neutral folution of tin in the nitrous acid, it is calcined, a calx is thrown down, and dephlogifticated or imperfect nitrous air is produced. Dephlogifticated nitrous air, according to the phlogiftians, contains no phlogifton; then I afk, what becomes of the phlogifton of the newly calcined metal? If tin contained phlogifton, either inflammable air or nitrous air would be produced, or a portion of the diffolved tin would be precipitated in its metallic ftate; neither of which will take place, if the experiment be well conducted. Hence I fhould fuppofe, that metals do not precipitate each other in their metallic ftate, in confequence of a double affinity proceeding from the matter of light inflammable air (or phlogifton), and likewife that metals part with no fuch thing during their calcination in acids.

Metallic calces do not precipitate each other, as the celebrated Bergman has fhewn, but are rather foluble even in neutral folutions

tions of different metals. Hence he inferred, that the fame acid takes up the different metallic calces without diftinction, provided they have loft a certain portion of their phlogifton; but, to fpeak in the language of the prefent time, provided they are not united to too much dephlogifticated air. To afcertain the different degrees of calcination the different metals require to render them equally foluble in the fame acid, is a difficult tafk; for, as the above excellent chemift obferved, a very fmall quantity of dephlogifticated air, over and above a certain portion, will render fome metals quite infoluble; and the fame may be obferved on the contrary extreme.

Hence apparent exceptions arife to this law; for the fame acid will take up the fome calces, although it will not affect others. Thus the acetous acid readily diffolves the calx of mercury, but fcarcely takes up any of the calx of bifmuth. Howeve, as the fame acid does not make that diftinction between the calces that it does between their refpective metals, it is evident that dephlogifticated air is the chief caufe of metallic folution; although this cannot take place

when

when the attraction of the acid bafis to the metal itfelf, and to the dephlogifticated air attached to it, is deftroyed. For, when the metal is fully faturated with dephlogifticated air, it cannot influence the acid bafis to which it muft have much lefs affinity; nor can the dephlogifticated air of the calx influence the acid bafis, being already faturated with dephlogifticated air; and the metal, having all its force of attraction to dephlogifticated air expended on the quantity already attached to it, cannot influence the dephlogifticated air of the acid bafis in the leaft: therefore, when perfect calces and perfect acids are mixed, they do not affect each other, except in a few inftances, which have been already obferved.

Mr. Lavoifier, who firft attributed the precipitation of metals in their metallic ftate by each other, to the fuperior attraction of the precipitant to dephlogifticated air, deduces the proportion of the oxygenous principle neceffary to the folution of different metals, from the quantity of one metal neceffary to the precipitation of a given quantity of another metal, by the following

lowing analogy, which, as I cannot at prefent refer to the author, I fhall give in Mr.
Kirwan's words: " As the quantity of
" the precipitant is to that of the precipi-
" tated metal, fo is the quantity of the
" oxygenous principle neceffary for the folu-
" tion of the precipitated, to that neceffary
" for the folution of the precipitant. Thus,
" fince 135 grains of mercury are neceffary
" for the precipitation of 100 gr. of filver
" from the nitrous acid, it is evident that
" 135 gr. of mercury require for their folu-
" tion the fame quantity of the oxygenous
" principle as 100 grains of filver; and
" therefore that the quantity neceffary to
" diffolve 100 gr. of mercury, is to that
" neceffary to diffolve 100 gr. of filver, as
" 100 to 135. His general formula may
" be expreffed thus: Let the weight of
" the precipitant be P, that of the preci-
" pitated p, that of the oxygenous principle
" neceffary for the folution by precipitation
" of 100 gr. of the different metals, to be
" as expreffed in the fecond column of the
" annexed table, and that neceffary for fo-
" lution only, as in the third column."

Metals.

Metals.	Oxygenous Principle.	
	Grains.	For Solution merely.
100 gr. of Platina,	81,690	
Gold,	43,612	
Iron, {	27	
	37	
Copper,	36,000	15, 85
Cobalt,	29,190	
Manganese,	21,176	
Zinc,	19,637	
Nickel,	14,721	
Reg. of Ant.	13,746	22, 383
Tin,	14	23, 555
Regulus of {	11,739	
Arsenic {	24,743	
Silver,	10,800	
Bismuth,	9,622	
Mercury,	8,000	
Lead,	4,470	14, 190

Mr. Kirwan objects to this part of the antiphlogistic doctrine *, 1st, Because a solution of gold in aqua regia is precipitable in its metallic state, by a fresh made solution of vitriol of iron, but not of copper or any

* Essay on Phlogiston, p. 131.

other

other metal. The precipitate of gold obtained in the above manner, is generally combined with more or lefs dephlogifticated air; and confidering that 100 gr. of iron frefh diffolved can take 10 grains of dephlogifticated air from 100 grains of gold, that a precipitation fhould take place is not to be wondered at, efpecially when gold is rendered infoluble on lofing a fmall portion of the dephlogifticated air neceffary for its folution. Befides, the iron does not precipitate an equal quantity of gold, which muft make a vaft difference. Mr. Kirwan thinks this manner of accounting for it infufficient; 1ft, Becaufe a folution of vitriol of copper takes up only 15,85 parts of the oxygenous principle, and yet is capable, by precipitation, of taking up 36 gr. and although it has greater attraction to the oxygenous principle than gold has (according to Mr. Lavoifier), it does not precipitate a particle of gold. 2dly, Becaufe platina is not precipitable by a folution of vitriol of iron, which, in the antiphlogiftic doctrine, muft retain its dephlogifticated air with very little force, when it cannot take it from

nitrous

nitrous air, as its infolubility in the nitrous acid indicates.

To the firft of thefe objections I would make anfwer, that the attraction of copper to dephlogifticated air is not near fo ftrong as that of iron; and its ftronger attachment to the acid of folution reduces this ftill lower, fo as to bring both folutions to an equilibrium. To the fecond caufe I would fay, that platina, by being foluble in various proportions of dephlogifticated air, may afford the martial folution a portion of it, and ftill remain in folution.

As copper is precipitated by iron, and likewife as copper is infoluble in diluted vitriolic acid, Mr. Kirwan fuppofes that the diffolution of copper in a diluted folution of vitriol of iron, by expofure to air or in a boiling heat, is difficult to be accounted for in the antiphlogiftic theory; and on this he grounds his fecond objection. In my opinion, it is very unfavourable to the phlogiftic doctrine; becaufe the copper is diffolved, and no inflammable air produced, and yet the iron is thrown down in a calciform ftate.

Mr,

7

Mr. Kirwan grounds his third objection, page 132, on the following fact: " Iron," he fays, " is diffolved by the concentrated " vitriolic acid only by the affiftance of " heat; yet, if to a folution of filver or " mercury, in that concentrated acid, a piece " of iron be inferted, the filver or mercury " will immediately be precipitated in their " metallic form, and the iron diffolved. " This feems inexplicable in the new " theory; for fince iron cannot without the " affiftance of heat deprive fulphur of its " oxygenous principle, how does it happen " that, without that affiftance, it deprives " filver or mercury of that principle, though " they have a ftronger attraction to it than " fulphur has?" This, certainly, is a very fair query, and deferves attention. Therefore, I fhall give my opinion of it in as clear a manner as I can.

Let the two diagrams, S be molecules of concentrated vitriolic acid; which let us fuppofe influence each other with the force of 2, which in addition to $5\frac{1}{18}$ makes $7\frac{1}{18}$.

Now,

Now, if iron be introduced
into this acid, it will not be
diffolved in it; for the force
of 7, with which we have
already fuppofed iron to attract dephlogifticated air,

being inferior to $7\frac{1}{13}$, a perfect neutrality
prevails until the force of 2, which we may
call the aggregate influence, is diminifhed; and this is done by fire or water.
Again, let us fuppofe mercury to attract dephlogifticated air with the force
of $6\frac{1}{4}$; in this ftate concentrated vitriolic
acid will not influence it, until its aggregate attraction is wholly removed by fire,
and then it will readily diffolve it. Let
us now fuppofe the mercury in a ftate of
folution, to be influenced by its dephlogifticated air and volatile vitriolic acid, which
is the acid of folution, with the following
forces. Let M be mercury, D the quantity
of dephlogifticated air neceffary for folution; let us fuppofe thefe, if there had not
been any thing elfe prefent to influence either,
to attract each other with the force of $6\frac{3}{4}$,

and

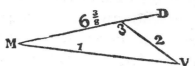

and let us fup-
pofe this to be
the utmoft fum
of their reci-
procal attractions. Let us likewife fuppofe
V, or volatile vitriolic acid, to be attached to
M——D, or the calx of mercury, with
the force of 3; let 1 of this proceed from
the mercury itfelf, and the other 2 from
the dephlogifticated air attached to it, which
muft reduce the attraction of M for D to
$3\frac{3}{8}$; which, in addition to the force of 1,
that prevails in confequence of the attachment of M and V, makes $4\frac{3}{8}$: thus, V
and D are attached to M with the force of
$4\frac{3}{8}$. Now,
if iron were
introduced
into fuch a
mixture, is
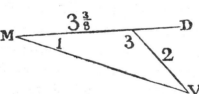
it not to be expected that it would with
the force of 7 readily overcome the above
force, and precipitate the filver or mercury,
even in the prefence of concentrated vitriolic
acid, which is always infeparable from
thefe folutions, and which, from its weak
attachment to the mercurial falt, may op-

pofe

pose the decomposition a little? Mr. Kirwan's fourth query, page 133, is very
much in favour of the antiphlogistic doctrine: for, as I had an occasion to observe
above, the precipitation of one metal by
another in its calciform state, without the
production of inflammable air, at the same
time that the precipitant is held in solution,
tends strongly to prove the non-existence of
the matter of light inflammable air in
metals; besides, it is very explicable in the
antiphlogistic doctrine. I have already endeavoured to shew upon what principle the
acid bases retain their dephlogisticated air
with less force, when fully saturated with
it, than when united to a small portion;
and I have shewn, in treating of nitrous
acid, that the attachment of its basis to
dephlogisticated air is in exact proportion
to the quantity united to it. The same
law holds good in all other combinations,
and is explicable on the same principles.
Almost all bodies will unite with the different substances to which they have an
affinity, in various proportions, until they
arrive at the point of saturation, which
limits their power of chemical attraction.
There

There are a few exceptions to the above law; for, the principles of water will only unite in one proportion, so that we can never obtain it in an intermediate state. The cause of this I have already attempted to demonstrate. I have my doubts whether the same may not be said of the aerial acid. Thus, metals will unite with dephlogisticated air in various proportions, until saturated. If 100 grains of a metal are capable of uniting to 15 gr. of dephlogisticated air only, they will attract and retain 5 gr. of dephlogisticated air with greater force than they will 10 gr. and 10 gr. with greater force than 15 gr.

Let us suppose every 100 gr. of tin, when in perfect solution, to be united to 15 gr. of dephlogisticated air with the force of 5½. Let iron attract dephlogisticated air with the force of 7, and let us suppose this force to be reduced to 6, by the accession of 7½ gr. of dephlogisticated air, and the attraction of the tin to its dephlogisticated air to be increased by losing 7½ of dephlogisticated air : in this case, iron cannot precipitate tin in its metallic state, although it may have greater attraction to

T 2

dephlo-

dephlogifticated air than the tin has. Hence it is evident, that a metal, in order to precipitate another in its metallic ftate, muft not only unite to dephlogifticated air in greater quantities, and attract it more forcibly, but that this fuperiority of force muft be very great indeed.

Mr. Kirwan's fifth, fixth, and feventh queries have been explained, pages 260—1. One ounce of the nitrated calx of mercury, two ounces of Pruffian blue, and twenty-four of water, boiled for a few minutes with conftant agitation, acquire a cineritious yellow colour. The mercury unites to the tinging acid of the Pruffian blue, and forms a foluble falt. If to the filtered folution a fmall quantity of iron filings and vitriolic acid be added, the whole mafs turns black, and the mercury is reduced*. As iron filings and vitriolic acid produce inflammable air, and as the Pruffian acid is difengaged and the mercury revived, Mr. Kirwan fuppofes, that a portion of the inflammable air unites to the mercury, revives it, and expels from it the Pruffian acid.

* Scheel, p. 162, French tranflation.

This

This being urged againſt the antiphlogiſtians by Mr. Kirwan, as unanſwerable in their doctrine *, I ſhall endeavour to inquire into it minutely.

In the firſt place we are to conſider, that the Pruſſian acid, being united to the calx in its perfect ſtate, cannot take any thing from it during its ſeparation; therefore the reduction muſt ſolely depend upon the attraction of the mercury to inflammable air. 2dly, Be it remembered, that Mr. Kirwan conſiders the calx of mercury as a compound of fixable air and the baſis of mercury. Now, I ſhould like to know how the inflammable air can act in this caſe; for it has two powers to encounter. Firſt, The attachment of the aerial acid to the metallic baſis. 2dly, The attraction of the Pruſſian acid to both, beſides its own attraction for fire, which is very conſiderable. I muſt confeſs, as the decompoſition depends upon a ſingle elective attraction, I cannot conceive how the inflammable air can expel both acids. If the inflammable air diſengaged by the acid and iron filings, ſhould

* Eſſay on Phlogiſton, p. 123.

T 3

unite

unite to the metallic bafis, its own proper
phlogiston would be difengaged, united to
dephlogifticated air in the ftate of fixable
air; for it cannot be faid that there is heat
fufficient to form water. Then what becomes of the fixable air ? for I repeated the
experiment with the utmoft caution, and
could not obtain a particle of fixable air.
It cannot be faid, that the inflammable air
united to the dephlogifticated air of the
calx, and formed water, if we fuppofe it to
be already attached to the matter of light inflammable air in the calx; for bodies of the
fame fort cannot difturb each other's affinity
to different fubftances fo materially, as to
caufe a decompofition.

Let us now inquire into the above procefs in the antiphlogiftic doctrine. I have
already fhewn, that bodies which have lefs
attraction to dephlogifticated air than fulphur has, may wholly decompofe the vitriolic acid, from the nature of its conftitution.
Thus mercury will calcine in concentrated
vitriolic acid by the affiftance of heat only,
and volatile fulphureous acid is difengaged.
The rationale of the production of this acid
has been given before. As water has no
effect

effect on mercury, it is evident that light
inflammable air attracts dephlogisticated air
with greater force than mercury does.

If sulphur and the calx of mercury be
distilled, volatile vitriolic acid is formed,
and the mercury is partly revived; and if a
large portion of sulphur be used, cinnabar
is formed. Hence it appears, that sulphur
has greater attraction to dephlogisticated air
than mercury has. These facts kept in
view, we can readily account for the reduction of mercury, when vitriolic acid
and iron are introduced into the solution of the mercurial calx in the Pruffian acid. Iron, as I have already endeavoured to explain, during its dissolution in
vitriolic acid, totally deprives the sulphur
of its dephlogisticated air; the sulphur
again, while in its ultimate division, and before it is influenced by fire, or by the aggregate attraction, recovers this from the
water, by which inflammable air is produced. If the calx of mercury reduced into
its ultimate division, in which state it must
be when held in solution, were in contact
with vitriolic acid thus decomposed, is it
not reasonable to suppose, that it would

yield

yield its dephlogisticated air to the sulpnur, more especially when it retains it with less force than water does? But as water is present, a portion of it is likewise decomposed, by which we obtain inflammable air. Whether the inflammable air itself, at the instant that it is deprived of its dephlogisticated air, may not contribute to the reduction of the mercury, by uniting to its dephlogisticated air, and reproducing water, is what I cannot pretend to determine; although, from the attraction of the matter of light inflammable air to fire, together with the interference of the Prussian acid, I am rather inclined to suppose it does not. The mercury being thus deprived of its dephlogisticated air by the superior attraction of sulphur to that principle, rejects the Prussian acid, as having no sensible attraction to it in its metallic state.

NOTE.

N O T E.

FINDING that Mr. Bertholette, in his notes to the French verfion of Mr. Kirwan's Effay on Phlogifton (which I had not feen until my fection on marine acid had been printed, which is now fome months fince, the prefs has been fo very tedious), affirms, that dephlogifticated marine air is not decompofed by inflammable air, as Mr. Kirwan has afferted, I made the following experiment :

I poured fome colourlefs nitrous acid highly diluted upon a quantity of manganefe, in order to feparate any calcareous earth it might contain (the perfect acid having no effect on the pure calx of manganefe), and triturated them for fome time; then filtered the folution, and wafhed the calx repeatedly with hot diftilled water, until the whole of the nitrous acid was wafhed away. Having introduced it into a retort, I poured fome pure marine acid upon it ; and, when it had worked fome time, received fome of the air in hot diftilled water:

ter : equal parts of this and inflammable air produced from vitriolic acid, which ſtood in lime liquor for two days, were mixed over lime water; the marine air was gradually abſorbed, no precipitation took place, and the inflammable air did not ſeem diminiſhed. I repeated the experiment with the ſame reſult. In haſtily peruſing the page in which Mr. Kirwan mentions his experiment on inflammable and dephlogiſticated marine air over lime water, I ſuppoſed, he meant, that no fixable air had been produced during the union of both airs : this was my chiefeſt motive to repeat the above experiment, the reſult of which tends to corroborate my arguments on that ſubject.

An Analysis of the Human Calculus, with Ob-
servations on its Origin, &c.

INTO a small earthen retort well coated, I introduced one ounce and three quarters (Troy weight), or 840 grains of dry and well powdered calculus, which, on being broke, appeared to be laminated with a small nucleus, which was likewise minutely laminated. It was composed of coats or layers somewhat like an onion; the outward crust appeared very porous, but increased in firmness of texture towards the centre. The retort thus charged was placed in a side furnace, with a conical glass tube, and an air apparatus adjoined to it. The first impression of fire after the air of the vessels was expelled, occasioned a flow emission of an elastic fluid, the first measure of which appeared to consist of equal parts of phlogisticated and fixed air.

The 2d measure $\frac{2}{3}$ fixable, $\frac{1}{3}$ phlogisticated.

3d $\qquad$ $\frac{2}{3}$ ditto, $\qquad$ $\frac{1}{3}$ ditto.

4th $\qquad$ $\frac{7}{8}$ ditto, $\qquad$ $\frac{1}{8}$ inflammable.

5th, 6th, and 7th measures same as the last.

laſt. Here the elaſtic fluids began to come over very faſt, attended with an urinous ſmell. The 8th meaſure conſiſted of $\frac{2}{3}$ fixable, $\frac{1}{3}$ inflammable, with an alkaline ſmell, 9th meaſure $\frac{2}{3}$ fixable, $\frac{1}{3}$ inflammable, and burned with a greeniſh flame. The elaſtic fluids now iſſued ſo rapidly, it was impoſſible to keep an exact account of the number of meaſures; and as I was obliged to work in mercury, the meaſure which I uſed was ſmall, containing but five cubic inches; therefore I only examined the elaſtic fluids at different periods of the proceſs. About the fourteenth meaſure by conjecture, a very pungent alkaline, urinous and ſuffocating ſmell was very ſenſible, not only on the ſurface of the mercury, but throughout the elaboratory. The ſixteenth meaſure was rapidly attracted by lime water to $\frac{1}{3}$, and the lime water was not rendered ſo turbid as it ought to have been, if all the air abſorbed had been fixable air: on continuing the agitation the contraction ſtill went on, though much ſlower than at firſt, until the air was reduced to $\frac{1}{5}$, which was inflammable; the laſt portion, that was ſlowly abſorbed, precipitated the lime very faſt. After loſing

about

about five meafures, the next was rapidly
contracted in common pump water partially
impregnated with fixable air, until reduced
to $\frac{2}{3}$, and here feemed ftationary, though
frequently agitated; but on removing it to
lime water, it was contracted $\frac{1}{6}$, render-
ing the lime water turbid. From thefe
facts it appears, that fixed and alkaline airs
iffued at the fame time; but why they did
not unite in their paffage, or when received
into the meafure, is a myftery to me; probably the fmall quantity of inflammable air
interfered. From the beginning of the
10th meafure, a black charry and greafy
matter began to line the conical tube and
the air veffel; and may not the alkaline air
diffolve this partially, though not in fuch
proportion as to render it folid, yet at the
fame time to weaken its attraction for fixable air? Were they to ftand for fome time,
I do not doubt but mild volatile alkali
would have been formed; but this circumftance did not occur to me during the procefs. The laft proportions continued for
four meafures, and then the alkaline air increafed to $\frac{1}{4}$, and the remainder was inflammable. It is remarkable, that this
proportion

proportion of alkaline and inflammable airs
fhould burn as well as if the whole had
been inflammable. At this period more
than two thirds of the procefs were over,
and the proportion of alkaline air decreafed,
while that of the inflammable air increafed,
until towards the end, when the laft nine
meafures were all inflammable, and the
operation ceafed, though the retort was
urged with a white heat.

On breaking the retort when cold, I
found a black powder on the bottom, which
weighed 95 grains; this I digefted in ten
ounces of diftilled water for one hour, and
then filtered and evaporated it to two ounces,
when a yellowifh powder was depofited; and
on letting the whole ftand for one night, no
cryftals were formed. I filtered the liquor
to feparate the powder, and evaporated the
filtered folution to one ounce, during which
time it continued to depofit more of the
fame powder; this again I paffed through
the fame filter I ufed laft, in order to have
it all upon one filter, and when the liquor
was all through, I wafhed the powder with
diftilled water, which I added to the reft
of the folution. This being evaporated to
eight

eight pennyweights, or half an ounce, began
to depofit a very white powder, and to emit
a fubacid aftringent vapour, not unlike
vitriolic acid. The white precipitate when
collected, wafhed, and dried, weighed one
grain : it had a fhining appearance, and
felt very foft, not unlike mica in powder : expofed to a white heat for ten minutes, it acquired no change, but looked
rather whiter. It diffolved in diftilled water;
cauftic volatile alkali caufed no precipitation ; mineral alkali, and the acid of fugar,
rendered the folution turbid, and likewife
nitrated terra ponderofa : hence I inferred
that this powder was felenite. After feparating the felenite, I evaporated the remaining part of the folution to drynefs,
with a gentle heat, during which time it
emitted fubacid vapours. The powder
weighed eleven grains, was of a dirty yellow colour, and had an aluminous tafte.
To this powder I added as much diftilled
water as was nearly fufficient to diffolve it ;
and then put it by for three weeks, being
interrupted by fome other bufinefs. At the
expiration of this time, fmall tranfparent,
and feemingly cubical cryftals appeared

2   on

on the fide of the veffel, above the furface of the folution ; and thefe likewife had an aluminous tafte. I diffolved the whole in diftilled water, and filtered the folution: acid of fugar had no effect on it at leaft for five minutes ; cauftic volatile alkali occafioned an immediate cloudinefs; and the folution when filtered, though the cauftic alkali predominated, was rendered turbid by a folution of mineral alkali ; nitrated terra ponderofa threw down a copious precipitate, and Pruffian alkali detected a fmall portion of iron. This aluminous folution, as I may now venture to call it, left on the filter a yellow fubftance, which when wafhed and dried weighed half a grain ; it diffolved in nitrous acid without effervefcence ; acid of fugar caufed no precipitation, but cauftic volatile alkali threw down a precipitate, which diffolved in diftilled water. This folution was rendered turbid by the acid of fugar, and muriated terra ponderofa ; but cauftic volatile alkali, or lime water, had no effect on it. The folution of felenite in either of the mineral acids, and its precipitation undecompofed by cauftic volatile alkali, fhould always be guarded againft by every experimentalift.

The

The yellow powder firſt depoſited during evaporation from the ſolution (page
286) weighed two grains and a half, and,
expoſed to a tolerably ſtrong heat, acquired
a deep orange colour. I digeſted it with two
ounces of diſtilled water in a ſand heat for
half an hour, and then filtered the ſolution,
which did not contain any thing but ſelenite. A yellow powder was left on the filter,
which weighed ¼ of a grain; it ſeemed to
be iron, and ſuch I found it, for marine
acid readily diſſolved it; phlogiſticated alkali
precipitated Pruſſian blue, and tincture of galls
turned the ſolution black; muriated terra
ponderoſa ſeemed to detect a vitriolic impregnation; but, on examining the marine acid,
it contained a ſmall veſtige of vitriolic acid,
though not ſo much as appeared to be preſent in this martial ſolution. Indeed the
acid vapour riſing from the ſolution of alum,
during the depoſition of this iron and
ſelenite, renders it probable that it may be
partially combined with vitriolic acid, in
ſuch a proportion as not to render it ſoluble in water, and in ſuch a ſtate as to be
diſengaged by marine acid. Thus ſepara-
ting all that was ſoluble in diſtilled water
from the charry ſubſtance left in the earthen

U   retort,

retort, I dried and weighed the remainder, and found the loss of weight by this treatment to be fifteen grains. I calcined the remaining eighty grains in an open crucible exposed to a strong red heat; it was difficult of calcination, and took three quarters of an hour to be reduced to a bright grey powder; it first burned with a flame, and afterwards calcined with very vivid sparks at every fresh surface exposed to the air; when thoroughly calcined and cold, it weighed twenty-one grains, having lost fifty-nine grains during calcination. I plunged it into six ounces of hot distilled water, and when it stood half an hour filtered it: the solution tasted like lime water, turned syrup of violets green, and diluted vitriolic acid had no effect on it; but aerated volatile alkali, and acid of sugar, rendered it turbid. The remaining part of this powder left on the filter, when well dried, weighed sixteen grains; therefore, five grains of lime seem to have been taken up by the distilled water; these sixteen grains dissolved in nitrous acid, first, with a little effervescence, and when this ceased the solution went on very slow, until the
whole

whole was taken up : acid of fugar caufed
no precipitation in this folution, but cauftic volatile alkali precipitated the whole;
about one grain of Pruffian blue was thrown
down by the phlogifticated alkali, or perhaps more, for I could not feparate it from
the filter. I digefted the precipitate, when
well wafhed and freed from the volatile
alkali, in diftilled vinegar, which took up
with effervefcence one grain and a half,
which was precipitated by cauftic volatile
alkali. I wafhed what was infoluble in the
vinegar, and digefted it in diftilled water
for half an hour, then filtered the folution :
cauftic volatile alkali had no effect on this
folution; but acid of fugar and nitrated
terra ponderofa caufed an immediate cloudinefs. Seven grains and a half of the powder, which was infoluble in diftilled water
and acetous acid, were readily taken up by
diluted vitriolic acid, and precipitated by
cauftic volatile alkali : fo the fixteen grains
laft treated, feem to contain of clay feven
grains and a half; of felenite fix grains;
of magnefia one and a half; and of iron one
grain. The proportions of the different
ingredients are as follow, viz.

U 2   Iron

Iron - - - - - - $2\frac{1}{9}$ Grains
Selenite - - - - - 11 Ditto
Clay - - - - - - $7\frac{1}{2}$ Ditto
Alum - - - - - - 8 Ditto
Pure calcareous Earth - 5 Ditto
Aerated Magnesia - - - $1\frac{1}{2}$ Ditto
Charry combustible Substance 59 Ditto

Total $94\frac{1}{9}$ Grains

I found a darkish yellow saline sublimate adhering to the neck of the retort, of a lamellar spongy texture, except the inner part next the retort, which was more compact, and coloured: this being carefully collected, weighed 425 grains, and readily dissolved in half a pint of hot distilled water. I filtered the solution, and separated a coally substance, which when washed and dried weighed ten grains, and, when exposed to a red heat, burnt with a greenish flame, and emitted white fumes, in smell not unlike vitriolic ammoniac: the residuum after calcination weighed half a grain, and was of a whitish colour; it seemed insoluble in distilled water, but nitrous acid dissolved it with effervescence; acid of sugar caused a very little precipitation,

tion, which did not take place until it ſtood ſome time; but cauſtic volatile alkali inſtantly threw down a precipitate, which was taken up, when waſhed, by acetous acid: The quantity was too ſmall to be examined more accurately, but it ſeemed to poſſeſs the properties of magneſia. The ſaline ſolution had the colour of ſmall beer, and, when evaporated to two ounces, did not depoſit any thing, nor on cooling yielded any cryſtals. The black matter which lined the conical tube and air veſſel, weighed twenty-eight grains; indeed it adhered ſo faſt to the glaſs, it was impoſſible to collect the whole from the broken fragments, ſo that a few grains may be loſt. I diſſolved it in diſtilled water, and ſeparated four grains of a black coal from it, which did not differ in the leaſt from that obtained from the former ſublimate: this ſolution likewiſe evaporated to one ounce, and, after ſtanding one night, did not ſhew the ſmalleſt appearance of a depoſition, or a cryſtallization. I mixed both ſolutions together, and evaporated them to one ounce; which, when cold, acquired the conſiſtence and colour of trea-

cle,

cle; fo that I was now affured this was not a cryftallizable falt, and that a fufficient knowledge of it could not be acquired by this treatment. I charged it into a fmall tubulated glafs retort, with fix ounces of diftilled water, in order to wafh it down; and then placed it in a fand bath, and diftilled over three ounces of water, which feemed to be impregnated with nothing but a fmall quantity of the folution, which adhered to the neck of the retort, and which gave it a light ftraw colour: this being removed, I applied a clean receiver; and when about half an ounce more of the liquor came over, the diftillation was attended with an alkaline fmell, merely fenfible, until an ounce and a half of the liquor paffed over; and then it got fo very pungent, though the diftillation was carried on very flow, and the veffel kept cool, that I was convinced of its being in a cauftic ftate; but a fmall quantity of mild volatile alkali adhered to the lower part of the neck of the retort, part of which was wafhed down by the diftillation, fo that it was in vain for me to attempt to afcertain the proportions which the mild and cauftic

alkali

alkali bore one to another. The volatile alkaline folution in the receiver, had the colour
andfmell of fpirits of hartfhorn, but more
empyreumatic, and like fpirits of hartfhorn,
when expofed to the air for fome time, acquired a deeper colour, in confequence of
part of the alkali efcaping, and the reft attracting fixable air, which rendered it incapable of keeping the charry matter in folution, which it had before diffolved.
When all the liquor had paffed over, and
nothing appeared in the retort but a fmall
black mafs, I raifed the fire ; and, according
as the heat increafed, this black fubftance
acquired a white colour, with a kind of arrangement on the furface, which was occafioned by the heat applied to the bottom of
the retort being only fufficient to raife the
falt to the top of the charge ; but when the
fand got nearly red hot, white fumes began
to appear, which condenfed on the upper
part of the retort, and a little way down
the neck. The procefs lafted until the
charge was nearly red hot, when the white
fumes ceafed, and nothing elfe paffed over.
On breaking the retort the following day,
I collected the fublimate, which weighed

U 4   feventy-

feventy-two grains, and a black porous
brittle fubftance was found on the bottom of
the retort, which weighed twelve grains; and
which, when expofed to a ftrong red heat,
emitted white fumes, with a flight alkaline
fmell: by this procefs it was reduced, with
very little appearance of combuftion, to a
grey powder, which weighed three grains:
this I cannot give any account of, as it has
met with an accident; but I could venture
to fay, that four grains of the black powder
were the fame as the fublimate, and that the
remaining five grains confifted of volatile alkali, and a charry combuftible fubftance.

Having the fublimate now, as I thought,
tolerably pure, and wifhing to know its
nature and properties (as I fufpected it to
be a combination of volatile alkali and fome
acid), I took five grains of well burnt
and powdered quicklime, and with it
mixed five grains of the fublimate, but
without the leaft fmell of volatile alkali; and thrown upon a red hot iron, it
emitted white fumes: the fame proportion of
vegetable alkali and fublimate had the like
effect. I made two equal divifions of the remaining

maining part of the fublimate, which was fixty-two grains; the one I mixed with two ounces of diftilled water; it readily dif- fufed through it, being in fine powder; and on the other poured fixty grains of vi- triolic acid, diluted with half an ounce of diftilled water: having thus mixed them in two large beer glaffes, I was obliged to fet them by for fix weeks, being inter- rupted by other chemical experiments; and at the expiration of that time, neither feemed to be much acted upon. I poured the vitriolic mixture into a fmall matrafs, and boiled it on fand for half an hour, with two ounces of diftilled water, when the whole was taken up: the folution looked clear, and depofited nothing on ftanding; mild mineral alkali had no effect on it; but mild vegetable alkali threw down a copious precipitate in white floculi, which was re- diffolved by cauftic alkali, lime water, and partially by mild mineral alkali. Phlogif- ticated alkali, acid of fugar, and acid of tartar, had no effect on this folution. The other portion of fublimate, which I mixed with water, was very little diffolved, and

4   in

in pouring it into a matrafs, fmall round lumps which appeared on the bottom of the glafs, drew my attention; they were fix or feven in number, fome weighing more than one grain, and the fmalleft about half a grain. They were very hard and compact, with a very fmooth furface, and in figure refembling the nucleus found in this calculus. I charged the whole into a matrafs, with three ounces of water, and boiled it on fand for three quarters of an hour, when about one half was taken up; the folution filtered very clear while hot, but on cooling it got turbid, and in time depofited white floculi, which were redif-folved by cauftic volatile alkali and lime water: it turned fyrup of violets green; but this may be occafioned by its retaining volatile alkali, though it had not the fmall-eft appearance of fuch impregnation. I have often obferved, that, fometimes, the pureft fixed vegetable alkali contains vola-tile alkali, notwithftanding the many ope-rations and different degrees of heat it muft undergo before it arrives at that degree of purity in which we find it fold at the fhops,

under

under the name of falt of tartar*. I filtered
the folution, to feparate what it depofited
on cooling: mineral alkali had no effect on
it; but mild vegetable alkali caufed a
cloudinefs, which was rediffolved by mineral alkali and lime water. Pruffian alkali
had no effect on this folution; the acids of
arfenic, of tartar, of fugar, and of borax,
had likewife no effect on it; and alfo the
three mineral acids. I was obliged to dif-
continue my experiments on this fublimate
here, having no more of it, and no calculus to obtain it from.

I introduced five pennyweights, or 120
grains, of the fame calculus into a fmall tubulated retort, and on this poured half an
ounce of ftrong nitrous acid, which acted
upon it with effervefcence I collected fome
of the air extricated during folution, and
found it to be fixable, with a fmall quantity
of nitrous air. When the effervefcence
ceafed, I added a quarter of an ounce more

---

* I have obferved that fixed alkali, when firft moiftened
with water, very frequently produced volatile alkali; and
as the conftituent principles of volatile alkali were not
well known when this paper had been written, I fuppofed
it to be ready formed in the fixed alkali.

of

of nitrous acid, and digefted it in hot fand
for one hour, during which time it emitted
nitrous vapour and nitrous air; but the
latter in very fmall proportion. When the
folution was perfected, I poured it into a
fmall matrafs, with the addition of one
ounce of diftilled water, and boiled it gently,
until the fuperabundant nitrous acid was
nearly expelled. The folution was of a
deep yellow colour, and appeared turbid;
but, on adding five ounces more of water,
and digefting it a quarter of an hour longer,
it acquired the colour and tranfparency of
what is called dephlogifticated nitrous acid.
On cooling it got a little turbid, and in a
few days depofited a darkifh yellow powder.
I filtered the folution to feparate this powder,
which, when wafhed and dried, weighed a
little more than a quarter of a grain: pure
nitrous acid had no effect on it, but marine
acid readily diffolved it; in fhort, it had all
the properties of calx of iron. Being again
interrupted, I was obliged to lay the folution by for fome time; and wifhing to know
what effect a long expofure to the heat of
the fun would have on it, I placed it in a
window, in one of the upper rooms of the
elaboratory at Oxford, where the fun had
full

full power over it four hours every day. A little moifture feemed to exhale from it daily, the weather being hot, and the matrafs, which had a fhort wide neck, being only covered with a piece of bibulous paper to keep out the duft. Thus fituated, in the courfe of a week a few very fmall cryftals appeared to float on the furface, which in time funk to the bottom, where they adhered together, fo as to form a hard concretion, ftill retaining a cryftalline appearance, but being fo fmall and confufed, it was impoffible to diftinguifh their figure: this depofition continued for near a month, and then feemed to ceafe. I filtered the folution to feparate the falt; and, to expedite the procefs, as I thought, evaporated half an ounce of the liquor.away, and then fet it by in the ufual place for a fortnight longer; but no more of thefe cryftals appeared. I digefted the falt, which, when wafhed and dried, weighed three grains, in four ounces of diftilled water for two hours, and no part feemed to be taken up. I decanted off three ounces of the water, and added to the remainder fix drops of vitriolic acid, which, by help of digeftion, feemed to diffolve it flowly; but on the

addition

addition of half an ounce more of diſtilled water, the whole was readily taken up. Acid of ſugar had no effect on the ſolution, but lime water rendered it turbid. I precipitated the whole with cauſtic volatile alkali, and filtered the ſolution, which likewiſe threw down the lime from lime water. I waſhed the precipitate, and poured diſtilled vinegar upon it, which did not take it up : marine acid diſſolved it ; phlogiſticated alkali had no effect on the ſolution ; and the acid of ſugar cauſed very little turbidneſs on ſtanding three or four hours. Theſe appearances induced me to ſuppoſe, that this ſalt was phoſphorated clay. The ſolution being now free from iron and phoſphorated clay, had a ſub-acid taſte, and looked clearer, but ſtill retained a yellow caſt : acid of ſugar had no effect on it ; but nitrated terra ponderoſa threw down a copious precipitate ; as did likewiſe the cauſtic volatile alkali. Mild fixed vegetable alkali (which at firſt ſurpriſed me much) cauſed no precipitation ; but, when I conſidered the ſolvent power of fixable air on calcareous earth and magneſia, which earths I knew were held in ſolution in ſmall proportions, and the quantity of fixable air diſen

3   gaged

gaged by the uncombined and combined acids, I could readily account for the above phenomenon. I charged two-thirds of this solution into a small glass retort, and distilled over two ounces of liquor, which seemed tasteless; but had a very agreeable smell, not unlike rose water. When all the liquor passed over, white fumes appeared in the retort, which were soon succeeded by a slow emission of an elastic fluid. I collected some of this fluid, and found that a candle immersed in it burned with an enlarged flame. Nitrous air did not diminish it in the least; it seemed to be that species of air that nitrous ammoniac is convertible into: no more than thirteen or fourteen cubic inches of this air were obtained; and as soon as it ceased to come over, I observed some salt in irregular crystals in the lower part of the neck of the retort. On increasing the heat, a white salt began to sublime, and adhere to the upper part of the retort. I continued the operation until the bottom of the retort was obscurely red hot, and then raised it in the sand. The following day, when I broke the retort, the quantity of sublimate was so trifling, I could collect but very little from

the

the broken glafs: however, there was fufficient to convince me, that it was the fame with what I obtained in my former analvfis. The falt mentioned above, which cryftallifed in the neck of the retort, was nitrous ammoniac; it inflamed and detonated *per fe*, &c. A grey powder was left on the bottom of the retort, which hot diftilled water partly diffolved; muriated terra ponderofa, acid of fugar, and vegetable alkali rendered this folution turbid, but cauftic volatile alkali had no effect on it. The remaining part of the powder which the diftilled water left behind, was readily diffolved with effervefcence by marine acid, and precipitated by cauftic volatile alkali: that part taken up by the diftilled water feems to be felenite, and that diffolved by the marine acid to be magnefia.

This laft mode of treating the calculus, was partly to correct my former analyfis, but chiefly in confequence of Dr. Beddoe's very judicioufly fufpecting, that it contained fomething which might be decompofed by the ftrong heat I firft ufed (how far this conjecture was right is very evident); therefore I only attended to the proportions of that which evaded my former analyfis.

The

The phofphoric acid muft have been united to volatile alkali in the calculus, previous to its treatment with the nitrous acid, notwithftanding its fuperior attraction to calcareous earth: the prefence of alum fhews how enveloped with an oleaginous matter the volatile alkali and pure calcareous earth muft have been; therefore it appears, that the calculus was compofed of the following different compounds blended together, viz. felenite, alum, microcofmic falt, mild volatile alkali, lime, and cauftic volatile alkali combined with oil, fo as to form a faponaceous mafs, calx of iron, magnefia combined with aerial acid, clay enveloped by a faponaceous and oily matter, and the fublimate already defcribed. Confidering this to be the true ftate of the calculus in the bladder, the fmall proportions of clay, felenite, magnefia, and iron, which are the moft infoluble of the ingredients, the great folubility of microcofmic falt, and alum, and the mifcibility of lime, volatile alkali, and oil in water, tend to fhew, that the fublimate is the cementing ingredient: indeed, its infolubility in water, and property of forming nuclei out of the body, as above obferved, leave no

X   room

room to doubt it. The proportion of the other ingredients, and very like.y their prefence, depend upon chance, volatile alkali and oil excepted ; therefore this fublimate fhould be the object of our inveftigation. May not ftrict refearches into the nature of this fingular fubftance throw new light on the original caufe of other diforders, as well as that of the calculus, particularly the gout, which hitherto has baffled the fkill of our phyficians ? The effect of mild mineral alkali on the fublimate, is worthy the attention of thofe who may have an opportunity of trying its efficacy. Mild mineral alkali may be taken in large dofes, and continued for a length of time with impunity to the moft delicate conftitutions, only obferving a few circumftances; but this alkali in a cauftic ftate muft very often be attended with mifchievous confequences. Befides, if we confider that it muft enter the mafs of blood before any part can reach the bladder, and the fmall portion of the dofe taken fecreted with the urine ; and, laftly, the action of cauftic alkali upon animal fubftances, we fhall be at a lofs to know on what principle cauftic

cauftic alkalies have been recommended in preference to the mild. Soap itfelf might as well be prefcribed at once ; for foon after cauftic alkali is taken, it muft be in a faponaceous ftate. Fixed vegetable alkali fhould be avoided, and the preference given to the other two alkalies. As it is evident that alkalies have no real action on the ftone in the bladder, though their efficacy has been experienced in alleviating the difeafe when timely adminiftered, their mode of action is only explicable in the following manner : They either prevent the generation of the fublimate in the fyftem, or elfe keep it in folution in the mafs of fluids; and being in the utmoft degree of divifibility, its ultimate particles are capable of paffing through the moft minute emunctories, by which it is carried off by other fecretions as well as by the urinary. Thus the urine not being faturated with this matter, acts as a folvent on the ftone ; and as the moft foluble parts are firft wafhed away, it in time falls into fragments of irregular furfaces, which, by their friction, irritate and inflame the bladder, as has been obferved by feveral practitioners.

Allowing

Allowing that the fublimate is the cementing fubftance in the calculus, and judg-
ing from the effects of alkalies upon it,
their *modus operandi* in the conftitution, it
remains now to inquire into the origin'of
the calculus. The immortal Scheele has
found this fublimate in the urine of different perfons, and hence inferred, that it was
a common fecretion; but it ftill remains
to be afcertained, whether there be a
greater quantity of it procured from the
urine of patients who have the misfortune
to labour under this diforder, than in that
of thofe who never felt its pangs. If this
latter fhould not be the cafe, another path
lies open for our refearches, which promifes
moft fuccefs. May not a deficiency of volatile alkali in the conftitution, be the caufe
of concretions in the bladder, kidneys, &c.
or, which muft have the fame effect, too great
a proportion of acid, which, uniting with
the alkali, may take up that portion which
would have kept the fublimate in folution,
until conveyed out of the fyftem by the urinary and other fecretions; and may not this
be the phofphoric acid? If this latter
fhould be the cafe, an increafe of microcofmic

cofmic falt muft be found in the urine; but
if the former, a decreafe of the volatile alkali, and no increafe of the neutral falt: The
fmall quantity of phofphoric acid found in
the calculus, proceeds from the folubility
of microcofmic falt. Do not volatile alkali
and phofphoric acid conftitute a great part
of the human frame? and is there not a procefs continually carried on to generate thefe
in the fyftem * ? and is not this procefs
liable

* It is nearly three years fince I firft had an opportunity
of making fome obfervations on volatile alkali, which
confirmed my opinion of its conftant generation in the human fyftem, to fupply its continual wafte; and likewife
enabled me to form a faint idea of its conftituent parts.
As others have publifhed fome experiments and obfervations, made fubfequent to mine, I find it neceffary to be
more minute in the following recital, than I otherwife
would wifh. About the latter end of March 1785, I
found that nitrous acid poured on tin filings, and immediately mixed with fixed vegetable alkali, generated volatile alkali in great abundance: fo fingular a fact did not
fail of deeply impreffing my mind, though at the time
I could not account for it. I mentioned this to Dr.
Higgins (for the obfervation was made in his elaboratory),
but he took little or no notice of it. Thus, unable to
awake his attention to fo fingular a fact, and having no
opportunity of making experiments of my own, I was
obliged to lay afide all thoughts of it.

About

liable to be retarded or checked by intem-
perance, &c. which may vary their quantities
and proportions? and may not a due proportion of these be necessary to a vigorous and
sound constitution? If so, no wonder that
an

About a fortnight after, I mentioned the circumstance
to Dr. Brocklesby. He told me he was going to meet
some philosophical gentlemen at Sir Joseph Banks's,
and desired I would generate some alkali for him to
exhibit before them: accordingly I did, and had the
pleasure of accompanying him thither.

The December following, I chanced to get acquainted
with my late worthy friend, Dr. Caulett, to whom I
mentioned the fact already related, respecting volatile
alkali, and likewise its copious generation from Prussian
blue, fixed vegetable alkali, and water. Pleased with what I
told him, we agreed to procure the necessary apparatus for
making a set of experiments on the subject. At present
it is needless to give a detail of our different experiments;
though at that time, when volatile alkali was less known,
they might have been of some importance: therefore I shall
only give an account of the following, which drew our
particular attention. Into a glass cylinder made for the
purpose, we charged three parts of alkaline air, and to this
added one part of dephlogisticated air; we passed the
electrical spark repeatedly in it, without apparently effecting the smallest change. When it had received about
a hundred strong shocks, a small quantity of moisture appeared on the sides of the glass, and the brass conductors
seemed

an increafe or deficiency in either or both of thefe, fhould be productive of feveral diforders. I make not the fmalleft doubt but a feries of accurate experiments, made by a facacious obferver on the latter part of this

feemed to be corroded: when we had paffed fixty more fhocks in it, the quantity of moifture feemed to increafe, and acquire a greenifh colour, though at this time the column of air fuffered no increafe or diminution. On examining the air, it burned with a languid greenifh flame, from which we inferred that the dephlogifticated air was totally condenfed; it ftill retained an alkaline fmell, and the alkaline part was not readily abforbed by water. This and another phenomenon obferved in the firft part of this paper, refpecting alkaline and fixable airs iffuing at the fame time, without forming an union, induce me to fuppofe, that volatile alkali, like other fubftances, may be found in an intermediate ftate, and in proportion as it is deprived of one of its conftituent parts, that it attracts fire fo much the ftronger, which counteracts its attraction to other bodies. Thus nitrous air is a compound of phlogifticated and dephlogifticated airs, requiring a larger proportion of dephlogifticated air to condenfe and render it combinable with alkalies. I often obferved, that fixable air obtained from different fubftances, was not under the fame circumftances always condenfed with equal facility *: hence muft arife the impof-

* Since the above has been written, I have been induced to fuppofe that fixable air is never found in an intermediate ftate, as obferved in the beginning of this volume.

fibility

this subject, would be attended with useful
discoveries. If God will grant me health
and opportunity, I shall persevere in this
task, and wish that others would do the
same; for the importance and extent of the
subject

fibility of ascertaining the specific gravity of the compound
elastic fluids. From Mr. Cavendish's famous discovery of
the constituent parts of water, we could readily account
for the loss of the dephlogisticated air in this experiment ;
but the quantity of water produced was more than we
could expect from this: therefore water must have been
precipitated from the decomposed alkali ; for volatile alkali, from its great attraction for water, must keep some
in solution, even in its aeriform state. From the above
circumstances, it might be expected that a contraction of
the column of air should take place; but be it considered, that the union took place gradually, in proportion as the alkali was decomposed; and that in this case
the expansion must equal the condensation. Being
obliged to set out for Oxford, our experiments were
suspended, and, alas! never to be resumed. If a young
man of uncommon sagacity, perseverance and industry, and whose philosophical mind was strongly bent
towards new investigations, promised to extend science,
the premature death of the late Dr. Caulett must be a
severe loss to society, as well as a grievous one to those
who had the pleasure of his acquaintance. During the
spring of the year 1786, I often had an opportunity of
mentioning different facts to Dr. Austin, relating to volatile alkali, who at that time was too much engaged to
pay attention to the subject. In the latter end of June

4   1787,

subject point out to me, that we shall all find work enough, and that our labours will not be in vain, provided they be attended with diligence.

The above Analysis is an exact copy of what has been read before the Royal Society. I am sorry I have not had an opportunity of prosecuting the subject as I would wish, as I promised two years since, when this paper was written. I have made some

---

1787, I received a letter from him at Oxford (for he then lived in London), requesting my exact mode of obtaining volatile alkali, as he was engaged in that subject. I mentioned the purport of his letter to Dr. Beddoes, our present lecturer in chemistry at Oxford, who had readily seen into the importance of what I told him, and candidly said, it ought to have been made public a long time ago. On my arriving in London the following August, Dr. Austin gave me an account of a set of experiments which he had made, and which actually proved, that volatile alkali consists of light inflammable and phlogisticated airs, not knowing at that time what Mess. Hausman and Bertholet had done. Without depreciating the merit of these two gentlemen, Dr. Austin has an equal claim to the discovery, laying aside priority; as his experiments are as decisive as theirs. Dr. Priestley made the first step towards our knowledge of volatile alkali. See his Sixth Volume on Air.

Y   experiments,

experiments, but they are not numerous
enough, or of fufficient importance, to afford a fatisfactory conclufion; for, in order to this, it would require at leaft 500
experiments. But I hope fhortly to
have it in my power, to offer the public
fomething on this fubject. That the urinary fublimate is prefent in tubercles found
in the lungs of perfons who die of pulmonary confumptions, and likewife in what are
vulgarly called chalk ftones, is what I have
experienced; but in what proportion, or
whether in quantities fufficient to caufe the
concretion, is what I cannot fay, for I have
had but a few grains of each to examine;
nor could I procure any more, notwithftanding a diligent inquiry amongft my friends.
I have every reafon to fufpect, that confumptions and fcorbutic complaints very
frequently arife from a fuperabundance of
this fublimate in the fyftem; and that it is
chiefly the caufe of the gout and rheuma-
tifm, and folely the caufe of the ftone in
the bladder. I make no doubt but thefe
diforders generally proceed from obftructions; and it is probable that either a precipitation of this fublimate in the fyftem, or
elfe

elfe a deficiency of fome other fecretion, which would hold it in folution until conveyed out of the body, may be the chief caufe of thofe obftructions; and likewife, that different degrees of precipitation may produce different fymptoms and different diforders.

That mineral or volatile alkali and bark have been ufeful in the above diforders, has been affirmed by experienced phyficians; and I know an inftance myfelf of mineral alkali and nitrous ammoniac being ferviceable in a pulmonary complaint of fome ftanding.

With refpect to the ftone, when it acquires a certain magnitude, it is abfurd to attempt to diffolve it in the bladder, it waftes fo very flowly, and during this time the patient muft fuffer vaft pain, particularly when the ftone acquires a rugged furface; therefore cutting for it at once is much preferable.

Mineral alkali taken in the beginning of the complaint, and before the ftone accumulates, will no doubt check its progrefs, and may in time change that difpofition in the habit. Patients who are cut for the

ftone

ftone fhould, I think, take mineral alkali for fome time when the wound is healed, but not before, for fear of bringing on a mortification. Thefe are my opinions, or rather queries, refpecting the effects of the above falt or fublimate found in the urine, calculus, &c. on the human conftitution; and my fole motive for laying them before the public, is to promote an inquiry into fo interefting a fubject.

I flatter myfelf, that at leaft an attentive perufal of the above experiments may point out the ignorance of thofe empirics who have too long impofed upon the public with their pretended lithontriptics, and likewife that it may tend in future to check fuch proceedings.

THE END.

EXPERIMENTS

AND

OBSERVATIONS

ON

THE ATOMIC THEORY,

&c. &c.

EXPERIMENTS

AND

OBSERVATIONS

ON THE

Atomic Theory,

AND

ELECTRICAL PHENOMENA.

───────────

BY

WILLIAM HIGGINS, Esq.

F. R. S. & M. R. I. A.

PROFESSOR OF CHEMISTRY TO THE DUBLIN
SOCIETY.

───────────

LONDON:

PRINTED FOR LONGMAN, HURST, REES, ORME,
AND BROWN.

────

1814.

TO

THE RIGHT HONORABLE AND HONORABLE

THE

DUBLIN SOCIETY,

AS A SMALL TRIBUTE OF GRATITUDE FOR
THEIR LONG CONTINUED PATRONAGE,

THESE PAGES ARE INSCRIBED,

BY THEIR VERY OBEDIENT

AND HUMBLE SERVANT,

WILLIAM HIGGINS.

ERRATA.

ERRATA.

EXPERIMENTS

AND

OBSERVATIONS,

&c. &c.

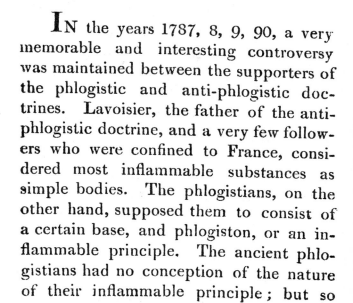

IN the years 1787, 8, 9, 90, a very memorable and interesting controversy was maintained between the supporters of the phlogistic and anti-phlogistic doctrines. Lavoisier, the father of the anti-phlogistic doctrine, and a very few followers who were confined to France, considered most inflammable substances as simple bodies. The phlogistians, on the other hand, supposed them to consist of a certain base, and phlogiston, or an inflammable principle. The ancient phlogistians had no conception of the nature of their inflammable principle; but so soon as hydrogen was discovered, the modern phlogistians adopted it as the real phlogiston, and according to their doctrine this was the cause, by its intimate union, of the combustibility of all bodies that were capable of burning, or uniting to oxygen. Lavoisier insisted that oxygen united to metals, phosphorus, sulphur, charcoal, &c. from its attraction to them as simple bodies, and that the supposition of their containing hydrogen was erroneous.

He made many experiments to support his doctrine, one of which I shall mention as sufficient for the present. He confined mercury and oxygen, of ascertained weights, in an apparatus calculated for the purpose, and exposed the mercury to the heat of 700° of Fahrenheit: in time the whole of the oxygen united to the mercury, and converted it into a red oxide which weighed more than the mercury in its simple metallic state: this additional weight corresponded with the weight of the oxygen absorbed. When this oxide was exposed to a red heat, the whole of the oxygen was expelled in its gascous state, without any change whatever, and the mercury was reduced to its metallic lustre and fluidity. This and many similar facts convinced Lavoisier that the agency of a third body, such as phlogiston, was fallacious and unnecessary, as the facts could be better explained without it.

The phlogistians denied these positions : they explained the process in the following manner. The oxygen united to the phlogiston and to the metallic basis conjointly, in a low degree of heat ; and, in a higher degree, the oxygen was expelled, while the phlogiston was retained by the metal so as to recover its metallic lustre.* At this time the phlogistians would not allow water to be composed of oxygen and hydrogen. According to Dr. Priestley, the water produced, when those gases were united, was what they contained before their union or condensation, and

---

* In this way every phenomenon was explained with equal plausibility by both doctrines.

that the compound which they formed was an acid.

These circumstances led me to enquire, very minutely, and upon new principles, into both doctrines at this critical period, and the work which I published on the subject was entitled " A comparative view of the phlogistic and anti-phlogistic theories." The following quotation from the preface of that work will give a clear idea of the nature of the controversy.

" The present controversy between the philosophers of the day rests upon the following questions. 1st, Is water composed of oxygen and hydrogen ? 2d, Does the union of oxygen to different bodies depend upon one inflammable principle, common to all combustible bodies ? Or, in other words, do all bodies that burn or oxydate, such as charcoal, sulphur, phosphorus, metals, azote, &c. contain the matter of hydrogen as one of their constituent principles ? One would suppose if these substances were composed of two elementary principles, namely, peculiar bases, and hydrogen in a solid state, that it would be no difficult matter to separate them, more especially when we consider the great attraction of the matter of hydrogen for caloric. Yet the phlogistians have not been able to accomplish this : Therefore the only ground they have to rest their hypothesis upon is, that these bodies unite to oxygen : according to this philosophy oxygen has the property of uniting but to one substance in nature, caloric excepted !

" If the above inflammable substances were simple elementary bodies, or even compounds free from hydrogen or phlogiston, the anti-phlogistians cannot do any more than what they have already done ; for instance, suppose sulphur or charcoal were decomposed into two principles, either gases or solids, different in their nature from any other substances with which we are at present acquainted, the phlogistians might still insist that they contained phlogiston (hydrogen) if they even were the most simple bodies in nature, provided they possessed the property of uniting to oxygen.

" The anti-phlogistians, therefore, in order to establish the truth of their doctrine, have to prove the non-existence of a substance in bodies whose presence, as one of their constituents, has not hitherto been ascertained. On this difficulty the phlogistic theory seems to rest and to maintain itself.

" Thus seeing upon what principles the antagonist theorists maintained their different doctrines, in order to accomplish any thing decisive. I was obliged to have recourse to a mode of philosophising quite novel in the science of chemistry.* I have introduced several diagrams in order to render the nature of my investigations the more intelligible : I considered this the surest mode of reasoning, and the most effectual means of establishing truth and removing errors."

---

* This alludes to the Atomic theory.

When I commenced my investigations of chemical theory in 1788 and 1790, at which time the work was sent to the press, all the chemical philosophers of Great-Britain, Sweden, Germany, Ireland, Holland and Italy, and also most of those of France, were phlogistians. Under these circumstances, a very young man, such I was at that time, might well be supposed to be intimidated, and even deterred from offering an opinion on the subject of chemical philosophy; however the new views which I fortunately adopted furnished me with some degree of confidence.*

---

* The following extract from a letter I received from Dr. Beddoes will shew the state of chemical theory at this period :—

"*Oxford, 10th of April,* 1789.

" Dear Sir,

.... I shall be glad to see your book, though I hope you have not taken Lavoisier's side of the question, or else have defended it by arguments totally unlike any thing that has yet appeared. Dr. Priestley's late admirable experiments have in my opinion totally overset that doctrine, and re-established the existence of phlogiston.

" Yours faithfully,

" THOS. BEDDOES."

I was very well aware of the importance as well as of the difficulty of the task which I proposed to myself. I had to frame a new system of investigation, in order to explore two doctrines that were, at the time, doubtful and abstruse.

I own it cost me many weeks, nay, many months of anxious meditation and study, before my plan was perfectly formed.

At length it occurred to me that chemical attraction only prevailed between the ultimate particles of simple elementary matter, and also between compound atoms.* The play of chemical affinities between those divisions were therefore only to be attended to.

---

* In my " Comparative View" the term *ultimate particle* means the last division of elementary matter, and the term *molecule* the last division of a chemical compound. I now adopt for the latter the term *atom*, and for a more complicate compound that of *molecule*. This makes no difference in the system.

These considerations gave birth to that doctrine which Mr. Dalton, eighteen years after I had written, claimed as originating from his own inventive genius. What his pretensions are, will be seen from the sketches which will soon follow, and which have been taken from my book.

In the application of my system to chemical theory, I expressed by numbers the relative forces of attraction subsisting between the different kinds of ultimate particles and atoms of matter to each other. This was of infinite use to me during my researches, and if followed up would mature the science into that mathematical precision in which it is at present deficient.

This I consider as one of the most important features of the system : it has not even been mentioned by Mr. Dalton in his work, and when he repeats experiments formerly made by me, he does not even glance at the source from whence he derived his information.

I cannot with propriety or delicacy directly say that Mr. Dalton is a plagiarist, although appearances are against him. Probably he never read my book; yet it appears extraordinary that a person of Mr. Dalton's industry and learning should neglect one of the few works that were expressly written on the subject of theory. At the time it was published, there were one thousand copies of it sold, and it was the principal means of putting an end to the controversy already alluded to, which otherwise might not be determined for several years.

It is not my intention at present, whatever may happen hereafter, to correct my own errors, or to mend such as may fall to the lot of Mr. Dalton, except in a few instances where we differ in proportion, as to the constituent principles of certain compounds. My sole object is to claim what I conceive is, in justice, due to me.

Mr. Dalton has represented the ultimate particles of elementary matter by means of symbols, and atoms are repre sented in the same way with the proportion of their elementary constituents.

These signs correspond with my diagrams, except that numbers, expressive of the relative force of attraction, are left out. Those symbols, I own, shew some ingenuity: they are, excepting the omission of numbers, preferable to my diagrams. This can only be considered a mechanical improvement. Definite proportions are also represented by those symbols, and the same is strictly attended to by my diagrams. Specimens of both will be exhibited hereafter. The relative weights of the different particles of elementary matter, that of hydrogen being a standard, have also been given by Mr. Dalton. I have done the same in many instances. After this the relative weight of compound atoms could readily be conceived, and Mr. Dalton has extended this to saline substances. Here indeed many obstacles which have not as yet been removed, stand in the way: the principal one is, the great attraction of saline substances to water, which must interfere with the estimate deduced from the weight of their respective ultimate particles.

I will allow that the relative weight of the ultimate particles of metals might be inferred from the additional weight which they acquire by calcination, when the operation is performed by heat and exposure to air; but in order to this the degree of oxydation should be accurately ascertained.

Metals, like all the rest of the solid and fluid materials of the globe, consist of particles, which, when separated from each other, are invisible, indivisible, and unalterable in their size or shape, whatever that may be, as Sir Isaac Newton first observed. These ultimate divisions are held together by the aggregate attraction, and although apparently in complete contact, they are not so in reality, and probably in proportion to their diameters their distance from each other is very considerable. We have every reason to suppose that the ultimate particles of every substance in nature possess the same specific gravity, and that the difference in the weight of metals depends upon the distance of their respective ultimate particles from each other.*   However this may be, no doubt the diameters of the particles of different bodies are not the same, and their weight is in proportion to their size. Every ultimate particle of a metal is surrounded with a small although dense atmosphere of caloric, together with a small portion of the electric or some other subtile fluid.†

When metals are presented under favourable circumstances to bodies that have a strong chemical affinity to their ultimate particles, those particles come into action independent of each other in the aggregate : they act as separate individuals, as has been demonstrated in many cases, in my Comp. View ; for instance, when a metal, in a temperature sufficient

---

* This I have shewn to be the case in respect to some gases.—See pages 14, 15, of my Comparative View.

† See page 14, Comp. View.

to diminish its aggregate attraction, is exposed to oxygen gas, each particle will enter into union with one, two, or more particles of oxygen, according to the nature of the metal operated upon, for different metals unite with different doses of oxygen. If an ultimate particle of a metal is only capable of uniting but to a single ultimate particle of oxygen, the aggregate mass of the atoms of such oxide are unable to influence any more oxygen. This seems to be a general law throughout the whole system of chemistry; even when two atoms unite, the compound becomes surrounded with one common atmosphere of caloric, and rejects a third atom of either of its constituents. In short, there is a limit to the proportions in which the particles of elementary matter, as well as those of atoms, unite, which the old chemists expressed by the term saturation, and the modern ones by that of definite proportions. The former having no knowledge of the atomic system, could not extend their ideas on this subject beyond gross volumes.

It is not easy to ascertain when a metal is saturated with oxygen, for if that saturation should be limited by the union of an ultimate particle of the one with an ultimate particle of the other, so as to form a binary atom, metallic particles might be mixed with such an oxide, for the particle of oxygen cannot divide itself, it can only remain attached to one particle of metal.

Metals, whose particles are capable of uniting to two of oxygen, can have no metallic particles mixed with their oxides, yet it is possible to have them composed of ternary and binary atoms mechanically mixed, for the binary, in order to become ternary, cannot deprive the latter atom of any of its oxygen so as to leave it in a binary state.

A metal which unites to three portions of oxygen, may also have its oxide mixed in two different states of oxydation. It might consist of ternary and quaternary atoms. Binary atoms cannot exist in contact with the latter.

Those important chemical laws **were** first demonstrated in my Comparative View. (See pages 136, 137.)

From the foregoing considerations it is not an easy matter to ascertain when a metal is perfectly oxydated in the hands of the most experienced operator. Hence it is difficult to ascertain the relative weight of an ultimate particle of a metal, from the additional weight a given quantity of a metal acquires by oxydation. Besides, moisture is absorbed during the process of calcination, which must increase the difficulty. Yet it must be allowed to be the most effectual mode of any to approximate towards accuracy. I was the first who attempted to ascertain the relative weights of the ultimate particles of matter, as shall be proved hereafter.

The foregoing short statement will, I presume, prepare my reader for the evidences which will soon follow. I have read Mr. Dalton's " New System of Chemical Philosophy," as he calls it, with great attention ; and also my " Comparative View," for the first time the last twenty years, and I cannot discover any improvement made in my doctrine, except what might reasonably be expected from any ingenious compiler, who had carefully perused my book. The nature of those improvements, such as they are, has been enumerated in the foregoing pages.

The atomic doctrine has been applied by me in abstruse and difficult researches. Its application by Mr. Dalton has been in a general and popular way, and it is from these circumstances alone that it gained the name of Dalton's Theory. Mr. Dalton's work is read; mine had been laid aside as soon as the controversy, which gave rise to it, ceased; and at that time the theory in question was not understood, nor did I expect it would for a considerable time. I calculated upon the middle of the present century. Probably it would have lain by since if it had not been for the genius and industry of Mr. Dalton.

As it is nearly five years since the first part of Mr. Dalton's " New System" ap-

c

peared, it might be asked why I had not taken notice of it sooner; I will only say that it is with much reluctance I do so now at the request of some scientific friends. Besides, I had it in contemplation, for some years past, to publish a system of chemistry on a new arrangement, which I am now determined upon. In such a work I thought my claim to the *new system* would appear less pointed, and with more grace.

I have shewn in my Compar. View, that simple elementary particles, whether in a solid or gaseous state, governed a certain quantity of caloric which formed an atmosphere round them, somewhat similar in structure to the atmosphere which surrounds our globe; and also that probably the caloric was accompanied with a certain portion of electricity, as has been already alluded to.

Caloric, thus attached to the particles, comes under the denomination of specific heat, and is in all probability chemically united. We have every reason to suppose so, as it is as latent as an acid in sulphate of soda, or an alkali in nitre.

The ultimate particles of different kinds of matter, whether in a solid or gaseous state, do not retain the same quantity of caloric in their respective atmospheres. This probably is occasioned by their different forces of attraction to it. Those particles which attract caloric with most force, are surrounded with more of it, in a less space than those particles that attract it with a smaller force.

No doubt the aggregate attraction of the particles themselves, particularly in solids, diminishes the quantity of caloric which they otherwise would have influenced : this has been ascertained by various facts.

That substances, of the same degree of condensation and temperature, contain different quantities of caloric, has been proved : this had been attributed, long before the nature of the union of caloric to bodies was known, to their relative capacities for it, and the expression is still applicable.

When two ultimate particles unite chemically, their individuality is destroyed, and they form one solid atom whose capacity for caloric is less than its constituents in a detached or simple state;* hence it is that caloric is liberated by chemical union. These atoms however retain a sufficient quantity of caloric to furnish them with atmospheres.

When two atoms unite chemically, the compound molecule governs still less caloric than its constituent atoms, yet it is enveloped with an atmosphere.

Molecules of this kind are as distinct from each other, or as insulated in conse-

---

* I have adduced some exceptions to this general law in my Comp. View, in treating on the subject of nitrous acid, as shall be shewn hereafter.

quence of their respective atmospheres, as either ultimate particles or atoms.

Molecules set bounds to chemical combination, for here it almost invariably stops. Molecules of different kinds mix mechanically, or produce decomposition and new formations.

We may distinguish these different compounds from each other by the terms single and double compounds, and the latter, with few exceptions, contain less caloric than the former.

Many ingenious experiments have been made to ascertain the specific heat of bodies; that is, the whole quantity of caloric contained in a given weight or bulk of substances; yet I must own I have never felt convinced of the accuracy of their result, or rather of the inference deduced from them.

It is not my intention to enter here on so important a discussion which would require a whole volume to itself; my object at present, in addition to that already related, is to give a cursory view of chemical theories in general, but particularly of the atomic system.

It is impossible to deprive any subtance of the whole of its caloric, although much of it may be extracted by means of artificial cold. The degree of cold that is capable of depriving an ultimate particle, or an atom, or molecule, of one tenth of their caloric, must probably require more than twice the degree of cold to separate two tenths, and so on progressively ; for in proportion as caloric is taken away, what remains is retained with the greater force. This law has been demonstrated in my Comparative View. (See page 41.) In short, this doctrine prevails throughout the whole of that work, and in many instances it has been there expressed by numbers. I do not intimate that this doctrine related to caloric : I confined myself to the atoms and ultimate particles of ponderable matter : the same law however holds equally good in either case.

The idea that ultimate particles of matter, which are so exceedingly minute that the molecule itself, which consists of many of them, is invisible, even by the help of microscopes, should be surrounded with an atmosphere of caloric, might appear too hypothetical and fanciful to many. What are the planets in our system, which we consider worlds, but small molecules in comparison to the immense space in which they move? They are all surrounded with some kind of matter, and probably this matter, whatever it may be, in a great measure prevents their coming into contact, at the same time that it presses them towards each other. Might not the projectile and rotatory motion of the planets be produced and preserved by the unceasing action of this subtile matter? Had Sir Isaac Newton been perfectly acquainted with the laws of electricity and caloric, at the time he had written his Principia, very likely his philosophy would have taken a different turn.

Our own planet is surrounded with an atmosphere, but the materials of which it

consists are terrestrial, for oxygen constitutes a great part of the solid masses of
our globe, such as the earths and water
(ice); and azote also exists in a solid state,
united to certain bodies. Our globe and
that atmosphere may be encircled with a
still more subtile fluid, so as to form an
atmosphere that extends to the confines
of that of its neighbouring planets.

The ultimate particles of ponderable
matter are exceedingly minute, but those
of imponderable elements, such as caloric,
electricity, and light, are beyond calculation. The utmost stretch of the human
mind can no more estimate the size of
those particles than it can measure space
and duration. However, their divisibility
is limited.

Probably a single ultimate particle of
caloric bears the same proportion, in its
size and weight, to a particle of oxygen,
as the latter does to our globe: hence
arises the impossibility of ascertaining the
weight of that element.

From the foregoing considerations we can readily conceive the nature and structure of the calorific atmospheres which are influenced by particles, atoms, or molecules, of ponderable matter.

The quantity of caloric in gases is very considerable, particularly in those which are uncompounded.

Solids also contain a prodigious quantity of caloric, as may be shewn by deflagrating together nitre, brimstone, and crude antimony, reduced to powder, and intimately mixed. The intensity of the heat, and brilliancy of the light, produced in this way, are dazzling to the sight. The greater part of this caloric exists in the nitre. If the quantity of caloric contained in any solid substance were accumulated upon another of the same bulk and temperature, the heat produced would be very great; for instance, if the caloric of ice were transferred to the same bulk of cast iron, it would be more than sufficient to effect its fusion.

There are only three ways of setting free any quantity of specific heat contained in bodies: the first is by chemical action; the second, by pressure on gases, or by hammering malleable metals so as to approximate their ultimate particles. The third, and last, is accomplished by means of electricity in the state of a certain degree of accumulation and density. This I only offer as a mere hypothesis, for the present, although well-known facts tend to support my opinion.

By strong electric sparks gunpowder and alkohol are inflamed. This inflammation is occasioned by caloric which is disengaged from these substances, or from the air in contact with them. Small metallic wires are also ignited and fused by a strong electric battery; and it frequently happens that by the same means silver and gold wires are dissipated into very minute divisions and converted into oxides. This I conceive to arise from a rapid dislodgment of the specific heat of the metals by the electric matter. Upon a similar principle it is, that small wires

of platina, copper, iron, &c. are ignited
or fused by a strong voltaic battery, particularly that composed of broad plates.*
When a platina wire, sufficiently thick to
resist fusion, is used, the glow of heat and
light produced is exceedingly bright. The
same effect is produced when charcoal is
made use of. These brilliant phenomena
are effected by the specific caloric of
those substances, which is disengaged in
a free state from their particles by the superior influence of the electric matter
which occupies its place during its presence. These phenomena are produced
in vacuo with equal brilliancy as in oxygen gas.

As the heat thus produced will continue while the battery acts with sufficient
energy, and as there must be a constant

* The order of the fusibility of metals by exposure to
heat in the common way, is somewhat reversed when the
electric fluid is made the medium of fusion. This circumstance is favourable to my hypothesis, for in this latter case
their fusibility depends upon the quantity of specific caloric
which they respectively contain.

waste of the specific heat of both the charcoal and metallic wires, this doctrine may appear defective. If it be allowed that the electric fluid is capable of disengaging specific heat on the principles which have been adduced, it must also possess the power of urging on, during its passage, through the battery and conductors, a sufficiency of caloric to supply the waste occasioned by the ignition.

When oxygen and hydrogen are mixed, their ultimate particles, notwithstanding their chemical attraction to each other, will not unite. This kind of neutrality does not proceed from the distance at which they are held by their caloric, but from the structure of the atmospheres which it forms round them, and which tend to preserve and press to their respective centres their gravitating particles.

When an electric spark is passed in this mixture of gases, it liberates the specific heat of that part which it meets in its passage from one conductor to the other; thus the atmospheres being destroyed, the gravitating particles unite, as meeting no resistance in a medium of uniform density : the caloric of that part of the gases condensed by means of the electric fluid produces a similar effect upon the atmospheres of the other part of the mixture. This is effected with a velocity almost equal to the passage of the electric spark. The same effect is produced by a flint spark upon the same principle, that of *blending* the atmospheres. Doctor Higgins was the first who advanced this ingenious doctrine in his excellent Treatise on Acetous Acid, a work which is shamefully passed over by modern writers on that subject, although his book was published when the nature of that acid, so far as related to its internal structure or constituents, was unknown to others. Dr. Higgins's idea of the *modus operandi* of the electric matter and mine are quite different, even in this experiment.

When a strong electric spark is passed in oxygen gas, or any other gas, a flash

of light is produced : this is occasioned
by the liberation of a portion of the specific heat, which resumes its former station
as soon as the influence of the electric
matter is removed, which is instantaneous.

The explosions produced on such occasions are the effects of expansion by the
liberated caloric and instantaneous absorption of it again by the particles of
the gas, by which means the gas becomes
condensed to its original dimensions.

The same effect is produced on the
large scale of nature. When the electricity of a cloud passes to another cloud in
a negative state, or to the earth, or from
the earth to a cloud, a portion of the
specific heat of the intermediate air, in
the direct line of its passage, is set at
liberty for a moment. This is the cause
of thunder and lightning. When this
operation takes place at a distance, we
perceive the flash of light before we hear
the thunder, in consequence of the greater
velocity of light than that of sound.

The effects of lightning in destroying edifices, fusing metals, setting fire to inflammable bodies, and depriving animals of life, are explicable on the foregoing principles.

The brilliant phenomena of the aurora borealis, in the upper regions of the atmosphere, are effected by electricity in the same manner.

By the help of this theory we are enabled to account for those fiery meteors which occur so frequently in our atmosphere.

Those meteors move with great velocity, partly in an horizontal direction, but approaching gradually towards the earth. When they reach within a certain distance of it, the phenomena of thunder and lightning are produced ; and at that moment they come down most frequently shattered into small masses with the effect of fusion on their surface, although their internal parts are quite free from any appearance of that kind.

From the analyses of these stones, it appears that they consist of iron in its metallic state, without any determinate form, small portions of nickel, oxide of iron, and sulphur.

The stone which fell in the county of Tipperary, a few years ago, was found by my analysis to consist of the same ingredients with others which had fallen on different parts of the globe, according to the analysis of Mr. Howard.

As those stones are different from any mineral substance hitherto discovered on our globe, we must consider them as foreigners. It is supposed by some that they never belonged to any planet, and that they were opaque wandering masses before they reached the confines of our atmosphere. This, certainly, is the most rational mode of accounting for their existence in the situation in which we first behold them.

However, my principal object is to account for their luminous appearance.

Those masses contain specific heat round their particles, like other bodies of similar nature. In moving through the atmosphere they collect electricity, and this continues increasing, as there is no other solid matter in those upper regions to prevent its accumulation. When they acquire a sufficient quantity of electric matter, a portion of their specific heat is liberated and thrown upon their surface : this gives the luminous appearance. As they are of an inflammable nature, a portion of oxygen unites to their external parts. The degree of heat occasioned by these different circumstances will account for that superficial fused crust with which they are found invariably to be surrounded.

Those electric stones, in descending towards the earth, when they meet with a cloud comparatively negative, lose their electricity, which, bursting forward with great vehemence, exhibits the phenomena of thunder and lightning : at the same time they are most commonly shattered into pieces. So soon as this takes place,

D

their luminous appearance ceases, and they are precipitated to the earth, still retaining a considerable degree of heat. The stone that fell in the county of Tipperary could not be touched with the hand for some time after its descent.

Thunder and lightning accompany volcanic eruptions; particularly at their commencement. Although the electric matter alone is not sufficient to produce all the effects, yet it might be the primary cause. During the interval of volcanic eruptions, the electric fluid is gradually accumulating on the inflammable materials (pyrites) and other substances which constitute the subterraneous strata whence the eruption issues; and when collected in a sufficient degree of concentration and density, specific heat is liberated; this heat produces the chemical action of all the elementary principles in the whole mass. By these means a considerable degree of heat is produced, gases are formed, and fixed substances are fused. The heat continues to increase, as there is nothing to carry it off, until the eruption takes place, which is occasioned by the expansive force of red hot gases that burst a passage in the direction in which they meet with the least resistance, that is, to the surface of the earth. The liquid part, or lava, is also forced to the surface upon mechanical principles so obvious that I need not dwell on them at present.

Violent earthquakes are also accompanied with thunder and lightning at their immediate source : hence we are induced to attribute those convulsions of nature to the force of subterraneous electricity, on the same principle that concussions are produced in our atmosphere by the same element.

The heat produced by friction, although it constantly takes place under various circumstances before our eyes, has not hitherto been accounted for upon any rational principle. It cannot be attributed to an union with oxygen gas, or to any chemical action of ponderable particles, as had been shewn by Count Rumford.

This philosopher, being struck by the heat evolved by the friction of bodies, took a solid cylinder of iron, near 8 inches in diameter, and 9,8 inches long. In this cylinder a hole was bored 3,7 inches in diameter, and 7,2 inches in length. A blunt steel borer was introduced into this hole, which by means of horses was made to rub against its bottom with a considerable weight. The cylinder was wrapt round with flannel to keep in the heat, and it was turned round at the rate of 32 times in a minute. At the beginning of the experiment the temperature of the cylinder was 60°; at the end of thirty minutes, when it had made 960 revolutions, its temperature was 130°.

To prove that the caloric produced was not occasioned by the union of oxygen, Count Rumford enclosed the cylinder and borer in a wooden box filled with water so as to exclude the air. The quantity of water was 18,77 pints, and at the beginning of the experiment it stood at the temperature of 60°. After the cylinder revolved two hours and thirty minutes, with the velocity already described, the water boiled.

Whether the water was excluded, or allowed free access into the hole in the cylinder where the friction took place, the result of the experiment was the same.

Mr. Pictet, of Geneva, made some experiments on the friction of bodies in air, and in vacuo, without any difference as to effect.

These facts led the above philosophers to suspect, that heat, like gravity, might be a mere property of common matter, and that it is produced by a peculiar vibration of their particles, more especially as there appeared no perceptible source from which, as a substance, it could possibly be derived.

Heat evolved by friction, however unaccountable and mysterious it may appear, is not sufficient to invalidate the doctrine of the materiality of caloric, being only a solitary fact opposed to thousands that tend to establish its existence as an elementary substance.

When bodies unite chemically caloric is given out : can this be effected by vibratory motion of the particles ? Were this the case, heat ought to be evolved during the solution of saline substances in water and acids, whereas cold is produced. The motion of the particles or atoms is the same in both cases. When a bell is rung, all its particles are made to vibrate strongly, yet no heat is produced by ever so long a continuance of those vibrations. Should heat be produced by vibration of the particles of ponderable matter, it ought to disappear the instant such motion ceases, which is not the case.

What keeps the particles of gases in solution, or at such a distance from each other ? It must be attributed to the caloric given out so copiously during their chemical union.

In my humble opinion the heat produced by friction can only be accounted for on those principles which I have already adduced.

Friction invariably excites and accumulates electric matter on the bodies rubbed : if they are good conductors, it circulates very quickly through them, and the quantity of the electric matter thus induced in a given time, is in proportion to the rapidity of the friction. Upon what principle this effect is produced, is totally unknown at present, although the fact is fully established, particularly by the operation of an electric machine.

Might not the heat produced in Count Rumford's experiment, arise from a dislodgment of a portion of the specific heat of the iron through the influence of electricity, which must flow in every direction to the centre of friction ? And might it not also, in its passage thither, force on before it another portion of heat from the calorific atmospheres which it meets ?

We have every reason to suppose that the particles of imponderable elements, like those of the ponderable, have their different forces of attraction to bodies.

The de-oxydizing rays which accompany those of light, separate ponderable elements, such as oxygen and metals, and oxygen and hydrogen, and oxygen and carbon. This elementary substance must therefore be inimical to the process of combustion : we should therefore be the less surprised at finding one imponderable element to disengage another imponderable element from its chemical union.

Caloric and the electric fluid are antagonist elements, whereas light and caloric seem to be kind and almost constant associates. The light of the sun, and that produced by artificial means, are accompanied by caloric.

Moon-light seems to be quite free from caloric, which on that account might appear an exception to the foregoing law : but we are to consider that this kind of light is reflected from a considerable distance, and from a great body that might retain the caloric that accompanies it from the sun, or reflect it back again to that luminary.

Electricity, in its pure simple state, is incapable of producing heat or light. When a Leyden jar is overcharged with the electric fluid, rays of light diverge from between the wooden cover and the edge of the glass : this light is so feeble, it is only visible in the dark ; but when the whole charge of the jar is made to pass in air at one sudden explosion, a very vivid flash of light is produced : when passed in air rarefied by partial exhaustion, by means of an air pump, the light is less vivid, and continues diminishing in proportion to the rarefaction, because in this state it meets with less caloric in its passage.

When the air is completely removed, which can only be effected by the Torricellian vacuum, it not only passes with some difficulty in such a medium, but neither light nor heat is produced. Philosophers do not agree as to this fact, which must be in consequence of the great difficulty of producing a perfect vacuum.

Substances that retain the calorific atmospheres of their particles or atoms with the greatest force, are the worst conductors ; because the electric fluid has to force its way by removing a certain portion of caloric which obstructs its passage. The quantity of caloric thus liberated depends upon that of the electric fluid, and the effects it produces as free caloric, are more or less sensible according to the thickness of the conductor. For instance, the electricity of a large cloud will melt a mass of metal, whereas that of an electric or voltaic battery will only fuse small wires.

Metals, charcoal, and living animals, are the best conductors of electricity, as a sufficient portion of their caloric is readily removed on its passage through those substances.

Dry oxides are non-conductors, as their calorific atmospheres are small and strongly attached to their atoms. Glass also, which consists of different oxides fused in one solid mass, is a non-conductor on the same principle, and so are resinous substances; yet glass and resins become good conductors when sufficiently heated so as to enlarge their calorific atmospheres.

The liquid oxides, namely, acids and water, are bad conductors of electricity, and, when it passes through them, a portion of their specific heat is removed for a moment. The same effect is produced in dry gases, which are also bad conductors, partly upon the foregoing principles.

We know very little, at present, of the internal nature of the imponderable elements. Although we are acquainted with many of the phenomena which they produce, yet the greater part of the duty allotted to each is veiled from our senses: every one of them has to perform an important office in the system of nature, not excepting the great scale of our planetary system. In our own little world (the earth) every thing is performed by them; animalization, vegetation, life, and motion, are their attributes, for in their absence the ponderable materials of our globe would be one chaotic inanimate mass, or, in the language of the old chemists, a *caput mortuum.* We must therefore consider them as agents in the hands of Providence to effect his all-wise and mighty purposes.

We shall never be perfectly acquainted with the laws of nature while we are ignorant of the properties and operations of those subtile elements that guide, animate, and move the whole of the universe.

Our ancestors, so late as sixty years ago, were as unacquainted with the nature of atmospheric air as we are at present with that of the imponderable elements. They considered it beyond the reach of human investigation, having no conception of the implements and apparatus calculated for such an intricate inquiry.

We are nearly in the same situation, as to the imponderable elements; we possess very imperfect means of examining them, consequently the rationalia of their most important functions are concealed. However, I entertain hopes that at some future period posterity will gain that power over them which we now possess in the extensive field of pneumatic chemistry.

The theory, or rather the hypothesis, which I have advanced, on electrical phenomena, is founded on well-known facts, and according to my knowledge is quite new. It is simple and uniform in its application, and capable of accounting for many phenomena which appeared hitherto inexplicable upon any rational principle whatever. Should it stand the test of further investigation, it will establish the materiality of the imponderable elements beyond a shadow of doubt.

So fully convinced am I, at present, of the truth of this doctrine, that no vague or superficial objections will be able to stagger my creed : at the same time I am ready to submit to convincing facts and arguments, for truth should be the sole object of every writer on philosophical subjects.

I will now return to the atomic theory, the principal object of this essay, and endeavour to submit to the philosophical world such testimony as will enable it to judge who is the author of that doctrine.

When I had written, the present chemical nomenclature was not adopted : azotic gas was then called phlogisticated air ; oxygen gas, dephlogisticated air ; hydrogen gas, light inflammable air ; and caloric was distinguished by the name of fire ; and so on, as to other substances. Modernising, therefore, that part of my book which must necessarily be transcribed, cannot be considered misrepresentation. In many instances, it will be necessary to render passages shorter and more perspicuous than they are in the original, particularly as this doctrine was applied to abstruse investigation, as I have already mentioned. There shall be no alteration whatever, as to the mere matter of fact; and reference will regularly be made to the pages of the old work. Any additional remarks that are made, will be in italics, or in a note at the foot of the page.

Although the theory in question runs throughout the whole work, consisting of 280 pages, I will only trouble the reader with certain passages, which circumstance must unavoidably mutilate the system which I advanced. It will, however, answer the purpose of ascertaining whether any and what part of this doctrine originated with Mr. Dalton.

It is almost unnecessary to quote any part of Mr. Dalton's work, it being so well known, and so recently published; yet I shall transcribe those passages at the end of this treatise that he or his friends would have adduced, were they to contest the present question. I shall also present specimens of his symbols and his ingenious method of exhibiting, by their means,

the constituents and proportions of atoms
and molecules.

I consider his definite proportions and
weight of atoms in many instances very
erroneous, as shall be proved in the course
of this work. The few experiments he
made were not sufficiently accurate to jus-
tify his conclusions. But let facts answer
for themselves.

Mr. Kirwan was the first who opposed
the theory of Lavoisier, in a treatise written expressly for the purpose, called
" Essay on Phlogiston." One of his first
objections was to the table of Lavoisier
on the affinities of the oxygenous principle
to different bodies, wherein he placed
charcoal above iron.

Mr. Kirwan supposed that charcoal,
according to the precedency given it in
this table, should decompose water in a
boiling heat, at least, (*which is not the
case*) considering that iron, which is placed
lower, will produce hydrogen under the
same circumstances.

The reply which I made to Mr. Kirwan, on this subject, will exhibit the first dawn of the atomic theory ; and the series of chemical affinities adduced on the occasion, as being still problematical, deserves the attention of modern philosophers. It is as follows : *

" The nature of charcoal should be first considered. Although the aggregate attraction of its parts appears weaker than that of iron, from its facility of pulverization; yet, when reduced to powder, or small molecules, its ultimate particles may cohere with greater force.

" The frangibility of charcoal is in a great measure owing to the number of minute cavities which intersect its texture; from the expulsion of hydrogen, and the succulent part of the wood.

" Independent of the aggregate attraction which counteracts chemical union

---

* Comp. View, p. 11.

more than we are aware of, it appears to me that the ultimate particles of charcoal are surrounded with some repelling fluid which defends them from the action of air and water. The same may be said with respect to alkohol, oil, and ether; for they all have greater attraction to oxygen than phosphorus has, which unites with it in the common temperature of the atmosphere.* Whether this be occasioned by caloric, the electric fluid, or some other subtile fluid, with which we are unacquainted, deserves attention.

" Nitrous air will rush into union with oxygen gas, in any moderate temperature, yet sugar will not do so, although it will deprive the nitrous air of its condensed oxygen.

---

* This holds good when phosphorus is exposed to atmospheric air. When dry phosphorus is confined over mercury in perfectly dry oxygen gas, no union will take place in a common temperature, so that the slow combination of phosphorus is promoted by the azote, which acts on it as a solvent.

" Pure calcareous earth (lime) will have no effect on muriatic gas, when both are perfectly dry; yet water, to which this gas has no chemical affinity, will condense it: in this state it will readily form an intimate union with the lime.

" Oxygen and hydrogen gases, when mixed in their simple state, will not unite, notwithstanding their chemical attraction for each other, unless exposed to an electric or a common spark, yet they will readily combine when one or both are partially condensed; instance, nitrous air, which, as will hereafter appear, consists of oxygen and azote, will condense hepatic gas.* Hepatic gas, as shall be shewn, is hydrogen in its full extent, holding sulphur in solution. When those gases are mixed, sulphur is deposited, and the residuary air is found to be the gaseous oxide of azote.† In this experiment a

---

* Comp. View, pages 12, 13.

† At the time the above was first written, nitrous air was considered by many chemists a compound of nitric acid and phlogiston.

portion of the oxygen of the nitrous air unites to the hydrogen of the hepatic gas, and forms water. It does not appear that this takes place in consequence of a double affinity.

" Azotic gas is made to unite with great difficulty to oxygen gas, by means of repeated electric shocks in contact with pure potash, although it attracts oxygen with greater force than nitrous air ; the latter being a compound of azote and oxygen.

" When iron is moistened with water, and confined in a glass jar over mercury, it will yield hydrogen. Iron, under the same circumstances in oxygen gas, will give no hydrogen, and the oxygen is condensed ; in both cases the surface of the iron is equally oxydized.

" Iron and dry oxygen gas, kept in contact ever so long, will not act on each other : the iron preserves its metallic brilliancy, and the gas its elastic state, and no hydrogen is evolved. Hence it appears, that iron has no effect on oxygen gas in a common temperature, and that it is the oxygen of the water which unites to it, while the oxygen of the gas is condensed by the liberated hydrogen in its nascent state, so as to reproduce water. *This is effected by a double influence, which is so obvious as not to require an explanation. This modification of chemical affinity escaped the observation of chemists before I had written. The process of bleaching is effected in this way.*

" The foregoing facts cannot be accounted for readily. It might be supposed that water condenses muriatic gas in consequence of its capacity for caloric. But why phosphorus, and not ether, oils, or sugar,

---

* A very ingenious treatise on this kind of affinity was published by Mrs. Fulham, about fifteen years ago, wherein she erroneously attempts to explain the phenomenon of combustion on the same principle, and boasts very much of her discovery, having met nothing like it in the works of Lavoisier, Fourcroy, Kirwan, &c. at the same time that she cautiously omitted mentioning the work from which she borrowed her ideas.

or why nitrous air, and not azote, unite to oxygen in a low temperature: And again, why iron takes the oxygenous principle from water, in preference to that in its gaseous state, when the hydrogen disengaged condenses it, are phenomena, in my opinion, not well understood.

"It is true all this may be attributed to caloric, which, from its attraction to bodies, counteracts their chemical union to each other: yet, from the following considerations, probably some other power interferes.

"It must be allowed that nitrous air consists of oxygen and azote, in the proportion of two of the former to one of the latter. The supposition of its containing phlogiston, will hereafter appear to be erroneous: therefore every ultimate particle of azote must be united to two of oxygen; and these molecules, surrounded with their respective atmospheres of caloric, constitute nitrous air. If these molecules were surrounded with an atmosphere of caloric, equal in size only to those of oxygen gas, 100 cubic inches of nitrous air should weigh 98,535 grains ; whereas, according to Kirwan, their weight is but 37 grains.* Hence we may fairly conclude, that the molecules of nitrous gas are thrice the distance from each other that the ultimate particles of oxygen gas are, in the same temperature ; consequently we may infer, that their calorific atmospheres are in proportionable size ; or some other repelling fluid must interpose.

" Having thus considered the size of the repelling atmospheres of nitrous air, and also the attraction of the molecules of this air to oxygen, which is weaker than that of the ultimate particles of azote in their simple state, it is unaccountable with how much more facility the former unite to oxygen than the latter.

---

* Chemists do not agree as to the proportions of the constituents of this gas.

" The decomposition of nitrous gas
by the hydrogen of hepatic gas, is also
extraordinary, considering, as I already
observed, that the hydrogen is not in a
condensed state, and therefore very probably combined with its full portion of
caloric.

" Do atmospheres of equal density
favour the union of their respective molecules or particles ? Or, do dense and rare
atmospheres, by readily blending and suffering them to approach nearer, promote
their chemical union ? Or, does the electric fluid interfere ?

" From the foregoing considerations
it appears to me that the attractive forces
of bodies are not to be estimated by the
facility of uniting, but rather by the difficulty of disuniting them. I therefore beg
leave to differ from Mr. Kirwan in his
objections to Lavoisier's table of affinities, &c. . . . .

" When steam is passed over the surface of fused sulphur in an earthen tube,

5

so contrived as to exclude atmospheric air, hydrogen and sulphurous gases are produced, which shews that sulphur has stronger affinity than the hydrogen to the oxygenous principle, as had been first shewn by Dr. Priestley.*

" According to Mr. Kirwan, 100 grains of sulphur require 143 grains of oxygen gas to convert them into sulphurous acid : they require much more to become sulphuric acid. This acid, exclusive of water, consists of 2 parts of oxygen and 1 of sulphur, by weight.†

" One hundred and forty-three grains of oxygen gas contain 41 of water ; quicklime will abstract 26 grains from it, and the remainder of its water cannot be separated by similar means ; therefore 100 grains of sulphur require only 100 or 102 of the dry gravitating matter of oxygen gas to form sulphurous acid. As sulphurous acid gas is very little more than double

---

* Comp. View. page 33.   † Ibid. p. 36.

the specific gravity of oxygen gas, we may conclude that the ultimate particles of sulphur and oxygen contain the same quantity of matter; for oxygen gas suffers no considerable diminution of its bulk by uniting to the quantity of sulphur necessary for the formation of sulphurous acid. *It contracts $\frac{1}{11}$ as shall be shewn hereafter.*

" Hence we may conclude, that an atom of sulphurous acid consists of a single particle of oxygen and a single particle of sulphur, chemically united; and that every molecule of sulphuric acid contains one particle of sulphur and two of oxygen, being the proportions necessary to saturation (*definite proportion*).*

" As two cubic inches of hydrogen gas require but one cubic inch of oxygen gas to condense them to water, we may presume that they contain an equal number of divisions, and that the difference of the

---

* Comp. View, page 37.

specific gravity of those gases depends on the size of their respective particles; or we must suppose that an ultimate particle of hydrogen requires 2 or 3, or more particles of oxygen to saturate it. Were this the case, water, or its constituents, might be obtained in an intermediate state of combination, like those of sulphur and oxygen, or azote and oxygen, &c. This appears to be impossible; for in whatever proportion we mix hydrogen and oxygen gases, or under whatever circumstances we unite them, the result is invariably the same. *Water is formed, and the surplus of either of the gases is left behind unchanged.*

" When water is decomposed, or resolved into its constituent gases, by the *voltaic battery,* or by an electric machine, the above proportions are constantly obtained.

" From those circumstances we have sufficient reason to conclude, that water is composed of a single ultimate particle of oxygen and an ultimate particle of hydrogen, and that its atoms are incapable of uniting to a third particle of either of their constituents."

It will, I should suppose, be needless to tell my reader, that the foregoing facts, relative to sulphurous acid, sulphuric acid, and water, suggested the first effort of ascertaining the comparative weights of the particles of different elementary matter, and that the weight of the atoms and molecules which they produced, might readily be ascertained, those facts being once established. This part of my theory Mr. Dalton strictly attends to.

" The proportions of the elementary principles of water, sulphuric and sulphurous acids, being thus laid down, let us now attend to their various effects on different substances, according to the antiphlogistic doctrine. *The phenomena which they produce, or rather their chemical action on bodies, were enquired into, on the phlogistic principle, in a part of my Comparative View, preceding that from whence the following extract is taken.*

" It has been observed, that certain metals attract oxygen with greater force than sulphur does, and that the ultimate particles of sulphur have greater affinity to oxygen than those of hydrogen.* It has also been shewn, that sulphuric acid, mixed with water in certain proportion, will oxydize and dissolve metals with more facility than concentrated sulphuric acid, and that water alone will have very little effect on metals in a common temperature.

" Although these facts appear inconsistent when lightly considered, yet they may be accounted for on the following principles, and are, in my humble opinion, inexplicable by any other means whatever.

" Let us suppose iron or zinc to attract oxygen with the force of 7, sulphur to attract it with the force of $6\frac{7}{8}$, and hydrogen with the force of $6\frac{5}{8}$. Let us again

---

* Comp. View, page 38.

suppose these to be the utmost forces of attraction that can subsist between particle and particle of those substances.

" Stating the relative forces in the foregoing proportion, which I am led to believe is perfectly correct, from facts already adduced, and from many more which will hereafter appear, one would expect that metals should oxydize in water more readily than in concentrated sulphuric acid. This undoubtedly would have been the case if other circumstances had not interfered. The following will be a sufficient illustration.

$$S\text{————}6\tfrac{7}{8}\text{————}O$$

" Let S represent a particle of sulphur, and O a particle of oxygen, in the annexed diagram, which attract each other with the force of $6\tfrac{7}{8}$, and let the compound be considered an atom of sulphurous acid; the force of union subsisting between S and O is greater by $\tfrac{2}{8}$ than that of hydrogen and oxygen in an atom of water, being but $6\tfrac{5}{8}$.

" As the attraction of bodies is mutual, let us suppose S to possess one half of this quantum of affinity, which is $3\frac{7}{16}$, and O to possess the other half; the two particles must unite with the force represented in the diagram.*

" When a second particle of oxygen unites to the particle of sulphur, its quantum of attraction must be equally divided between both. This will reduce the attachment of sulphur and oxygen in the molecule of sulphuric acid, formed by this triple compound, to $5\frac{1}{13}$.

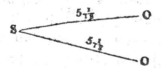

" *In order to more perfectly understand this part of the doctrine, which I consider to be the most important in the whole system that I advanced,* let S represent a particle

---

* Comp. View, page 39.

of sulphur, and O O two particles of oxygen united to it with the numerical forces annexed to them in the diagram. If one of the particles of oxygen were removed, S and O would remain united with the force of $6\frac{7}{8}$, and, when restored, this force would be diminished again to $5\frac{1}{15}$, and so alternately.* This seems to be a general law: all bodies unite with greater force to half the quantity of those substances to which they have an affinity, than to the entire. Instance, carbonate of potash will part with a portion of its carbonic acid in a moderate degree of heat, yet it requires a very intense heat to expel the whole. In like manner, crystallized sulphate of potash will part with most of its water in a heat below ignition, but it requires a strong red heat to drive away the entire of its water. Thus we find, in proportion as the potash is deprived of a part of its carbonic acid, its power of retaining the remainder is increased; and the same holds good as to the expulsion of water from the salt †

---

* Comp. View, p. 40.　　† Ibid. p. 41

" The internal structure of water and sulphuric acid being ascertained, what play of affinities must take place when iron or zinc is introduced into dilute sulphuric acid, may readily be conceived.

" The iron will attack the oxygen of the sulphuric acid with the force of 7, which resists only with the power of $5\frac{1}{18}$, in preference to the oxygen of the water, which is held by the hydrogen with the force of $6\frac{1}{2}$. We are not to suppose that the iron will only partially decompose the molecules of acid in contiguity with it, but that it will deprive the sulphur of the entire of its oxygen, more especially when it presents such a multiplicity of metallic particles in a small compass.*

" The sulphur being thus despoiled of its oxygen by a superior power, and still preserving its ultimate division, instantly exerts its whole force $6\frac{7}{8}$ on the

---

* Comp. View, page 42.

F

oxygen of the water, which it readily gains, meeting with the resistance only of 6⅕. Thus hydrogen is disengaged."

The principal object of the foregoing demonstrations was to ascertain that the hydrogen came from the water, and not from the metal, as was almost generally supposed at the time.

Lavoisier and his few followers imagined, that the sulphuric acid first united to the metal, and that the compound, demanding more oxygen, decomposed the water. This is the theory of modern chemists. I have proved the fallacy of this doctrine, as shall be stated presently.

" The phlogistians might object to this mode of accounting for the decomposition of water, by saying that sulphur cannot effect it in the temperature of the foregoing process. I will agree with them, when sulphur is in small aggregates, or molecules ; but it should be considered, that fused sulphur, as already observed, will decompose water when brought in contact with it, in the state of steam. This decomposition is effected by means of caloric, which removes the aggregate influence of the ultimate particles of sulphur. If the aggregate attraction should not interfere in a low temperature, which is the case during the rapid decomposition of the molecules of sulphuric acid by metals, the decomposition of water ought to take place the more readily.

" The ultimate particles of sulphur, on being deprived of their oxygen, cannot recover more of it from the water than what is sufficient to form sulphurous acid. This sulphurous acid unites instantly to the metallic oxide, and acts as a solvent."

These movements and arrangements of particles take place with inconceivable velocity.

" When iron is put in concentrated sulphuric acid, scarcely any effect is produced until heat is applied, which removes the aggregate influence of the molecules of the sulphuric acid, and diminishes that of the iron. During this process the iron is oxydized and partly dissolved ; sulphurous acid gas is evolved in great abundance, with little or no hydrogen.*

" When water is mixed with the sulphuric acid in sufficient quantity, it interposes itself between its sluggish molecules, and removes them beyond the sphere of their mutual influence : it answers the same purpose that caloric does; so that the solution goes on rapidly without the application of heat.

" The sulphurous acid gas that is produced by the action of concentrated sulphuric acid on iron, may be satisfactorily accounted for in the following manner :

" The first effort of the metallic particles deprives the molecules of sulphuric acid within their reach of the whole of their oxygen, and the particles of sulphur instantly exert the force of $6\frac{7}{8}$ on the

---

* Comp. View, page 43.

oxygen of the neighbouring molecules of sulphuric acid, which resist only with the force $5\frac{1}{18}$. As the particles of sulphur can take but one of oxygen from the molecule of sulphuric acid, two portions of sulphurous acid are formed.*

" The following demonstration will render this play of affinity between the particles perfectly clear. Let us suppose a particle of sulphur, recently deprived of its oxygen by the metal, and still possessed of the power of $6\frac{7}{8}$ to recover a portion of it, to be in sufficient contact with a molecule of sulphuric acid, will it not take one particle of oxygen from the sulphuric? And will not the compounds $s\underline{\quad 6\frac{7}{8}\quad}o$, and $s\underline{\quad 6\frac{7}{8}\quad}o$, which represent atoms of sulphurous acid, be formed? One portion will pass off in a gaseous state, and the other will unite to the metallic oxide.†

---

* Comp. View, p. 44.   † Ibid. p. 46.

" When sulphuric acid is so diluted with water as to afford only hydrogen, the atoms of water, by surrounding those of the acid, or rather by the intermixture of their more numerous surfaces, are exposed to the immediate action of the particles of sulphur the instant they are deprived of their oxygen by the metal : thus only one portion of sulphurous acid is formed, which unites with the oxide, while the hydrogen of the water is disengaged in a gaseous state.

" Agreeable to the foregoing explanation, a fresh made solution of iron in sulphuric acid should contain three portions of oxygen. The following fact will prove this to be the case.

" When potash in solution is poured into a solution of sulphate of iron, immediate decomposition takes place, sulphate of potash is formed, and the metal is disengaged of a darkish blue colour, united with one third the quantity of oxygen necessary to its perfect oxydation. The metal could not receive this oxygen, from the sulphuric acid being found united to the alkali in its perfect state, otherwise we should obtain a sulphite of potash. . . ."

*This decomposition, and also that which the solution of iron undergoes by long exposure to the oxygen of the atmosphere, have been demonstrated by means of diagrams, upon unerring mathematical principles, in continuation of the foregoing extract, in my " Comparative View."**

Its full quantum of influence has been given to every particle, distinct from each other. And I am certain that chemical philosophy will never reach its meridian splendour, except by means of such principles.

The maintainers of the phlogistic doctrine allowed that metals must part with their phlogiston (hydrogen) in order to become soluble in acids. As no hydrogen is given

---

* Comp. View, pages 47—49.

out when metals are dissolved in highly concentrated sulphuric acid, they insisted that
the sulphurous gas evolved contained the
phlogiston of the metal ; that is, this acid
gas is a compound of sulphuric acid and
hydrogen. The foregoing demonstrations
were intended to prove the fallacy of that
part of their doctrine. They were, however,
considered inadequate : more decisive experiments were necessary for the purpose.

It occurred to me, if sulphurous acid contained hydrogen, should it dissolve metals,
that a double quantity of hydrogen would
be obtained, (its own hydrogen and that of
the metal). The chemical properties of sulphurous acid were scarcely known at this
time.

The following experiment was of considerable importance, as it helped very materially to upset the phlogistic doctrine, and
to establish the new philosophy which I
adopted, in order to investigate the antiphlogistic system.

" I introduced some iron nails, free from rust, into strong sulphurous acid; in a few minutes it acquired a milky appearance, and the solution went on, *to my great astonishment*, without ebullition or extrication of gas, of any kind. On standing a few hours, the solution acquired a darkish colour, and cleared soon again by the deposition of a black powder. This powder, when collected and washed, burned on red hot iron like charcoal with a small quantity of sulphur."*

This acid is an excellent menstruum for analyzing iron or steel, for the whole of the carbon they contain is left behind in the solution, which is not the case when they are dissolved in other acids. The French chemists brought this forward as a new discovery of their own, seven years after my Comparative View had been published. As I have taken sufficient notice of this transaction in the preface to my Essay on Bleaching, together with the change which nitrous acid

---

* Comp. View, page 49.

*produces on blood, which Fourcroy assumed
to himself, it is needless to comment on the
subject here.*

" A neutralized solution of sulphite
of iron is quite clear, of a light greenish
colour, and free from any sulphurous
smell. When nitrous acid is dropped into
the solution, a cloudiness is produced,
which immediately disappears without
ebullition, although sulphurous acid is
disengaged, in its peculiar degree of pungency, which was not expected : on the
contrary, nitrous gas was looked for.*
The sulphuric, muriatic, and acetous acids,
decompose this solution, and no hydrogen
is disengaged.

" The prussiate of potash throws down
a white prussiate of iron, which, by exposure to the atmosphere, gradually acquires
a blue colour: this change is produced
instantaneously, when exposed to oxymuriatic gas."

---

* Comp. View, page 50.

I will pass over the various applications of those facts in the enquiry which engaged my attention at this remote period, and confine myself to the following extract :

" It may appear extraordinary that hydrogen is not produced during the solution of iron in sulphurous acid, whereas it is so copiously evolved by its solution in dilute sulphuric acid, which contains double the quantity of oxygen."[*]

Should the hydrogen be obtained by the decomposition of water, one would suppose that the sulphurous acid, which contains less oxygen by one half than the sulphuric acid, would effect it more readily. If the decomposition were occasioned by the compound resulting from the acid and iron, it would be the case.

" I confess I was much puzzled for a considerable time, before I could reconcile these seemingly clashing phenomena to my theory.[†] It appears to me that they

---

[*] Comp. View, p. 50.   [†] Ibid. p. 59.

are demonstrable in the following manner, and in no other way whatever.

" Let us suppose iron to attract oxygen with the force of 7, and sulphur, from the divided attachment of its particles to a double portion of oxygen, to retain it with the force of $5\frac{1}{18}$, as usual; let us also suppose iron, from the density of its texture, to present a greater number of ultimate particles in a given surface than the sulphuric acid, particularly the dilute acid, from the interposition of water.*

" From the foregoing statement of the relative forces of attraction subsisting between the particles of those substances, the following decomposition must take place. When dilute sulphuric acid and iron are exposed to each other's chemical influence, the martial particles will take the whole of their oxygen from the mole-

---

* Some diagrams are omitted here, which were considered unnecessary, therefore instead of referring to the letters of those diagrams which represented particles, I shall mention them by their proper names.

cules of the acid, or their particles of sulphur, in consequence of an attraction for iron, which is very small, comparatively to the opposite powers, will move along with their oxygen. This is not likely to take place; for the force of 7, exerted by the iron on the oxygen, separates it from the particles of sulphur with such celerity that the latter are left far behind, and being in contact with water, they exert their whole force on its oxygen.

" Therefore it is the superior force of the metal, and the proportional velocity of the motion of oxygen towards it, that leave the particles of sulphur so circumstanced as to enable them to decompose water in the manner already described."

It might appear strange to persons not intimately acquainted with chemical philosophy, that velocity and motion should be taken into consideration when bodies seem to be in contact with each other. The particles of the most solid substances are not in complete contact; and the atoms or molecules of fluids are still more remote from each other

Probably if the diameters of those divisions could be ascertained, the space they have to move through, in order to form a chemical union, would be very considerable.

We will now attend to the effect of sulphurous acid on iron, which places my doctrine on the decomposition of water beyond the smallest doubt.

" When sulphurous acid is poured on iron, although its particles attract the oxygen of this acid with the force of 7, yet it meets with the resistance of $6\frac{7}{8}$, as the diagram, which represents an atom of sulphurous acid, will shew.

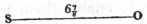

" The same superiority of force does not prevail here between the particle of sulphur and that of the iron for oxygen which evinces itself in the molecule of sulphuric acid.

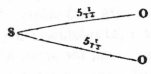

" Had there been a greater inequality of force between S and the particle of iron for oxygen, S from its intimate union to its oxygen O and a small degree of attraction to iron, would move with its oxygen towards the iron, and form the molecule of sulphite of iron already described.*

" The following diagram will help to render those affinities very clear.

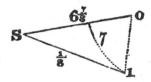

S represents a particle of sulphur, O its oxygen united with its usual force. I represents a particle of iron, figure 7 represents its force of affinity to oxygen, and the fraction $\frac{1}{8}$ represents its influence on the sulphur. This shews, although the particle of iron attracts the oxygen with the numerical force annexed

---

* Comp. View, page 60.

to it, that the sulphur is influenced with
the same force by the particles of iron and
oxygen conjointly, which is the power
of 7; therefore the oxygen and its sulphur
will move with equal speed, and unite to
the particle of iron. Hence it is that no
separation of the principles of the sulphurous atom takes place, that water is
not decomposed, and that no hydrogen
is produced.

" The foregoing facts and demonstrations, relating to the sulphuric and sulphurous acids, confirm each other, and
throw light upon many abstruse chemical
phenomena." *

*Still, however, it occurred to me, at this
time, that it was necessary to ascertain the
proportions of the principles of the sulphurous acid, more especially as it was considered
by eminent philosophers a compound of hydrogen and sulphuric acid. In order to this
I made the following experiments.*

---

* Comp. View, page 61.

" I mixed equal parts of sulphuretted hydrogen obtained from iron filings and sulphur, (previously exposed to heat sufficient to unite them,*) and oxygen gas produced from nitre. The sulphuretted hydrogen was absorbed by water to a very small bubble, and the oxygen contained but one tenth of azote.†

" Nine measures of this mixture (3 cubic inches) were reduced by the electric spark to $2\frac{1}{2}$; the nitrated solution of barytes condensed them to one twelfth of a measure, or somewhat less ; and the solution did not appear in the smallest degree turbid ; and no cloudiness was produced by the addition of lime water. The residuum left unabsorbed was too small to be examined ; the portion condensed by the solution seemed from the smell to be sulphurous acid. In order to be convinced

---

* The sulphuretted hydrogen is obtained from this compound by means of dilute sulphuric acid.

† Comp. View, pages 78—81.

G

of this, I inflamed another charge of the same mixture of gases, and transferred the residuary air to a clean tube, which the sulphur, deposited on the sides of the inflaming jar, obliged me to do. To this residuum an equal bulk of sulphuretted hydrogen was added, which instantly rendered it turbid, and reduced it to about one third.

" This assured me that the gas was sulphurous acid, and also that this acid will not decompose nitrate of barytes.

" These experiments not only prove the constituent principles of sulphuretted hydrogen, but absolutely prove what I have advanced respecting the proportion of the elementary particles of sulphurous acid.

" It has been shewn by Dr. Austin, that hydrogen gas suffers no diminution or increase of its volume by the union of sulphur; therefore one half of the mixed airs was hydrogen independent of its sulphur, that is, $4\frac{1}{2}$ of hydrogen gas. These $4\frac{1}{2}$ measures require $2\frac{1}{4}$ of oxygen gas to condense them into water. $2\frac{1}{4}$ more of oxygen were expended in the experiment, two of which must exist in the sulphurous acid; and, as much of the azote disappeared, we may conclude that the remainder of the oxygen ($\frac{1}{4}$ of a measure) was expended in the formation of nitrous acid.

" From the foregoing facts it is evident, that the two measures of sulphurous gas contain two measures of oxygen; and as the specific gravity of sulphurous gas is double that of its constituents, excluding the hydrogen, we may infer that only the sulphur of two measures united to the oxygen gas, and that the sulphur of $2\frac{1}{2}$ measures was precipitated.*

" We may also infer from these data, that the atoms of sulphurous gas are sur-

---

* Comp. View, page 81.

rounded with as large atmospheres of caloric as the particles of oxygen gas, or
that they are as far asunder; and that the
number of the ultimate particles of sulphur in sulphuretted hydrogen are to those
of the hydrogen as 9 to 5." *According to
the experiment, they are as* 18 *to* 9. *Further experiments must correct inaccuracies.
These will soon follow.*

*This was the first experiment of the kind
made, and, had there been no other evidence
brought forward, ought to be sufficient for
the purpose, as it establishes three important
facts which comprehend the whole of what
has been unjustly called Dalton's Theory.*
1. *The proportion of the constituents of an
atom of sulphurous gas, and the relative
weight of those elementary principles.* 2.
*The weight of the atom, and comparative
diameter of its calorific atmosphere. And
lastly, The proportion of the ultimate particles of hydrogen, and of sulphur, in sulphuretted hydrogen gas.*

The following experiments were made since I commenced writing this essay. They will confirm what I originally advanced respecting the quantity of oxygen and sulphur in sulphurous acid.

I introduced a small bit of brimstone into a glass tube 37 inches long, previously filled with quicksilver and inverted in the same fluid : it was curved at the sealed end, in order to separate the brimstone from the surface of the mercury. The brimstone was partially fused in the vacuum, to make it stick to the glass when cold. Five cubic inches of oxygen gas were then thrown up ; the sulphur was melted by the flame of a spirit lamp, and when sufficiently heated, a flash was produced with a slight concussion of the apparatus. Upon increasing the heat, a second flash took place with a blue flame : no further effect could be produced. On suffering the apparatus to cool, and restoring the pressure of the atmosphere, by an inclination of the tube, evident contraction appeared : when water was introduced the diminution was very considerable.

These appearances induced me to change my apparatus, and make more accurate trials. A small quantity of sulphur was introduced into a glass tube a foot long, curved as the former; the sulphur was made to adhere to its extremity by fusion; when cold, it was filled with mercury, and a cubic inch of oxygen gas was thrown up; and the space, occupied by the gas in the measure used, was accurately divided into twelve equal parts.

When sufficient heat was applied, the combustion of a portion of the sulphur was effected with a sudden flash, accompanied with a considerable concussion, similar to what takes place when oxygen and hydrogen are fired by the electric spark. In about a minute after, a second explosion took place, and a languid blue flame appeared on the surface of the fused sulphur, which lasted a few seconds. No further change was produced by a continuation of the heat, although the end of the tube, where the sulphur was placed, was made obscurely red.

When the apparatus cooled to the temperature of the air of the elaboratory, the gas was transferred to the cubic inch measure ; the contraction appeared nearly $\frac{1}{11}$. When water was sent up to condense the sulphurous gas, one part remained unabsorbed, which was found to be oxygen gas.

If the whole of the oxygen had united to sulphur, the contraction, upon the most accurate calculation, would have been $\frac{1}{11}$. The experiment was repeated with similar result.

It is impossible to convert the whole of the oxygen into sulphurous acid, in these experiments, from the interference of the acid gas formed, which excludes a portion of the oxygen from contact with the sulphur.

When the oxygen gas was increased so as to have nearly a cubic inch of it expended, the contraction was invariably $\frac{1}{11}$.

The foregoing fact being ascertained, the results of the following experiments can readily be accounted for.

Five measures of a mixture of 23 of oxygen gas and 10 of sulphuretted hydrogen, were fired by the electric spark, and reduced to $2\frac{1}{4}$; no sulphur was left, and a residuum of oxygen gas remained when the sulphurous gas was condensed by water. Sulphuric acid was formed in this experiment.

When the oxygen gas was reduced to 21 parts, and 10 of sulphuretted hydrogen, sulphuric acid was also formed, but in less quantity than in the last experiment, and some oxygen was left.

In one experiment 2 cubic inches of oxygen and 1 of sulphuretted hydrogen (in all 30 measures) were fired, and reduced to 13 measures, and no oxygen remained;

5

about $\frac{1}{75}$ of azote was the only residuum.

This last experiment was repeated with gases carefully made; the sulphur was completely consumed, and 4 measures of oxygen gas were left. Several trials gave the same result.

These experiments led to the proportion of the gases sufficient to saturate each other, which was the principal object.

A mixture of 16 of oxygen gas and 10 of sulphuretted hydrogen was prepared; of this $6\frac{1}{3}$ measures were fired, and reduced to $2\frac{2}{3}$; no oxygen was left. When water was introduced, the sulphurous gas was condensed, and a very small bubble remained, which must be azote: by the test of muriate of barytes a very slight vestige of sulphuric acid appeared.

In this experiment 5 parts of the oxygen must have been expended in condensing the hydrogen into water; 11 parts more must go to the sulphur, in order to produce sulphurous gas : making an allowance for contraction and for azote, the whole of the oxygen is thus accounted for.

The following experiment was made with a view to ascertain, whether the last proportions of the gases were sufficient to saturate each other.

A mixture of 15 of oxygen and 10 of sulphuretted hydrogen were fired ; a small portion of sulphur was deposited, and the sulphurous gas measured little more than 9 ; muriate of barytes shewed a slight appearance of sulphuric acid : there was a small bubble of azote left as usual.

The gases used in these experiments were dried by means of fused muriate of lime, and they were examined under the same pressure of mercury before and after their union.

The foregoing facts prove that 10 measures of sulphurous gas contain 11 measures of oxygen gas, and as the specific gravity of this compound gas, making an allowance for the contraction of the oxygen on uniting to sulphur, is but twice that of its constituents, it is evident that a particle of sulphur contains the same quantity of solid matter which a particle of oxygen does, and that a sulphurous atom consists of a single particle of oxygen and a single particle of sulphur.

Should sulphurous gas, according to Mr. Dalton, contain two portions of oxygen and one of sulphur, considering that there is no expansion produced by the union, it would be more than one third heavier. But whence could this second portion of oxygen come? For, the whole of the oxygen expended in my experiments has been accurately accounted for.

Besides, the quantity of sulphurous acid, which a given measure of oxygen is capable of producing, puts the question beyond a doubt; and also confirms the inference drawn from the first experiments, which 1 made *twenty-three years ago* on

this subject, " that the proportion of ultimate particles of sulphur in hepatic gas
is to those of the hydrogen as 2 to 1
nearly."*

As sulphurous gas and sulphuretted
hydrogen gas, when mixed, decompose
each other, in the common temperature
of the atmosphere, water being formed
and sulphur deposited, I was anxious to
know the exact proportion in which these
gases condense each other. After a few
trials I found the following proportions to
answer.

22,50 measures were passed into a
graduated glass tube filled with quicksilver ; 28 measures of sulphuretted hydrogen were introduced : the whole of the

---

* Mr. Dalton supposes that this gas consists of 3 of
hydrogen and 1 of sulphur. In this he corrects himself in
the second part of his work, and considers the gas to consist
of 1 of hydrogen and 1 of sulphur. This amendment is
equally incorrect, so that he falls from one error into
another.

gases was reduced to one measure, and the part of the jar, in which the condensation took place, was lined with sulphur.

I did not expect that the sulphuretted hydrogen would decompose such a quantity of sulphurous gas; for the 22,50 measures, allowing for contraction, contained 24,50 of oxygen nearly; 14 of this quantity was sufficient to convert 28 measures of hydrogen into water. The remaining 10,50 must have been carried down, in the state of sulphurous acid, with the precipitated sulphur of both gases.

Mr. Dalton and many more chemists suppose, that there is an oxide of sulphur formed in this process, which consists of a particle of sulphur and one of oxygen.

This cannot be the case; for I have proved that sulphurous acid consists of these proportions. It is more probable that the sulphurous atoms are somehow or other influenced by a portion of the particles of the sulphur, at the moment of their liberation, in the same way that sulphurous acid is condensed by the sulphuric, without a decomposition of their respective atoms and molecules ; instance the glacial oil of vitriol of the ancient chemists, which is obtained from sulphate of iron by a strong heat. However, this can only be ascertained by experiments.

A portion of the sulphur deposited from the gases was collected from the glass jar, as free from globules of mercury as possible. It was then pressed and kneaded between the fingers, in order to force out any remaining quicksilver : by this mechanical process the mass acquired a considerable degree of cohesion and elasticity, had a strong acid taste, and the smell of sulphurous acid, although it was formed with an excess of sulphuretted hydrogen. By continuing the process, it became softer and more pliable, and the acid taste and smell were scarcely perceptible, and in a short time vanished altogether.

While working it up, I dipped my fingers at intervals in a small glass of distilled water, in order to collect the acid pressed out, and they were perfectly dried each time before the operation was resumed. On examining the water, it was found to contain sulphuric acid.* Neither cold nor warm water had any effect on this substance; but, when boiling water was poured on it, the cohesion of its parts was destroyed, and the water exhibited a milky appearance : the solution was evaporated to dryness, and a small quantity of distilled water was added; when filtered,

---

* This fact proves that the sulphuric acid is formed t the moment of the condensation of the gases, and that w? .er is not necessary to its formation, as Dr. Thomson and M. Dalton supposed. By what play of affinities it is produced I know not, unless it be the following. The ultimate particle of sulphur, the instant it is set free in the gases, exerts its aggregate influence on the particle of sulphur of its neighbouring atom of sulphurous acid, while the oxygen of this atom passes over to another atom of sulphurous acid in its vicinity, so as to constitute a molecule of sulphuric acid. This double influence might produce the effect. The small quantity of sulphurous acid, which appeared, might be carried down mechanically by the sulphur and sulphuric acid.

muriate of barytes produced a very slight
cloudiness, which shewed that the whole
of the acid was not removed by pressure.
What remained on the filter was sulphur
mixed with some black matter. Potash,
by means of heat, dissolved the whole of
the sulphur which this substance contained, and left a black powder behind,
which burned on red hot iron like charcoal, without the smallest appearance of
sulphur. Carbonate of potash seemed to
have very little action on it ; for the small
piece, exposed to it in a very moderate
degree of heat, retained its shape and
bulk, but readily crumbled between the
fingers into a black powder, consisting,
apparently, of carbon and some sulphur.*
Alkohol produced no change, and ether
had no effect on this substance.

Presented to the flame of a candle, it
burned somewhat better than sulphur,

---

* These are to be considered the properties of the gummy
substance, when produced in its perfectly elastic state and
deprived of the acid.

and nearly its bulk of a very porous and light black substance remained. This black matter I suspected to be carbon.

A portion of this black powder was introduced into a curved tube filled with oxygen, and inverted in quicksilver. The carbon was confined to the curved part. When it was sufficiently heated by the flame of a spirit lamp, it burned with very brilliant scintillations, and no residuum was left. Lime water was thrown up as soon as the apparatus cooled, which became turbid in a few minutes. These facts assured me that this black substance was pure carbon. To perfect the combustion of the carbon in oxygen, it must be previously freed of the whole of the sulphur by heat, which should be gentle at first, to avoid the joint combustion of the carbon and sulphur: when the latter is nearly expelled, the heat may be raised to any degree that will not promote the combustion of the carbon.

To ascertain the quantity of charcoal in this gummy substance, I exposed three grains of it, on a watch glass, to a moderate heat, and although it parted with a small quantity of sulphur, its elastic property was very little impaired.

When the heat was increased by the flame of a spirit lamp, it ignited, and the remaining sulphur burned with a blue languid flame with a few scintillating sparks. As soon as the combustion of the sulphur ceased, the black matter remaining was considerably heated, in order to expel the whole of the sulphur. It weighed half a grain.

It is probable from the foregoing facts, that this kind of elastic gum consists of hydrogen, carbon, and oxygen. It is extremely difficult to ascertain whether sulphur is necessary to its constitution. As the pure sulphur deposited from the gases incorporates with it when worked up together, we have reason to suppose that the union of most of the sulphur is somewhat mechanical.

To ascertain as nearly as possible the quantity of sulphur produced by the gases, and to obtain it free from mercury, a stratum of water was sent up in a jar filled with quicksilver; 7,6 cubic inches of sulphurous acid were then passed up, and 10,8 of sulphuretted hydrogen. Almost the whole of the sulphur remained suspended, and passed through a filter. The liquor was evaporated to dryness, in a gentle heat; sulphur and a very small quantity of sulphuric acid were left. The weight of the sulphur could not be ascertained, as it contained some minute globules of mercury.

The experiment was repeated, with the difference of employing ether instead of water. The sulphuretted hydrogen was first sent up; it was readily condensed by the ether without any degree of turbidness whatever.* The sulphurous gas, in the

---

* Ether unites to 7 times its bulk of sulphuretted hydrogen gas without any apparent change. This hydro-sulphuretted ether might be found of some use when its properties are fully ascertained.

H 2

proportion last mentioned, was introduced: the sulphur fell down in the ether, in small flocks; when it had stood for a few hours, the ether became nearly clear, and the sulphur rested on the surface of the mercury. Atmospheric air was suffered to pass into the jar in sufficient quantity to displace the whole of the quicksilver; the sulphur was separated by means of filtration, and the ether passed through quite limpid; but, when partly evaporated in a moderate heat, it became milky. When the whole of the ether was evaporated, a very minute quantity of sulphuric acid and sulphur, of a dark colour, were left behind, the weight of which could not be ascertained.

The sulphur, which the ether left on the filter, was washed with distilled water. When this water was evaporated, no residuum remained. When the sulphur was dried, it weighed 10 grains. It was exposed to a sufficient heat to volatilize the whole of it, except a small quantity of charcoal.

The foregoing experiment was repeated, and water was used to depress the quick-silver, in order to obtain the ether and sulphur free from mercurial globules, which is almost impossible. The liquid was evaporated to dryness, and then exposed to heat sufficient to expel the sulphur; a dark brown residuum remained, which formed a kind of varnish on the bottom of the saucer, in which the experiment was made. The heat applied to produce this effect was about 700° of Fahrenheit. When a small portion of this varnish was collected, it burned with some difficulty on red hot iron, and a minute quantity of grey ashes was left.

Some ether was passed up into a tube filled with mercury; about thirty times its bulk of sulphurous gas was afterwards introduced; the whole was absorbed, yet the ether was not sufficiently saturated with it; sulphuretted hydrogen was then sent up in as small quantity as possible at a time: some sulphur was deposited on the surface of the sulphurous ether, which, in descending in streaks through the liquid, was re-dissolved.* When one third or thereabout of the sulphurous acid was thus saturated, water was introduced ; the ether and sulphur rested on the surface of the column of water. When the two fluids were mixed, a portion of the sulphur disappeared. When the liquid was evaporated, sulphurous acid was expelled, and sulphur and carbonic matter remained behind, with a small portion of sulphuric acid.

In order to ascertain whether the sulphur, the moment it was disengaged from the hydrogen, had been dissolved by the sulphurous acid or ether, water was substituted for the latter, and no evident re-dissolution appeared. It is therefore probable that the two former fluids co-operate in producing the effect.

---

* The quantity of sulphur thus dissolved is barely perceptible.

The following experiment was made, to ascertain the quantity of sulphur deposited by a certain portion of the two gases, and also to ascertain the quantity of carbon.

7,6 cubic inches of sulphurous gas, and 10,8 of sulphuretted hydrogen, were mixed over quicksilver; after the condensation was effected, the sulphur was carefully collected; very dilute nitrous acid was poured on it to dissolve some small globules of quicksilver which adhered to it; when it stood for two days, the quicksilver was taken up. The sulphur was collected and washed, and when perfectly dry weighed 7¼ grains. It was exposed to heat sufficient to expel the whole of the sulphur; half a grain of charcoal remained.

As the quantity of sulphur obtained in this experiment was less than could be expected, some of it must have been oxydized by the nitrous acid. The quantity of sulphur obtained (10 grains) in a former experiment, from 18,4 cubic inches of the gases, is the nearest approximation to the real portion which they contain, as may be deduced from the additional weight, which oxygen and hydrogen acquire by their union to sulphur.

It is remarkable that the gummy matter is never formed when water or ether is used, although charcoal and sulphuric acid are constantly produced, unless we except the experiment, in which a varnish was formed. In the latter I succeeded but once, although the experiment was repeated. Probably the large quantity of ether, which was used in this experiment, contributed to the effect, by affording an additional quantity of carbon and hydrogen; for the portion of ether used was not attended to with any degree of accuracy, being considered of very little consequence.

The object of my enquiry was to ascertain whether a compound of the fixed oxide of sulphur existed. And my experiments tend to prove *that there is no such substance.**

---

* A glass jar, fitted with a brass cap and stop cock, was filled with quicksilver; about sixteen ounce measures of sulphuretted hydrogen were then passed up, and transferred into an exhausted glass globe of the same capacity. The glass jar was then filled with sulphurous acid gas; a communication being formed by means of the stop-cocks, the latter gas was gradually pressed up into the globe. A rapid condensation of the gases took place, and the quicksilver ascended so as to fill the jar. The whole of the inside of the globe was encrusted with sulphur, of a deep lemon colour, and, when collected, exhibited a crystalline appearance in very minute and brilliant spiculæ. The globe was considerably heated by the union of the gases, but not so much as one would expect from the condensation of such a large quantity, which shews that these gases contain very little caloric, notwithstanding the size of their respective atmospheres.

A portion of this sulphur was examined for carbon, in the manner already described, and the quantity obtained was nearly equal to that found in former trials.

When hot distilled water was poured on some of the sulphur, it became milky, and a strong smell of sulphurous acid was produced. This milky liquor, being separated from the sulphur, and evaporated to dryness, left a small residuum of sulphuric acid and carbon, and the washed sulphur also gave carbon. This experiment proves that none of the carbon, or black matter, comes from the mercury.

A large quantity of sulphuric acid was mixed with sulphur. This mixture was exposed in a glass cup to sufficient heat to fuse the sulphur, and to evaporate a great part of it and the whole of the sulphuric acid. No sulphurous acid was produced, and the remaining sulphur was not changed in the smallest degree.

I exposed fused sulphur to sulphurous acid in a glass tube over mercury for a considerable time, and no change whatever was produced in the gas or sulphur.

Now, were it possible to produce an oxide of sulphur, it ought to have been formed in the last two experiments, particularly by the sulphuric acid, as containing, according to Mr. Dalton's proportions, 1 of sulphur and 3 of oxygen, proportions different from the estimate, which I advanced in my "Comparative View," and which is founded on unerring principles. It is upon that account I have dwelt so much upon this subject.

The carbon obtained in the foregoing experiments must come from the sulphuretted hydrogen, and this gas received it from the sulphuret of iron, the substance, together with sulphuric acid, which produced it; yet the whole of the sulphuretted hydrogen was condensed by water, and no residuum of carbonated hydrogen remained.

I was anxious to produce this gas from iron free from carbon, but I found by my excellent test, (the sulphurous acid) that all kinds of iron contain more or less of it, except native meteoric iron: of this I had not a sufficient quantity. I attempted to reduce pure oxide of iron to its metallic state in hydrogen gas, by means of a lens; but the sun was not sufficiently powerful at this season of the year (December) to produce the desired effect.*

---

* When I used sulphuretted hydrogen obtained from the sulphuret of potash, no carbon was produced.

I could not conceive the cause of the dark colour of the sulphur precipitated, when equal measures of sulphuretted hydrogen and oxygen were fired, until I discovered the presence of carbon in the gummy matter already described ; and in proportion as the quantity of oxygen was increased, the colour of the sulphur was still darker, because the whole of the carbon was deposited, and less sulphur. From what we know of chemical affinities, the carbon should first unite to the oxygen, the sulphur next, and the hydrogen last of all ; yet this, strange as it may appear, is not the case, for the very reverse takes place in this experiment.

But what is still more singular, when a mixture of sulphuretted hydrogen and oxygen, in a small excess of the latter, was fired, the carbon was deposited and appeared in very minute divisions on the surface of the quicksilver ; lime water was thrown up,which condensed the sulphurous acid ; no degree of turbidness appeared, and a small residuum of oxygen was left ; therefore no carbonic acid was formed.

This subject deserves more attention than I can bestow on it at present.

Nitre and nitrous acid helped very much to prove, during my researches, the fallacy of the phlogistic doctrine, and also to establish the atomic system. My first object was to ascertain the quantity of azote and oxygen, that existed in this acid. This was accomplished in a variety of ways, but particularly by resolving those principles into gases, which is readily effected when nitrate of potash is exposed to a strong heat. As the gases are obtained mixed in various proportions at different stages of the process, the whole of the product was received in one mixed volume, and carefully examined.* The proportions were 1 of azote and 5 of oxygen. Lavoisier, at the same time, estimated the proportions as 1 to 4. If his inference rested on the decomposition of the pale nitrous acid, he must have been correct.

---

* Comp. View, p. 83.

The quantity of oxygen contained in nitre being once ascertained, its expenditure could readily be accounted for, when metals, charcoal, or sulphur, decomposed this salt by means of heat, as the oxides or acids produced must contain the whole of the oxygen, or else some of it must be expended in uniting with the hydrogen or supposed phlogiston of those inflammable bodies so as to form water.

I shall not now detail the great variety of experiments made for this purpose. I will only attend to that part, which more immediately relates to the atomic doctrine.

. . . . "Thus two parts of nitre and one of sulphur will detonate, when exposed to sufficient heat, at the same time that the whole of the acid is decomposed.* Sulphur will not unite to more oxygen, in the degree of heat necessary to conduct this process, than is suffi-

* Comp. View, pages 121, 122.

cient to convert it into sulphurous acid ; or, if it even should, its attraction is not strong enough to take any more of it from the nitre, as has been shewn in the third section of this work. Therefore we obtain from the above proportions sulphurous acid gas, oxygen gas, and azotic gas ; there is also some sulphur sublimed at the commencement of the process.

" When one part of sulphur, and four of nitre, are used, the products are quite different; for the quantity of sulphur being very small, it presents but a few surfaces to the nitre, so that it can only take the portion of oxygen from it, which is over and above the quantity contained in nitrous gas: the nitrous gas, being thus deprived of its oxygen, can no longer be retained by the alkali. The reason no deflagration takes place in this experiment is, the atoms of sulphur being few, relatively to the molecules of nitre, and so separated by their interposition, the quantity of caloric disengaged by the more intimate union of the oxygen of the nitre to the sulphur is insensibly dissipated; that is, it is not liberated in a sufficient degree of accumulation to present the phenomenon of combustion. The reverse of the foregoing takes place, when a larger quantity of sulphur is used; for in this case, the atoms of sulphur being more numerous, and of course closer to each other, caloric is disengaged in a more concentrated state, at the same time that the whole, nearly, of the oxygen of the nitre is taken up.*

" In order to deprive the nitre of all its oxygen, it is necessary to use sulphur in excess. First, because an ultimate particle of sulphur can only take a particle of oxygen from the nitre. 2. As every molecule of nitre contains, most commonly, four ultimate particles of oxygen and one of azote, which, forming little aggregates, and being enveloped by water of crystallisation, and

---

* Comp. View, page 123.

the alkali, are in a great measure defended from the action of the sulphur.*

" Therefore, as the nitre cannot be divided so ultimately as sulphur, if only that quantity of the latter be mixed with nitre, which will expose only surfaces sufficient to deprive its molecules of one half of their oxygen, nitrous gas is evolved ; but if, on the contrary, a sufficiency of sulphur be used to deprive the molecules of nitre of $\frac{3}{4}$, or thereabout, of their oxygen, we obtain azotic, sulphurous, and oxygen gases.

" Charcoal detonates with nitre in various proportions, but in no proportion will it disengage nitrous gas.

---

* The weight of the nitric acid molecule, united to an atom of potash, can readily be deduced from the weight of its constituent gases, when perfectly dry ; but the weight of the compound molecule of the salt described above cannot, in my opinion, be ascertained, in consequence of the interference of doubtful quantities of water.   Mr. Dalton has attempted to ascertain the weight of the molecules of many saline substances.

" Charcoal and nitre, distilled in many proportions, will afford azotic gas, and carbonic acid gas, and no nitrous gas whatever. I would ask the phlogistians, &c. . . . .*

" Charcoal not only unites to a larger quantity of oxygen than sulphur does, in order to become sulphurous acid, but it also attracts the portion necessary to its conversion to carbonic acid with greater force.† Thus it is, that charcoal, mixed with nitre in a very small proportion, will detonate, and that azotic gas and carbonic gas are produced. Every single molecule of charcoal (for we cannot reduce it to its ultimate particles by attrition) is capable of depriving a single molecule of nitre of the whole of its oxygen; this decomposition is so rapid that the molecule of charcoal directs the whole force of its attraction towards the molecule of

---

* Comp. View, p. 125.

† At this early period I was aware that a molecule of carbonic acid consisted of 1 particle of carbon and 2 of oxygen.

nitre, which first influences it; otherwise the charcoal would take a portion of oxygen from different nitrous molecules at the same time, so as to disengage nitrous gas."*

I will pass over several experiments made on different metallic filings and nitre. As they were intended to prove the non-existence of hydrogen in those substances, they could not be interesting at present.†

I shall adduce one of many experiments made on arsenic, as it, in some measure, relates to the principal object of this work:

" When regulus of arsenic, and nitre in powder, are mixed, and projected into

---

* This passage proves that I considered the molecules of this salt distinct and independent of each other; and of course, the idea extended to all saline bodies; for what holds good in one, must relate to the whole tribe. Mr. Dalton may weigh those molecules, but he must allow that they were first *identified* by me.

† Comp. View, page 128.

a red hot crucible, a rapid deflagration
ensues; the nitric acid is completely decomposed, and of course no nitrous gas is
produced.

" When the oxide is treated in the
same way, the nitric acid of the nitre is
only partially decomposed ; for nitrous
is evolved, and no deflagration takes gas
place.

" The regulus of arsenic having greater
attraction to oxygen, and being capable
of uniting to more of it than its oxide,
which is already half saturated with it,
wholly decomposes the nitrous acid of the
nitre ; and, as a great number of the
particles of oxygen accumulate with such
rapidity in a given time and space, the
phenomenon of combustion is produced.*

" The reverse of this takes place, in a
great measure, when the oxide is used
instead of the regulus ; for it can only

---

* Comp. View, p. 129.

take a certain portion of oxygen from the nitre, and it attracts this quantity with less force than that which is barely necessary to its calcination, (*to its first stage of oxydation.**)

As no hydrogen is produced during the solution of metals in nitrous or nitric acid, the nitrous gas evolved was supposed to contain it. This induced me to make the experiment with the oxide of arsenic, which, although it could impart no inflammable principle, produced nitrous gas.

Nitric acid was known to consist of azote and oxygen some time before I wrote my Comparative View, and the volumes of the gases, which compose it, were ascertained by Lavoisier and myself; but its internal structure or disposition, or arrangement of its particles, was totally unknown until I had

---

* The different degrees of the oxydation of metals were as well known to me at this period as those of other inflammable substances; but there was no nomenclature to designate them.

written on the subject. It is somewhat singular that no chemical writer has ever glanced at this circumstance, although it is twenty-four years since I published my book. This appears still the more extraordinary, as this kind of anatomy exhibited the most leading features of the atomic theory and definite proportions. Posterity, no doubt, will be surprized at this oversight, and will do my efforts that justice, which my cotemporaries have withheld. Here follows the extract on this subject, without any material alteration whatever.

" Having treated on the decomposition of nitre, let us now attend to the nature of nitrous acid in its simple state.* To account for the variety of changes, which this acid is capable of undergoing by the mediation of different inflammable substances, it will be necessary to be acquainted with the force, by which its constituent principles are united.

---

* Comp. View, pages 132-3.

" In my opinion, the most perfect nitrous acid contains 5 of oxygen and 1 of azote. Nitrous gas, according to Kirwan, contains 2 volumes of oxygen gas, and 1 of azotic gas. According to Lavoisier, 100 grains of nitrous gas contain 32 grains of azote and 68 of oxygen. I am of the former philosopher's opinion. I also am of opinion, that every primary particle of azote is united to 2 of oxygen, and that the molecule, thus formed, is surrounded with one common atmosphere of caloric.

" As this requires demonstration, let A in the annexed diagram represent an ultimate particle of azote, which attracts

$$A \overset{3}{\underline{\hspace{1cm}} \overset{6}{\hspace{1cm}} \overset{3}{\underline{\hspace{1cm}}}} a$$

oxygen with the force of 3 ; let a be a particle of oxygen, whose attraction to A we will suppose to be 3 more ; hence they will unite with the force of 6 : the nature of this compound will be hereafter explained. Let us consider this to be the

utmost force of attraction, that can subsist between oxygen and azote.

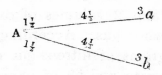

" We will now suppose a second particle of oxygen *b* to combine with A,
they will only unite with the force of $4\frac{1}{2}$;
that is, the whole quantum of the attractive power of A, which is but 3, will be
equally divided, and directed in two
points towards *a* and *b*; so that A and
a b will unite with the forces annexed to
them in the diagram: *a* and *b* having
no influence on each other, will suffer no
diminution of their respective attractions
for A. This I consider to be the real
structure of a molecule of nitrous gas.

" Let a third particle of oxygen *c*
unite to A, it will combine only with the
force of 4. This is the state of the molecules of the red nitrous vapour, or, when

condensed, the red nitrous acid. The diagram represents this molecule.*

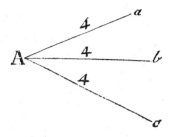

" We will suppose a fourth particle of oxygen *d* to combine with A; it will unite with the force of $3\frac{3}{4}$, and so on, with the rest of the particles of oxygen, as the diagram represents. This I consider to be the state of a molecule of the pale or straw-coloured nitrous acid.

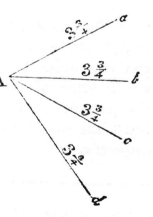

---

* Comp. View, page 134.

" When a fifth particle of oxygen *e* unites, the force of union existing between the particles of the molecule are still diminished, as is represented by the diagram. The fractions shew that the chemical attraction of azote for oxygen is nearly exhausted.

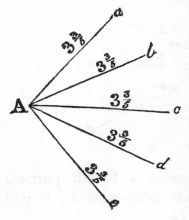

" This is the state of colourless nitrous acid;* and, in my opinion, no more oxygen can unite to the azote, having its whole force of attraction expended on the particles *a, b, c, d, e.*† This illustrates the nature of saturation, or *definite proportions.*

---

* Since my book was written, this acid has been distinguished by the name *nitric acid.*

† Comp. View, page 135.

" We can readily perceive from the foregoing demonstrations, that oxygen is retained with less force in the colourless nitrous acid than in the straw-coloured; and the latter acid retains it with less force than the red nitrous acid; and nitrous gas holds it still with more force than the red nitrous acid. This accounts for the separation of oxygen gas from the colourless nitrous acid, (nitric acid) when exposed to the sun, at the same time that the acid becomes coloured. Nitrous acid, in any other state, will afford no oxygen when exposed to the sun."*

---

* Although oxygen can be separated from nitric acid very readily, and with little force, yet it would require the chemical power of about 16 to take the azote from its oxygen, so as to set the latter free in its gaseous state. We are not acquainted with any substance in nature, that has one third the force of this affinity to azote. The same law holds good with respect to carbonic acid and water, &c. No affinity to their inflammable base can set free their oxygen. This kind of separation is only effected by electricity and the de-oxydizing rays, or by the living power of growing vegetables, probably with the assistance of these imponderable elements.

The molecules, described above, being surrounded with atmospheres of caloric, are perfectly distinct and independent of each other, in their respective acids.

" The different acids will mix mechanically, in the following order, without disturbing or decomposing each other's molecules. 1. Red nitrous acid will mix with the pale, or straw-coloured, and the mixture acquires a light orange colour. 2. The pale mixes with the nitric, and imparts a slight shade of a yellow colour to it.*

" When the red nitrous acid is mixed with the nitric acid, the former takes one portion of oxygen from the latter, and the straw-coloured acid is produced; that is, new molecules, containing four particles of oxygen, are formed.

" Nitrous gas will not decompose the red acid, on the same principle that the

---

* Comp. View, page 136.

latter will not decompose the pale; for the third particle of oxygen is retained by the acid molecules, with as great force as those of the gas attracts it. Nitrous gas will deprive the pale of one portion of its oxygen, and red nitrous acid is formed. Nitrous gas will also decompose the nitric, and a mixture of the molecules of the red and pale acids will be formed.

" Having premised thus much on the different states of nitrous acid, I shall now proceed to its decomposition.

" If a metal be introduced into the red, pale, or colourless nitrous acid, it will be calcined, and nitrous gas will be extricated; that is, the metal will deprive the nitrous gas of the portion of oxygen necessary to the formation of the acid. The metal deprives the molecules of acid, within its immediate influence, of the whole of their oxygen. The force of 7, with which we have supposed metals to attract oxygen, being so much superior to $3\frac{3}{5}$, if we make use of the nitric, or $3\frac{3}{4}$, if we use the pale nitrous acid, together with the number of ultimate surfaces a metal must present, deprives the azote of its oxygen with such rapidity, that it is at once left destitute of both caloric and oxygen : but before it has time to collect an atmosphere of caloric, which would prevent a second union, it exerts the force of 3 on its neighbouring molecule of acid, which had not reached the metallic influence, and recovers that portion of oxygen necessary to the formation of nitrous gas. This again, in passing in the acid, if it be the pale or nitric acid, will receive sufficiency of oxygen to form red nitrous acid.* Hence it is, when first a metal is introduced into the pale or nitric acid, though solution goes on, that little or no nitrous gas is evolved until the acid becomes coloured. As the metallic oxide formed requires red nitrous acid to hold it in solution, (for nitric acid will not answer) the acid, which the azote deprives of a portion of oxygen, unites to it.

---

* Comp. View, page 138.

" The foregoing demonstration may appear, at first sight, more fanciful than real. But does not the decomposition of nitre by metallic filings, whether they be deflagrated in a red hot crucible, or distilled by a gradual heat in a retort, tend to its confirmation ? The acid is completely decomposed in this way, in whatever proportions the materials are used. In this case, the metallic particles deprive the nitrous molecules within their influence of the whole of their oxygen ; and the azote, having no sensible attraction to the alkali, passes off in a gaseous state ; for it cannot recover any oxygen from the molecules of nitre, in consequence of the united force of their azote and potash.

" I introduced iron filings into a mixture of about 1 of pale nitrous acid and 16 of water.* When they stood some time, azotic gas was produced, but no nitrous

---

* The objcet of this experiment was to prove the non-existence of hydrogen in metals. At the same time it helped to develope the atomic system.

gas.* In this experiment, the few molecules of the nitrous acid, which come in
contact with the metal, are deprived of
the whole of their oxygen; and as the
azote is liberated at a distance from the
molecules of nitrous acid, and as its attraction is not sufficient to decompose
water, it collects atmospheres of caloric,
which defend it, in its passage through
the solution, from the action of a portion
of the oxygen of the suspended acid.

" This experiment not only confirms
the foregoing explanations of the decomposition of nitre and nitrous acid by
metals, but also tends very much to overset the phlogistic theory. Here the metal
is oxydized, and neither hydrogen nor
nitrous gas is produced.†

" Let us add to this an experiment
already described, viz. the solution of iron
in sulphurous acid without the production
of hydrogen; and the decomposition of

---

* Comp. View, p. 140.   † Ibid. p. 141.

it again by nitrous acid, without the formation of nitrous gas or azotic gas, although the metal is calcined and held in
solution.

*Here follows an explanation on the prin-
ciples of my theory, (the atomic).*

" The sulphurous acid dissolves the
iron, and of course it is reduced into
ultimate particles. Nitrous acid, dropped
into this solution, is diffused through it,
and, from the quantity of water which
must necessarily be present in the sulphite
of iron and in the nitrous acid, the molecules of both substances are in a great
measure removed from each other, so that
a single ultimate particle of iron can meet
only a single molecule of nitrous acid,
which supplies it with oxygen of calcination and acid of solution. Thus it is that
no nitrous gas is produced at the same
time that the whole of the sulphurous
acid is disengaged.*

---

* Comp. View, page 142.

K

" The great number of ultimate particles, which are concentrated in so small
a compass in metals, from the nature of
their texture, is the principal cause of the
decomposition of nitrous or nitric acid
during their solution in them."

*I shall pass over a great many facts
which were adduced, in order to ascertain
the relative quantities of oxygen contained
in nitrous gas and in gaseous oxide, particularly as they are at present known to almost
every chemical reader, and confine myself to
the following extract :*

" The method of obtaining gaseous
oxide from the solution of metallic nitrates favours the foregoing notions ;* for
we cannot procure it from nitrous or
nitric acid, until they are nearly saturated
with a metal; and then, by introducing
more of the same metal, or a different

---

* That the atoms of the gaseous oxide consist of a
single particle of azote and one of oxygen.

metal, we obtain this gas, instead of the nitrous gas.

" To understand the rationale of this fact, we must consider, that the nitrous acid, which holds the metallic oxide in solution, is in the state of the red nitrous acid. Therefore, although the newly introduced metal deprives the acid of solution in contact with it, of the whole of its oxygen, yet the particles of azote recover a portion of it from their neighbouring molecules of acid, on principles which have been already explained.*

" The following demonstration will render this play of affinity sufficiently clear.

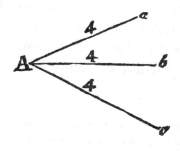

" Let the diagram **represent the mole-**cules of the acid of solution; if **a metal** be introduced into such a solution, it will deprive A of the whole of its oxygen; A being in contact with another molecule of acid of solution, will instantly seize on *a*, or *b*, or *c*, so as to constitute the gaseous oxide, and another particle of azote will at the same moment unite to a second particle of oxygen; thus the oxygen of the molecule of acid is expended in forming three portions of the gaseous oxide, while the metals are thrown down in the state of oxides.*

" It might be supposed, that a metal, when introduced into the red nitrous acid, in its simple state, should, on the foregoing principle, produce gaseous oxide. But we are to take into account that, although a particle of azote can only take

---

* It has already been shewn, by means of a diagram, that the atoms of gaseous oxide consist of a single particle of azote and one of oxygen, united with the force of 6. Sir Humphry Davy gave a very minute account of the nature and properties of this gas, in a work which he published in the year 1800.

one particle of oxygen from a single molecule of acid, another molecule in its vicinity will supply it with a second particle of oxygen, so as to constitute nitrous gas. This cannot happen in the metallic solution; for, when once the atom of gaseous oxide is formed, its attraction for more oxygen is not sufficient to take any of it from the united influence of the azote of the acid molecule and the particle of metal attached to it." *

The most ready way of obtaining the gaseous oxide is, by exposing nitrate of ammonia to heat in a pneumatic apparatus. This mode of procuring it was known when I wrote my Comparative View ; but it was not immediately connected with the new philosophy, which I advanced.

" Having endeavoured to shew the nature of nitrous gas and nitrous oxide, so far as relates to the proportions of their respective elements, we can readily ac-

---

† Comp. View, pages 171-2.

count, to a degree of certainty, why these gases do not affect each other when they are mixed; for the molecule of the nitrous gas retains its two particles of oxygen with as much force as the atom of the gaseous oxide can attract either of them.

This neutrality of the two gases, when mixed, is demonstrated by means of diagrams in the original work.

" Why the gaseous oxide should be more soluble in water than the nitrous gas, is what I cannot account for, unless it be occasioned by the smaller size of its calorific atmospheres, which may admit its atoms to come within the gravitating influence of that fluid.

" It is somewhat strange that the gaseous oxide should support combustion, while the nitrous gas, which contains more oxygen, has the reverse effect. It is also very singular, that nitrous gas will unite to more oxygen in a common temperature, and that the gaseous oxide will not, although it must have greater affinity to oxygen, as containing less of it than the former gas.

" That the red nitrous vapour, which contains much more oxygen, with less force, than the former gases, should not favour combustion, is still more singular.* Again, why Homberg's pyrophorus will burn in nitrous gas, and not in the gaseous oxide, is a fact-which we cannot account for, unless it be occasioned by a larger supply of moisture in the former gas.†

" When we consider that neither carbonated hydrogen, nor hydrogen, nor azotic gases, will unite to oxygen gas, notwithstanding their great attraction to it, without the aid of the electric or a common spark ; and compare these facts with the ease, with which oxygen gas and nitrous gas unite ; we are led to attribute

---

* This is not the case : but it was thought proper not to make any alteration in the extract.

† Comp. View, page 173-4.

them to something, which surrounds their gravitating particles, and this we must suppose to be caloric, partly, as it is disengaged during their chemical union or condensation.

" But why caloric should not exert this power, when nitrous gas and oxygen gas are mixed together, is rather extraordinary; more especially when we know, as I have shewn upon a former occasion, that the calorific atmospheres of nitrous gas are much larger than those of azotic gas; and also, when we have every reason to suppose, that nitrous gas contains nearly all the caloric, which its component particles of oxygen and azote contained in their simple gaseous state.

" It is true that caloric is not given out by the union of nitrous gas and oxygen gas, which might favour their combination by a predisposing affinity of the acid molecule for the whole of the caloric of its constituents. This mode of reasoning, however, is not sufficient to account for the fact. The question is, how do their extensive atmospheres blend, so as to suffer their respective gravitating particles and molecules to approach within the reach of each other's chemical influence? The condensation of oxygen gas by nitrous gas, without the evolution of caloric, is a very striking fact.*

" That nitric acid contains nearly as much caloric as its constituent principles held before their union, can scarcely be questioned; and that it parts with very little caloric, on uniting to alkalies, is well known. Therefore, nitrate of potash contains, in its solid state, caloric sufficient to preserve the elasticity of, at least, 100 times its bulk of oxygen gas.

" Hence arise the deflagration of carbon and nitre in close vessels, and the quantity of caloric which is liberated,

---

* " Heat is produced, but not more than should be expected from the re-action of the newly formed acid upon the suspended water of the gases."

✻

although carbonic acid gas is copiously evolved at the same time.

" These facts must convince us, that caloric unites chemically to bodies, and consequently that it gravitates towards them. Can we therefore doubt that caloric is a substance, and not a quality, as some philosophers are pleased to suppose ? "

As chemists differ from each other respecting the proportions of the volumes of oxygen and azotic gases, which nitrous gas and gaseous oxide contain, I repeated the following experiments, which were formerly made by myself and others.

Ten measures of pure nitrous gas were charged into a glass jar, previously filled with quicksilver : some well-prepared pyrophorus was then sent up, which instantly inflamed, and reduced the gas. The residuary gas was passed into a graduated measure, where the reduction appeared to be only $\frac{4}{10}$. When the experiment was made with a larger quantity of pyrophorus, the 10 measures were reduced to 5½, and the residuary gas was found to be azote. Two trials more gave the same result.

The pyrophorus was sent up in a small glass tube open at both ends, one of which was closed by means of a cork, and it was perfectly filled with the pyrophorus: when passed under the jar, which contained the gas, the cork was withdrawn, and the tube, with its contents, was suffered to ascend. The whole of the pyrophorus, by agitating the jar, was readily exposed to the gas. From the inflammability of the pyrophorus, no time could be gained to press it into the tube; it was therefore only quickly filled, and immediately covered, and passed up. Hence it occurred to me, that some atmospheric air might have been mixed with it. To ascertain whether this was the case, the measure was filled with powdered charcoal, and passed up in the jar, which was filled with quicksilver. In this way half a measure of gas was produced.

My assistant, Mr. Wharmby, repeated these experiments over and over again, with the same result. Suspecting that the residuary gas contained carbonic gas, it was exposed to lime water ; but no precipitation whatever appeared, and the gas was in no sensible degree diminished. When a lighted taper was plunged in it, the ignition instantly ceased, and oxygen gas had no effect on it.

We may infer from the foregoing facts, that a given measure of nitrous gas con tains equal volumes of its constituent gases. The weight of 100 cubic inches of oxygen gas is 34 grains, and that of the same volume of azotic gas about 30 grains; therefore, the weight of the molecule of nitrous gas must be the multiple of the weight of its constituent particles ; and, if the two gases were condensed by their chemical union to the dimensions of either of them, 100 cubic inches of nitrous gas should weigh 64 grains, where- as they weigh but 37. Therefore, the calorific atmospheres of the molecules of this gas are twice larger than those of either of its constituent gases.

I exposed potassium to dry nitrous gas over mercury, and no change whatever was produced in either of them, although they were suffered to stand until the potassium was absorbed by the mercury, which had taken three days. When water was thrown up, hydrogen was given out by the amalgam.

A small quantity of potassium was passed into a jar, containing $6\frac{1}{2}$ measures of nitrous gas, and a quantity of water, barely sufficient to ignite it, was sent up; as soon as they came in contact, a sudden flash was produced, accompanied with a concussion of the apparatus, and the gas was reduced to five measures, which consisted of hydrogen, azote, and nitrous gas.

When a larger proportion of potassium was used, ten measures were reduced to six, which contained azote in a free state, hydrogen, and nitrous gas. The rapidity,

with which nitrous gas is decomposed in
this way, can only be equalled by the
firing of oxygen and hydrogen, or oxygen
and any other inflammable gas, by the
electric spark.

The experiments with potassium were
made, with a view to ascertain the effects
of this new metal on the gas; for I was
perfectly satisfied with its analysis by
means of the pyrophorus.

The various ways of decomposing this
gas by moistened iron filings, and by sulphuretted hydrogen, were repeated for
the first time (by me) since I wrote my
" Comparative View," and I observed
nothing particular, except in one experiment, when equal parts of sulphuretted
hydrogen and nitrous gas, which stood
separately over dry mercury for several
days, were mixed, no decomposition took
place, although the mixture was suffered
to stand for three weeks. When water
was sent up, the whole of the gases, except a large bubble of azote, disappeared

in the course of seven days. The water
contained no free acid nor ammonia, and,
when filtered and evaporated to dryness
in a gentle heat, a small quantity of nitrate of ammonia was left.

By repeated trials I could never succeed in this experiment, but when the
gases and mercury, which confined them,
were perfectly dry. This curious fact has
escaped the observation of chemists.

The following experiments were made
to ascertain the proportion of the constituents of gaseous oxide.* 43 measures
of hydrogen and 46 of gaseous oxide
were fired in a glass jar, over mercury, by
the electric spark: the residuary gas
was of the standard of atmospheric air.
3 measures of gaseous oxide, and 4 of
hydrogen, when fired, were reduced to
nearly 4 measures, which consisted of

---

* Similar experiments were made by Sir Humphry Davy,
in the year 1800.—*See his Researches.*

azote and hydrogen. When equal volumes of the gases were fired, the mixture was reduced to one half. This residuum was not diminished by water, and when a lighted taper was plunged into it, the ignition instantly ceased; therefore we have every reason to suppose that it was azote. These experiments were repeated with the same result.

The foregoing experiments on nitrous gas and gaseous oxide shew, that the former contains equal bulk of oxygen gas and azotic gas, and that the latter consists of one measure of azotic and half a measure of oxygen gases condensed into the volume of one measure. The nitrous gas is found as much expanded as its constituent gases would have been, were they only mechanically mixed; so that little or no diminution of their volume is produced by their chemical union. This accounts for the greater specific gravity of the gaseous oxide; and this difference in their weights must depend on the size of their respective atmospheres of caloric.

The principal question is, in what proportion of their ultimate particles do their respective atoms or molecules exist? The estimate which I formerly gave, when I first introduced the atomic system, as may be seen in some of the foregoing pages, is, that a molecule of nitrous gas consists of a single ultimate particle of azote and two of oxygen, and that an atom of gaseous oxide contains one of azote and one of oxygen.

Mr. Dalton and most chemists suppose that the atoms of nitrous gas consist of one ultimate particle of azote and one of oxygen, and those of nitrous oxide of two of azote and one of oxygen. The quantity of the simple gases, which are necessary to constitute these compounds, I must own, favours this estimate. However, I do not see any reason why I should relinquish my former opinion.

The specific gravity of oxygen gas is very little more than that of azotic, and this I attribute to the dimensions of their

L

respective atmospheres of caloric, those of the latter gas being more extensive and less dense.

In my opinion, the ultimate particles of azote are larger, and of course heavier, than those of oxygen. I also conceive that a measure of oxygen gas contains twice the number of ultimate particles, that are contained in the same volume of azotic gas.

Indeed, the great number of particles of oxygen, which a single particle of azote is capable of uniting to and governing, for instance, in nitric acid, justifies in a great measure this hypothesis.

According to the philosophy which I laid down in my " Comparative View," and which I have proved to be correct in most instances, an ultimate particle of an inflammable base is capable of uniting to 1, 2, 3, 4, or more of the particles of oxygen, according to the nature of the inflammable substance; while, on the

other hand, a single particle of oxygen,
as I mentioned on a former occasion, cannot unite to more than one particle of
any inflammable matter. To suppose the
contrary, would be reversing that delight-
ful symmetry, which nature uniformly
presents to our view on every occasion.

Besides, were a particle of oxygen
capable of uniting to 2 or 3, or more
particles of inflammable base, there would
be no end to compounds and monstrous
compounds, which never occur in chemical investigations.

The chemical action of the muriatic
acid on metals was explained on the
atomic principle, and demonstrated by
diagrams, somewhat like those which I
have already adduced on the subjects of
sulphuric and nitrous acids.* When I
wrote, oxymuriatic acid was supposed by
the phlogistians to be muriatic acid, deprived of phlogiston or hydrogen. This

---

* Comp. View, page 190—3.

L 2

was also the opinion of Scheele, who first discovered this singular substance. Berthollet, I believe, was the first who considered oxymuriatic acid to be a compound of muriatic acid and oxygen. Some of the experiments and demonstrations, which I brought forward at that time, appeared very favourable to Berthollet's hypothesis, as the following extract will shew.

" When muriatic and nitric acids are mixed, nitrous gas is produced. This, however, depends upon proportions. If they are mixed in the proportions of two of the nitric to three of the muriatic, provided the acids are strong, nitrous gas is evolved, and the mixture becomes very hot. When it cools, the nitrous gas ceases to come over, and numerous bubbles are generated in different parts of the acid, which are absorbed almost as soon as they are formed. They sometimes appear at the bottom of the liquor, and pass upwards in slender streams, rapidly diminishing in their progress until they can no longer be traced. This phenomenon is

attended with a hissing noise, which must
be occasioned by absorption. I endeavoured, but without success, to obtain
some of this gas.

"Thus we find, that muriatic acid will
take oxygen from the nitric with as great
facility as from the oxide of manganese,
and that it acts on this acid in a similar
manner as it does on the metals, by withdrawing oxygen from it, and not, as the
phlogistians imagine, by imparting phlogiston to it. . . . .

"It is well known that nitrous gas
will not form nitrous acid without the
addition of oxygen. Yet Pelletier produced nitrous acid and muriatic acid, by
mixing oxymuriatic gas and nitrous gas.*
This is a convincing proof of the existence
of oxygen in oxymuriatic acid.†. . . . . .

*I considered muriatic acid at this period
to consist of an unknown inflammable base*

'26 Iroz. 393.   † Comp. View, p. 207.

and oxygen, and that they were united with
the force of 6. *This is considerably greater*
than the force, with which oxygen was sup-
posed to be attached to its azotic base in
nitric, pale, or red nitrous acids, as has been
already mentioned.

" Stating the comparative forces, with
which oxygen is retained in those acids
rather than their absolute forces, which
cannot be ascertained, we shall be the
more enabled to account for the following
facts. Pelletier has observed, that nitric
acid is completely decomposed, when
added in a small proportion to muriatic
acid, and that its azote is disengaged in a
gaseous state, although azote attracts the
quantity of oxygen necessary to the formation of nitrous gas with greater force
than the muriatic acid.

" The foregoing fact is only explicable
on the following principles. When a
small portion of nitric acid is diffused in
a large quantity of muriatic, the latter
exposes surfaces sufficient to separate,
with one uniform or co-operating influ-

ence, the whole of its oxygen from the azote.* For the force of 4, on the side of the muriatic molecules, is sufficient to overcome, if the nitric acid be used, the force of $3\frac{3}{7}$, or, should it be the pale acid, the force of $3\frac{3}{4}$. Red nitrous acid, in its pure state, will not be decomposed; for it retains its oxygen with as great force as the muriatic acid attracts it : therefore they will form a kind of union without decomposition.

" When a larger quantity of nitric acid is mixed with the muriatic acid, nitrous gas is produced : for, as a molecule of the muriatic can only deprive a single molecule of nitric acid, at most, but of two ultimate particles of oxygen, there are not a sufficient number of the former within the reach of the latter to effect a total decomposition, that is, a separation of the whole of its oxygen from the azote; for such a decomposition cannot take place, but by the simultaneous influence, at the same instant, of different molecules

---

* Comp. View, page 210.

of muriatic, while the nitric molecule is perfect. Thus it is that nitrous gas is formed, and as it retains its oxygen with greater force than nitric acid, it passes off through the muriatic acid in its gaseous state. *Muriatic gas and nitrous gas, when mixed over mercury, have no action whatever on each other*

"It appears to me, that oxymuriatic gas retains its oxygen with as great force, nearly, as nitrous gas; for, when these gases are perfectly dry, and mixed over mercury, no decomposition takes place until water is introduced. Hence I infer that water assists in the decomposition, from its attraction to muriatic acid."*

While writing these pages, I made the following experiments.

Fused muriate of lime was introduced into a small glass globe, which, when exhausted as much as possible, by means

---

* Comp. View, p. 211-2.

of a good air pump, was filled with oxymuriatic gas : it was a second time exhausted, and this process was repeated
three times, which induced me to suppose
that the whole of the atmospheric air was
pumped out : it was then filled with oxymuriatic gas. A glass jar was filled with
nitrous gas over quicksilver ; and both
gases were suffered to rest in contact with
muriate of lime for forty-eight hours.
When a communication was formed, by
means of stop cocks, the two gases exchanged situations with each other in a
few minutes. The nitrous gas, being the
lighter, ascended at the same time that
the oxymuriatic gas descended, and occupied its place in the jar. The globe exhibited a red appearance, which proved that
nitrous vapour was formed. On standing
for some time, the gases and nitrous vapour mixed with each other, and the
surface of the quicksilver was much
corroded.

When a portion of the gas in the jar
was passed into a glass tube, and agitated

in contact with quicksilver, until the whole of the oxymuriatic gas was condensed, water produced no diminution in the residuary gas, which was found to consist of nitrous and azotic gases. As no muriatic gas was formed, no interchange of elementary principles took place between the oxymuriatic gas, the nitrous gas, and water. The red colour, produced by the nitrous gas, must proceed from some atmospheric air, which remained in the receiver, notwithstanding the pains taken to get rid of it.

The result of the foregoing experiment induced me to make the following :

Oxymuriatic gas was quickly passed into a glass jar, half filled with dry nitrous gas over mercury : no apparent change took place : and when water was introduced, the oxymuriatic gas was condensed, and the nitrous gas remained unaltered ; for the whole of it was converted into red nitrous vapour by oxygen gas. As soon as this vapour was absorbed by the water, it acted on the quicksilver, and a slight degree of effervescence ensued : this was occasioned by the reproduction of nitrous gas, which gradually condensed a small residuum of oxygen remaining in the jar.

This experiment proves that oxymuriatic gas and nitrous gas do not decompose each other, and that no affinity exists between them, and also that red nitrous vapour has little or no action on oxymuriatic acid.

These facts, together with many others, adduced by Sir Humphry Davy, tend to shew, that oxymuriatic gas does not contain oxygen so loosely combined as has been heretofore imagined ; and the probability is, that it contains no oxygen. This, however, remains to be proved.

Having repeated experiments, which I formerly made, I shall drop the subject at present, particularly as it does not immediately relate to the object of this essay.

I will pass over different sections, which treat on the oxydation of metals in different ways ; on their reduction again to their metallic state ; and on the solubility of metals in acids.

Those different processes were strictly and impartially enquired into, on the principles of both antagonist doctrines, at this period ; and, assisted by the atomic system, I was able to draw fairer and juster conclusions than I otherwise could.

In the section which relates to the precipitation of metals by each other, from their solution in acids, the structure of the compound molecules of the metallic salt is represented by diagrams ; and the relative forces, with which their elementary particles influence each other, is expressed by numbers. The following extract will give one example of this kind, which will be sufficient.

" A neutral solution of sulphate of copper consists of an oxide of copper and sulphurous acid, chemically united. The sulphurous acid is less intimately attached to the copper than the oxygen. Iron will throw down the copper in this solution, in its metallic state, by taking from it the acid and the whole of its oxygen, with one sudden and uniform effort.

" To account for this decomposition, it is necessary to have recourse to the following illustration.*

" C in the diagram represents a particle of copper, O oxygen, which, we will suppose, attract each other with the force of $2\frac{2}{3}$; to avoid perplexity, reciprocal attraction is not considered. Let S, which represents sulphurous acid, be united to this oxide with the force of 3; and let us suppose 2 of this force to proceed from the oxygen attached to the copper, and the remainder, which is but 1, to be occasioned by the influence of the copper

---

* Comp. View, p. 262.

itself on the sulphur and oxygen of the sulphurous acid: therefore let G designate the centre of gravity of S.

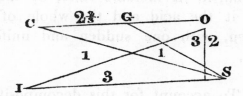

" Let us now suppose this to be the state of a molecule of sulphate of copper: here the copper attracts S and O with only the force of $3\frac{2}{3}$; and C and O conjointly influence S with the force of 3. Let us again suppose I, which represents, in the diagram, a particle of iron, to attract S, or sulphurous acid, with the force of 3; it cannot take it from C and O, which hold it with the force of 3; but it so counteracts the attachment of O and S to C, as to reduce it to $\frac{2}{3}$. Let us suppose I, from its attraction to oxygen, to influence O with the force of 1 more: in this case, C will be deprived of O and S;

for the force of $3\frac{2}{3}$ must yield to the power of 4.*

" Should the iron unite first to the sulphurous acid, the resulting compound would have no action on the oxide; for the sulphite of iron does not take any of its oxygen from the oxide of copper, when both are mixed. Hence it appears, as observed above, that the whole force of the iron, in order to throw down the copper in its metallic state, must be exerted at the same instant towards S and O conjointly.†

---

* Comp. View, page 263.

† A molecule of sulphate of copper contains as much oxygen as that of sulphate of iron; it is composed of 1 particle of copper, 1 of sulphur, and 3 of oxygen, attached to each other in such a way as to consist of two compounds, viz. an oxide and sulphurous acid.

When potash is introduced into a solution of this sulphate, it takes from it the acid of solution, with the full portion of oxygen necessary to constitute sulphuric acid. Therefore a molecule of sulphate of potash consists of the oxide of potassium and sulphuric acid, intimately united;

" All metallic precipitations are effected on the foregoing principles. Should the precipitant be unable to take up the whole of the oxygen of the precipitated metal, it falls down in the state of a semi-oxide. Thus lead and silver will precipitate gold from its solution of a dull purple colour, while copper and iron throw it down in its metallic state."

The precipitation of one metal by another from its solution in an acid, in the state of an oxide, was, at this distant period, urged

---

or of the following proportion of its constituent elements, 1 particle of potassium, 1 of sulphur, and 3 of oxygen. A molecule of sulphite of iron consists of a particle of the metal, united to an atom of sulphurous acid. Sulphite of potash contains one third less oxygen than its sulphate.

When the metallic oxides and sulphur are mixed, and exposed to sufficient heat, sulphurous acid is formed. When the alkaline or earthy oxides are treated in the same manner, no decomposition is effected ; the sulphur unites to them, and forms as perfect a sulphuret as if there had been no oxygen present : this is owing to the strong affinity of the metallic bases to their oxygen.

*as unfavourable to the anti-phlogistic doc-
trine, particularly by Mr. Kirwan in his
Essay on Phlogiston. The answer, which I
made on this occasion, shall terminate this
essay.*

" Mr. Kirwan's fourth query is very
much in favour of the anti-phlogistic
doctrine ; for, as I observed on a former
occasion, the precipitation of one metal
by another, in the state of an oxide, without the evolution of hydrogen, at the
same time that the precipitant is held in
solution, is a strong proof of the non-
existence of that principle in metals : besides, the fact is very explicable by the
anti-phlogistic theory.*

" I have already shewn, upon what
principle the different inflammable bases
retain their oxygen with less force, when
perfectly saturated with it, than when
united to smaller proportions ; and I have
also shewn, in treating on nitrous and

---

* Comp. View, page 274.

M

nitric acids, that the force of union of their base to oxygen is inversely to the quantity of oxygen, with which it is united.

" The same law holds good in all kinds of chemical combinations, and is explicable on the same principles. Almost all bodies, particularly elementary bodies, will unite to the different substances, to which they have an affinity, in various proportions, according to their nature, until they arrive at the point of saturation, which limits the power of chemical attraction.

" There are some exceptions to this law; for the principles of water will only unite in one proportion, so that we never have obtained them in an intermediate state of combination. I have some doubts whether the same observation might not be applied to the carbonic acid.

" Metals unite to oxygen in various proportions, until they are saturated. If

100 grains of a metal are only capable of uniting to 15 grains of oxygen, they will attract and retain 5 grains of oxygen with greater force than they will 10 grains, and 10 grains with greater force than 15 grains.*

" Suppose 100 grains of tin, when in perfect solution in an acid, should be united to 15 grains of oxygen with the force of $5\frac{1}{2}$, and that iron should attract oxygen with the force of 7, and let us suppose this force to be reduced to 6, by the accession of $7\frac{1}{4}$ grains of oxygen, and the force of the attraction of the tin to the remainder of its oxygen to increase by this loss: under these circumstances, iron could not precipitate tin in its metallic state, although it may have greater attraction to the oxygen and acid of solution than the tin has. Hence it is evident, that a metal, in order to throw down another in its pure metallic state, must

---

* Comp. View, pages 275-6.

M 2

not only unite to oxygen in greater quantities, and attract it more forcibly, but that this superiority of force must be very considerable."

Having produced a number of facts, taken from the philosophy, which I advanced many years before the close of the last century, I will now lay before the reader a sample of Mr. Dalton's " *New System of Philosophy*," published in the eighth year of the present century. I have fixed, according to my judgment, on the very best part of his work, so far as relates to the atomic doctrine. It will be found very nearly the ditto of the principles which I established, excepting his omission of numbers, which represent the relative force of the chemical attraction of particles and atoms to each other, and which appears to me to be one of the most important features of my system.

Here follows Mr. Dalton's third chapter, on chemical synthesis.

" On Chemical Synthesis. *

" When any body exists in the elastic state, its ultimate particles are separated from each other to a much greater distance than in any other state; each particle occupies the center of a comparatively large sphere, and supports its dignity by keeping all the rest, which, by their gravity, or otherwise, are disposed to encroach upon it, at a respectful distance. When we attempt to conceive the *number* of particles in an atmosphere, it is somewhat like attempting to conceive the number of stars in the universe; we are confounded with the thought. But if we limit the subject, by taking a given volume of any gas, we seem persuaded that, let the divisions be ever so minute, the number of particles must be finite; just as in a given space of the universe the number of stars and planets cannot be infinite.

" Chemical analysis and synthesis go no farther than to the separation of particles one from another, and to their re-union. No new creation or destruction of matter is within the reach of chemical agency. We might as well attempt to introduce a new planet into

---

* New System of Chemical Philosophy, p. 211.

the solar system, or to annihilate one already in existence, as to create or destroy a particle of hydrogen. All the changes we can produce, consist in separating particles that are in a state of cohesion or combination, and joining those that were previously at a distance.

" In all chemical combinations, it has justly been considered an important object to ascertain the relative *weights* of the simples, which constitute a compound. But unfortunately the enquiry has terminated here; whereas from the relative weights in the mass the relative weights of the ultimate particles or atoms of the bodies might have been inferred, from which their number and weight in various other compounds would appear, in order to assist and guide future investigations, and to correct their results. Now it is one great object of this work, to shew the importance and advantage of ascertaining *the relative weights of the ultimate particles, both of simple and compound bodies, the number of simple elementary particles which constitute one compound particle, and the number of less compound particles which enter into the formation of one more compound particle.*

" If there are two bodies, A and B, which are disposed to combine, the following is the order in which the combinations may take place, beginning with the most simple; namely,

1 atom of A + 1 atom of B = 1 atom of C, binary.

1 atom of A + 2 atoms of B = 1 atom of D, ternary.

2 atoms of A + 1 atom of B = 1 atom of E, ternary.

1 atom of A + 3 atoms of B = 1 atom of F, quaternary.

3 atoms of A + 1 atom of B = 1 atom of G, quaternary.

&c. &c.

" The following general rules may be adopted as guides in all our investigations respecting chemical synthesis.

1st. When only one combination of two bodies can be obtained, it must be presumed to be a *binary* one, unless some cause appear to the contrary.

2d. When two combinations are observed, they must be presumed to be a *binary* and a *ternary*.

3d. When three combinations are obtained, we may expect one to be a *binary*, and the other two *ternary*.

4th. When four combinations are observed, we should expect one *binary*, two *ternary*, and one *quaternary*, &c.

5th. A *binary* compound should always be specifically heavier than the mere mixture of its two ingredients.

6th. A *ternary* compound should be specifically heavier than the mixture of a binary and a simple, which would, if combined, constitute it, &c.

7th. The above rules and observations equally

apply, when two bodies, such as C and D, D and E, &c. are combined.*

" From the application of these rules, to the chemical facts already well ascertained, we deduce the following conclusions; 1st. That water is a binary compound of hydrogen and oxygen, and the relative weights of the two elementary atoms are as 1:7, nearly; 2d. That ammonia is a binary compound of hydrogen and azote, and the relative weights of the two atoms are as 1·5, nearly: 3d. That nitrous gas is a binary compound of azote and oxygen, the atoms of which weigh 5 and 7 respectively; that nitric acid is a binary or ternary compound, according as it is derived, and consists of one atom of azote and two of oxygen, together weighing 19; that nitrous oxide is a compound similar to nitric acid, and consists of one atom of oxygen and two of azote, weighing 17; that nitrous acid is a binary compound of nitric acid and nitrous gas, weighing 31; that oxynitric acid is a binary compound of nitric acid and oxygen, weighing 26; 4th. That carbonic oxide is a binary compound, consisting of one atom of charcoal and one of oxygen, together weighing nearly 12; that carbonic acid is a ternary compound, (but

---

* The terms, *binary, ternary, quaternary,* &c. were introduced long before Mr. Dalton had written; and in the same sense.

sometimes binary) consisting of one atom of charcoal,
and two of oxygen, weighing 19; &c. &c. In all these
cases the weights are expressed in atoms of hydrogen,
each of which is denoted by unity.

" In the sequel the facts and experiments, from
which these conclusions are derived, will be detailed;
as well as a great variety of others from which are inferred the constitution and weight of the ultimate particles of the principal acids, the alkalies, the earths, the
metals, the metallic oxides and sulphurets, the long
train of neutral salts, and in short all the chemical compounds which have hitherto obtained a tolerably good
analysis. Several of the conclusions will be supported
by original experiments.

" From the *novelty* as well as importance of the
ideas suggested in this chapter, it is deemed expedient
to give plates, exhibiting the mode of combination in
some of the more simple cases. A specimen of these
accompanies this first part. The elements or atoms of
such bodies, as are conceived at present to be simple, are
denoted by a small circle, with some distinctive mark;
and the combinations consist in the juxta-position of
two or more of these; when three or more particles of
elastic fluids are combined together in one, it is to be
supposed that the particles of the same kind repel each
other, and therefore take their stations accordingly.

" **EXPLANATION OF THE PLATE.**

" This plate contains the arbitrary marks, or signs, chosen to represent the several chemical elements, or ultimate particles.

Fig.

			Fig.		
1 Hydrogen, its rel. weight	1	11 Strontites	-	-	46
2 Azote - - - -	2	12 Barytes	-	-	68
3 Carbon, or charcoal	3	13 Iron -	-	-	38
4 Oxygen - -	7	14 Zinc	-	-	56
5 Phosphorus -	9	15 Copper	-	-	56
6 Sulphur - -	13	16 Lead	-	-	95
7 Magnesia - -	20	17 Silver	-	-	100
8 Lime - - -	23	18 Platina	-	-	100
9 Soda - - -	28	19 Gold -	-	-	140
10 Potash - -	42	20 Mercury	-	-	167

21. An atom of water, or steam, composed of 1 of oxygen and 1 of hydrogen, retained in physical contact by a strong affinity, and supposed to be surrounded by a common atmosphere of heat; its relative weight = - - - - - - - 8

22. An atom of ammonia, composed of 1 of azote and 1 of hydrogen - - - - - - - - - 6

23. An atom of nitrous gas, composed of 1 of azote and 1 of oxygen - - - - - - - 12

24. An atom of olefiant gas, composed of 1 of carbon and 1 of hydrogen - - - - - - - 6

25. An atom of carbonic oxide, composed of 1 of carbon and 1 of oxygen - - - - - - 12

26. An atom of nitrous oxide, 2 azote + 1 oxygen - 17

27. An atom of nitric acid, 1 azote + 2 oxygen - - 19

28. An atom of carbonic acid, 1 carbon + 2 oxygen 19

29. An atom of carburetted hydrogen, 1 carbon + 2 hydrogen - - - - - - - - - 7

(FAC-SIMILE OF PLATE.)

ELEMENTS.

SIMPLE.

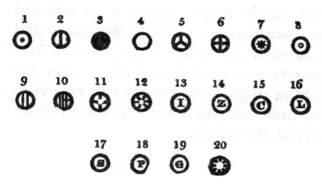

BINARY.

TERNARY.

The respect which I feel for truth and justice, rather than ambition for fame, induced me to undertake this task. The grateful acknowledgment of the public is all the reward men of science expect; and should they be liable to be stripped of that feather, through flippancy and manœuvre, the grand object must be frustrated; men of true science will quit the field in disgust; and many will be deterred from entering into it, to the great injury of the science.

APPENDIX.

SINCE writing the foregoing pages, an extract, taken from a very ingenious essay on the cause of chemical proportions, written by Berzelius, Professor of Chemistry at Stockholm, appeared in a periodical work, called " Annals of Philosophy, &c." (for December, 1813) of which Dr. Thomson, it seems, is the editor. The celebrated author of this essay makes the following remarks on the atomic system.

. . . . " When we reflect on this cause, it is first evident that it must be of a mechanical nature; and what presents itself as the most probable idea, most conformable to our experience, is, that bodies are composed of atoms or of molecules, which combine 1 with 1, 1 with 2, or 3, 4, &c. and the laws of chemical proportions seem to result from this with such clearness and evidence, that it seems very singular that an idea, so simple and probable, has not only not been adopted, but not even proposed, before our own days.

" As far as I know, the English philosopher, Mr. John Dalton, guided by the experiments of Bergman, Richter, Wenzel, Berthollet, Proust, and others, was the first person who endeavoured to establish that hypothesis.

" Sir Humphry Davy has lately assured us that Mr. Higgins, in a book, published in 1789, established the same hypothesis. I have not seen the work of Mr. Higgins, and can only notice the circumstance on the authority of Davy."

Here follows Dr. Thomson's remarks on this passage, in a note at the foot of the page.

"The work of Higgins on *phlogiston* is certainly possessed of much merit; and anticipated some of the most striking subsequent discoveries. But when he wrote, metallic oxides were so little known, and so few exact analyses existed, that it was not possible to be acquainted with the grand fact that oxygen, &c. always unite in determinate proportions, which are multiples of the minimum proportion. The atomic theory was taught by Bergman, Cullen, Black, &c. just as far as it was by Higgins. The latter, indeed, states some striking facts respecting the gases, and anticipated Gay Lussac's theory of volumes; but Mr. Dalton first generalized the doctrine, and thought of determining the weight of atoms of bodies. He shewed me his table of symbols, and the weight of the atoms of six or eight bodies, in 1804; and I believe the same year explained the subject in London, in a course of lectures delivered in the Royal Institution. The subject could scarcely be broached sooner. But about the same time several other persons had been struck with the numbers in my table of metallic oxides, published in my Chemistry; and the doctrine would have certainly been started by others, if Dalton had missed it.

"T."

If Dr. Thomson thought so much of my work on phlogiston, as he, erroneously, is pleased to call it, why not take notice of it in his Chemistry? As a compiler, he should not have passed it over.

This curious note of his accounts for the omission. He wished to leave the work itself in undisturbed oblivion; but whatever was valuable in it, he generously chose to bestow on Mr. Dalton.

"*When he wrote, metallic oxides, &c.*"

When I wrote, I was as well acquainted with metallic oxides as I am at this present moment.* And I was the first that established " *the grand fact, that oxygen, &c. always unite in determinate proportions, which are multiples of the minimum proportion,*" as almost every page of this essay, which relates to the subject, will prove.

" *The atomic theory was taught by Bergman, Cullen, Black, &c.*"

I have read the works of those chemists repeatedly, and I have not met with a single page, that relates to the atomic theory. Were these philosophers now in existence, they would shrink from the compliment with honest indignation.

---

* See the following pages in this essay, viz. 70, 116-17, and 163 ; and in Comp. View, 229—30.

It is true, at the time I wrote, I thought the ultimate particles of most metals were capable of uniting to three particles of oxygen. I am now of opinion, that there are but two distinct oxides of any one metal, and that the mis_ take of modern writers arises from a mixture of those oxides in different proportions.

N

" The latter, indeed, states some striking facts respecting the gases, and anticipated Gay Lussac's theory of volumes."

I have also attended to their particles, and to the relative weight of the particles and atoms of the different gases, as may be seen in many pages of this essay.

*" But **Mr.** Dalton first generalized the doctrine, &c."*

The doctrine was as extensively applied by me, and, what is still more important, it was founded on well-chosen facts and mathematical demonstrations, which **Dalton** omitted for reasons best known to himself. In a word, it will be found that Dalton has not done justice to my doctrine, with all his ingenuity ; and his attempt to weigh a few atoms, no matter how, or whether he is correct or not, gives him no claim whatever to the system, which I established several years before he or Dr. T. were known as chemical writers.

" The subject could scarcely be broached sooner."

This and the remaining part of the Doctor's note exhibit such self-evident misrepresentations, that I need hot say a single word on the subject, but refer the reader to the pages of this work. Indeed, I did not expect that such prejudice on the one side, and partiality on the other, should flow from the pen of so respectable a writer as Dr. Thomson.

The generous age of chemical science is no more. In my early days, it was my fortune to live at the same time, and to associate with, many of the venerable fathers of our present system. In that auspicious period, the ultimate and ardently expected object of research was truth : not the advancement of an individual's reputation. Philosophers were then eager to attribute the merit of discovery to its rightful owner, not to appropriate it to themselves or others. But now, in the vale of life, I am myself obliged to rescue the labours of my youth from the claims of those, who have adopted them without ceremony, and who have even attempted to force them from me by means of their combined exertions. However, justice will force its way sooner or later against all obstacles and prejudices. The subject is not, now, confined to the decision of a few individuals, but is laid before a grand tribunal, and it rests with them to give a verdict.

FINIS.

Graisberry and Campbell, Printers,
10, Back-Lane, Dublin.